Math from Three to Seven

The Story of a Mathematical Circle for Preschoolers

Alexander Zvonkin

Translated by Alla Yarkho
Translation edited by Paul Zeitz

Mathematical Sciences Research Institute
Berkeley, California

AMERICAN MATHEMATICAL SOCIETY
Providence, Rhode Island

2010 *Mathematics Subject Classification.* Primary 00A08, 00A09, 00A35, 97A20, 97A80, 97C30, 97U60.

This work was originally published in Russian under the title Малыши и математика, © 2007 A. K. Zvonkin and Moscow Center for Continuing Mathematical Education. Illustrations by Mikhail Panov. The present translation was made for MSRI by Alla Yarkho and edited by Paul Zeitz and is published by permission.

This volume is published with the generous support of the John Templeton Foundation.

For additional information and updates on this book, visit
www.ams.org/bookpages/mcl-5

Library of Congress Cataloging-in-Publication Data

Zvonkin, A. K. (Aleksandr Kalmanovich), 1948–
  [Malyshi i matematika. English]
  Math from three to seven : the story of a mathematical circle for preschoolers / Alexander Zvonkin ; translated by Alla Yarkho ; translation edited by Paul Zeitz.
    p. cm. — (MSRI mathematical circles library ; 5)
  Includes bibliographical references and index.
  ISBN 978-0-8218-6873-7 (alk. paper)
  1. Games in mathematics education. 2. Mathematics—Study and teaching (Preschool). 3. Mathematical recreations. I. Zeitz, Paul, 1958– II. Title.
  QA20.G35Z8613 2011
  372.7—dc23

2011016999

Contents

Foreword to the American Edition   vii

Introduction   1
  A Parent's Journal   1
  Why a circle? Why a journal?   2
  Should journals be edited?   4
  A novice's reflections on pre-school math   5
  Opinions   8
  A Short History of Our Circle   9
  Acknowledgments   12
  Two Disclaimers   13

Chapter 1.   The First Session: Narrative and Reflections   15
  A session in action   15
  Piaget's phenomena: reality or illusion?   24
  Why read psychology books?   28
  Why do we need theories?   32

Chapter 2.   The Boys' Math Circle, Year One   35
  Session 21. The Möbius band   35
  Session 22. What is bigger, the whole or its part?   37
  Session 23. The Tower of Hanoi   41
  Session 24. A bit of topology   45
  Session 25. The boy in the elevator   47
  Session 26. Intersecting classes   48
  Session 27. Pegboard quadrilaterals   50
  Session 28. We start probability theory   52
  Session 29. Total failure   54
  Session 30. Pouring water   56
  Session 31. Probability theory, again   60
  Session 32. Diplomas   62
  A few more problems   63
  How to draw a cube?   67

Chapter 3.   Children and $\binom{5}{2}$: The Story of One Problem   69
  A combinatorial puzzle   70
  Equivalent problems   71
  Denoting...   74
  Proof   76
  Physics and logic   79

Chapter 4.   The Boys' Math Circle, Year Two   83
  Session 33. Geometric similarity   83
  Session 34. An uneventful session   86
  Session 34. Almost calculating probabilities   87
  Session 36. A game of three dice   90
  Session 37. How many rectangles?   92
  Session 38. Losing my grip   94
  Session 39. Back on track   96
  A short excursion into the past.   97
  The programming language *Kid*   100
  Session 40. First encounter with Dienes blocks   105
  Session 41. More of the same (robots and Dienes blocks)   107
  Session 42. Snowflakes   109
  Session 43. On certain properties of addition   111
  Session 44. Magic squares   115
  Session 45. Generalized chains   117
  Session 46. Isomorphic problems   119
  Session 47. The end of the story about $\binom{5}{2}$.   120
  Session 48. True and false statements.   122
  A bit of programming, just with Dima   123
  Session 49. Thinking about symbols   125
  Session 50. A double anniversary   128
  Session 51. Which path is longer?   129
  Session 52. Breaking a code   131
  Session 53. A genealogical tree   132
  Session 54. The end of the school year   134

Chapter 5.   Notation, abstraction, mathematics, and language   137
  Symbols for words   137
  "Simplified" notation?   139
  Each person has more than one type of intelligence   141
  Teaching mathematics as a native tongue   144

Chapter 6.   The Boys' Math Circle, Year Three   149
  Session 55. Logical problems   149
  Session 56. Construction foreman   152
  Session 57. Who is booter, Gobr or Stoon?   154
  Session 58. Floor plans   158
  A long hiatus   160

Session 59. What does the other person see?   164
Session 60. Reflection   167
Session 61. How do you add invisible numbers?   169
Session 62. Which room is larger?   172
Session 63. Reason versus chance   173
Session 64. We battle against the odds, again   176
Session 65. Homeomorphism   180
Session 66. Topology   183
Session 67. Four colors   184
Miscellaneous jokes, conversations, and puzzles   185

Chapter 7. The Boys' Math Circle, Final Six Months   195
Session 68. Calendar conundrum   195
Session 69. Oral puzzles   197
Session 70. More programming   200
Session 71. Classroom puzzles ... almost   203
Session 72. Subprograms   205
Session 73. Odd numbers and squares   208
Session 74. The geometry of numbers   210
Session 75. The Mayans   212
Session 76. All things must end, sometime   214

Chapter 8. At Home and in School   217
Mathematical discussions, with sad digressions about school   217
First graders   234

Chapter 9. The Girls' Math Circle, Year One   239
Introduction   239
Session 1. Piaget's phenomena, again   246
Session 2. Princes and princesses   251
Session 3. How many differences?   253
Session 4. Building from diagrams   256
Session 5. Permutations   259
Session 6. The boy's morning   261
Session 7. Play trumps science   262
Session 8. Between two mirrors   264
Session 9. In the courtyard   266
Session 10. Bi-colored cubes   270
Session 11. Fives   271

Chapter 10. The Girls' Math Circle, Year Two   273
Session 12. Something's amiss with probability theory   273
Session 13. Intersecting classes again   275
Session 14. The Tower of Hanoi   277
Session 15. Towers of equal height   278
Session 16. Turning $90°$ 280

Session 17. Snowflakes   281
Session 18. Faces, vertices, and edges of a cube   282
Session 19. The wolf, the goat, and the cabbage   286
Session 20. A chain with one difference   290

Epilogue   295

Index of Math, Pedagogy, and Psychology   299

Foreword to the American Edition

A question of culture

When I was a grad student at UC Berkeley (in the late 1980s), it was understood, among my American classmates, that the Eastern Europeans were simply *better*. They weren't genetically superior; indeed, many of my American classmates, myself included, were themselves descended from Eastern European immigrants. And we knew that we weren't stupid. Many of us had excelled at mathematical olympiads, even at the international level. But at Berkeley, the Eastern Europeans — students and faculty alike — were known for their *intensity*. American-dominated seminars might last for one polite hour; in contrast, a Russian or Rumanian seminar would go on for an entire argumentative evening. Some of us joked that the Russians really came from the planet Krypton, attaining super powers when they came to live among us.

All joking aside, we fledgling mathematicians understood that the single most important thing was not raw intelligence or knowledge (Americans tend to lag behind in the latter compared to all international students). What mattered was *passion*. The way to become successful in mathematics, like almost every endeavor, is to care about it, to love it, to obsess over it. And in this, Eastern Europeans had a clear superiority, a *cultural* advantage. They had been trained, from an early age, to love mathematics more intensely.

For many years, dating from at least the Sputnik era, America has suffered from educational inferiority complex. We try to catch up, hunting for the secret ingredients that other nations use. Should we adopt the Singapore curriculum? Put our kids in after-school *Kumon* programs? Teach them meditation? Yoga?

There's nothing wrong with any of this; examining the practices of others' is bound to be enriching. But it's not the ingredients that really matter. There is no single magical special sauce. What you need is a *culture* of intellectual inquiry, and one that fits.

Of the many laudable practices around the world, one that resonates particularly well with the American mathematical community is the Eastern

European notion of a *mathematical circle*.[1] Most math circles have several features that distinguish them from simple math clubs.

First, they are *vertically integrated*: young students may interact with older students, college students, graduate students, industrial mathematicians, professors, even world-class researchers, all in the same room. The circle is not so much a classroom as a gathering of young initiates with elder tribespeople, who pass down *folklore*.

Second, the "curriculum," such as it is, is dominated by *problems*, rather than specific mathematical topics. A problem, in contrast to an exercise, is a mathematical question that one doesn't know how, at least initially, to approach.[2] For example, "Compute 4 times 3" is an exercise for most people, but a problem for a very young child. Computing 4^{37} is also an exercise, conceptually very much like the first, certainly harder, but only in a "technical" sense. And a question like "Evaluate $\int_2^7 e^{5x} \sin 3x \, dx$" is also an exercise — for calculus students — a matter of "merely" knowing the right algorithm, and how to apply it.

Problems, by contrast, do not come with algorithms attached. By their very nature, they require *investigation*, which is both an art and a science, demanding technical skill along with psychological strategies, what I call the "three Cs" of concentration, confidence, and creativity. Math circles teach students these skills, not with formal instruction, but by *doing math* and observing others doing math. Students learn that a problem worth solving may require not minutes, but possibly hours, days, or even years of effort. They work on some of the classic folklore problems, and discover how these problems can help them investigate other problems. They learn how not to give up; how to turn errors or failures into opportunities for more investigation. A child in a math circle learns to do exactly what a research mathematician does; indeed, he or she does independent research, albeit on a lower level, and often — although not always — on problems that others have already solved.

Finally, many math circles have a culture similar to a sports team, with intense comaraderie, respect for the "coach," and healthy competitiveness (managed wisely, ideally, by the "coach"). The math circle culture is often complemented by a variety of problem solving contests, often called "olympiads."

For a number of years, I and many others have worked hard to bring this math circle culture to the United States, not by imposing any rigid models, but simply by getting mathematical "grownups" together with youngsters to work on interesting problems. The past dozen years or so have seen an

---

[1]*P. Z.'s Note:* The term in English comes from the Russian математическии кружок (matematicheskiĭ kruzhok), which literally means "mathematical little circle."

[2]*P. Z.'s Note:* Many people use the two words "problem" and "exercise" interchangeably. I am much in debt to Titu Andreescu (originally from Romania), who first explained to me the utility of explicitly distinguishing between them. In fact, this distinction is quite explicit in all Russian textbooks, starting in the first grade.

explosion of math circles around the country, aided by organizations such as the Mathematical Sciences Research Institute (MSRI) in Berkeley. These circles are not that similar to one another, nor are they exact replicas of Russian circles. They have varying degrees of intensity, competitiveness, rigor. And virtually none of them involve very young children. Math circles for preschoolers are rare!

What this book is, what this book is not, and why you should read it

Which brings us to the book that you hold in your hands. In 2006, MSRI sponsored a trip to Russia, to visit specialized math schools and math circles in St. Petersburg and Moscow. Our host in Moscow was the remarkable Moscow Center for Continuous Mathematical Education (MCCME), described below on p. 13.

MCCME had just published Alexander Zvonkin's *Malyshi i Matematika* (Kids and Math), and we were captivated by his account of his experiences conducting a math circle in his apartment for *preschoolers* in the 1980s. We brought the book back, one of the "artifacts" that we collected, in the hopes of translating it into English.

Luckily, Zvonkin's wife Alla Yarkho was an English teacher, and she prepared a preliminary translation, which was then modestly edited and annotated into the version you see now.

As anyone who has taught or raised young children knows, mathematical education for little kids is a real mystery. What are they capable of? What should they learn first? How hard should they work? Should they even "work" at all? Should we push them, or just let them be?

There are no correct answers to these questions, and Zvonkin deals with them in classic math-circle style: He doesn't ask and then answer a question, but shows us a problem — be it mathematical or pedagogical — and describes to us what happened. His book is a narrative about what he did, what he tried, what worked, what failed, but most important, *what the kids experienced.*

This book is *not* a guidebook. It does not purport to show you how to create precocious high achievers. It is just one person's story about things he tried with a half-dozen young children. On the other hand, if you are interested in running a math circle, or homeschooling children, you will find this book to be an invaluable, inspiring resource. It's not a "how to" manual as much as a "this happened" journal.

Zvonkin writes in great detail about the various creative activities he did. But it is much more than a mathematical narrative. His focus is much more on the children than on the mathematics. He constantly struggles to get into their heads, to see the world as they do.

Does he succeed? Not always! Indeed, what is remarkable about this book, one of its greatest charms, is that it is partly a chronicle of failures.

An exemplary problem solver, Zvonkin tries things, sees if they work. If they don't — which happens more often than you'd think — he tries to figure out why, and moves on, trying something different. That's how math gets done, and that's how preschool math circles happen, as well.

But don't worry, Zvonkin did not subject his kids to a variety of weird experiments. His "failures" were minor compared to what he accomplished. Whether an activity "worked" or not, what he did was to get very, very young children seriously, and lovingly, engaged in mathematics.

How did he do it? You'll need to read the book to *really* find out. Just about every page contains a really clever teaching idea, a cool math problem, and an inspiring and funny story. It is impossible, not to mention unfair, to reduce this book to a few bullet points. Nevertheless, since this is the *American* edition, here's an "executive summary:"

(1) *Have fun!* Of course, if it's not enjoyable, kids will be turned off; this is just common sense. But it's deeper than that: humor relieves stress, builds community, enhances confidence. Zvonkin gives many examples that show how laughter saves the day.

(2) *Prepare carefully*, even though things never turn out the way you planned. Zvonkin sometimes criticizes his lack of preparation, and often thinks things up on the spot, but a remarkable feature of his circle was the loving attention that he (and his wife, Alla) gave to conceiving and creating a multitude of cards, pictures, games, etc. The serendipitous moments, of which there are many, some quite successful, do not happen in a vacuum; they are nourished by hours of prior thininking and working.

(3) *Recognize the individuality of each child.* Another common-sense idea, but one that is easy to forget. Not only is every kid different, but they change from minute to minute. Zvonkin is a harsh judge of himself, frequently confessing to impatience and insensitivity. But in fact, this introspective self-criticism is what keeps him connected with his kids. It is only the teachers who worry about their insensitivity who have a chance to actually listen to their students. And indeed, this book is nothing if not a detailed record of listening, observing, and mind-reading.

(4) *Use physical objects ("manipulatives") whenever possible*, engaging children with the "real" world. Little kids don't learn by listening to lectures. They have to touch, move, count, cut, glue, draw, etc. This is especially important in our modern computer-dominated age. Zvonkin tells a poignant story, "You can touch it!" (p. 237) about kids in a computer lab who'd rather play with an antique calculator that has a handle that *turns*. Throughout the book, we learn that people, not just young children, do not think in a vacuum; part of what makes us human is our connection to the physical world. Teachers who ignore this do so at their peril.

(5) *Don't explain much. Let them figure it out.* Any teacher or parent knows that this is easier said than done, and Zvonkin relates many examples of his own struggles to let his kids flounder and grapple with difficulties, and the joy he feels when kids tackle hard questions that *they raise themselves.*

(6) *Be flexible, including when interpreting the above rules.* A recurrent theme in the book is the danger of rigidity. Zvonkin discovers that his best sessions are the well-prepared, yet serendipitous ones; where he tries something that he invested a lot of planning in, but it doesn't go as planned, so he changes gears. Conversely, some of his worst experiences happen when he sticks to his guns, against his better judgement.

A final rule may be, "don't hesitate to get help from other disciplines." Zvonkin himself ventured rather deeply into computer science and developmental psychology, and his book includes interesting ruminations about how kids learn in general. He is not an expert, his sample is small, so these ruminations are admittedly speculative. But they are thought provoking. For in the end, the goal is not really getting kids to think about math, as wonderful as that is. The goal is just getting them to think, period.

The American reader may be surprised, as I was, by Zvonkin's strong critique of the Soviet school system. Our inferiority complex conditions us to think that other school systems must be better. This book paints a more complex picture: it's not the schools themselves that make the difference, but the extra-curricular culture that supplements, or as Zvonkin may argue, counteracts them. School, in Zvonkin's eyes, is not unlike its American counterpart: something to be endured, while the real learning happens elsewhere. In school, you learn algorithms. At the circle, you learn investigation, and you have fun.

How to use this book

We hope that this book finds a wide audience: teachers, parents, mathematicians, and students. Since some of our readers may not be professional mathematicians, we have endeavored to make the book as accessible as pos-sible. There are extensive explanatory footn index, which only references mathematical, pe topics. Bold-faced topics are especially importa comer to mathematical circles, for example, yo up the items referenced as **folklore problems** the **manipulatives** references will show you th that Zvonkin used.

Using the index and notes in this way will a jump right in and get ideas for his or her own e you should, at some point, read the entire book it is not just a catalog of enrichment resources!

And if you are a beginner, you may want to explore a few other resources to help you get started. Zvonkin describes many books that he used, but most are in Russian. Here are some excellent English-language companions to this book. Please note, however, that all of them involve more advanced mathematics than this book!

- If you read nothing else, read anything by Martin Gardner, the former editor of the "Mathematical Games" column of *Scientific American*. His columns have been collected in many books, and now most of them are available on a single CD.

- There are a number of excellent books that describe other math circles. Two of them are also volumes in the *Mathematical Circles Library* series: *Circle in a Box* by Sam Vandervelde, and *A Decade of the Berkeley Math Circle: The American Experience, Volume I*, by Zvezdelina Stankova and Tom Rike. Both are filled with specific and practical details about many different activities. In addition, *Mathematical Circles*, by Fomin, Genkin, and Itenberg (American Mathematical Society, volume #7 of the *Mathematical World* series) is a highly recommended account of Russian math circle activities for older children.

- Many recently written books contain delightful ideas of interesting problems and activities. My two personal favorites are Ravi Vakil's *A Mathematical Mosaic* and James Tanton's *Solve This*. Both books concentrate on fairly elementary material; the second one in particular is one of the few books that pays attention to *physical* activities.

- Besides Wikipedia (which is quite reliable for mathematics, compared to, say, politics), there are a number of good online resources. The aforementioned MCCME has many English-language items[1]. Cut the Knot[2] is an extensive "Interactive Mathematics Miscellany," maintained by a Russian immigrant, Alexander Bogomolny. Visiting the National Association of Math Circles[3] and the Math Teachers' Circle Network[4] will introduce you to an ever-growing community of math circles in this country, providing you with useful contacts as well as mathematical help.

  At a more advanced level, the premier site in the world for problem-solving activities, at least in English, is the Art of Problem Solving.[5] This site includes forums, online classes, books, etc.

---

http://www.mccme.ru
://cut-the-knot.com
/www.mathcircles.org
ww.mathteacherscircle.org
problemsolving.com

About Russian names and schools

Russian names

Most of the names used in this book are nicknames. For recurring characters we mostly use the English equivalents of these nicknames.[1] Here is a table of equivalents.

Translated Nickname	Russian Nickname	Birth Name	Gender
Andy	Andryusha	Andrei	male
Dima	Dima	Dmitry	male
Dinah	Dina	Dina	female
Jane	Zhenya	Evgenia	female
Gene	Zhenya	Evgenii	male
Pete	Petya	Pyotr	male
Sandy	Sanya	Aleksandra	female
Sasha	Sasha	Aleksandr	male

Grades and grading

In Russia, children start primary school between 6 and 7 years of age, about a year later than American children go into kindergarten. Primary school is four years long; what we call "grades" in the United States are called "classes" in Russia. A child in his or her first year of school is thus called a "first-classer" (первоклассник; pervoklassnik). We've translated this by "first-grader", but have sometimes used the expression "school year" or just "year" for later years, since the Russian tenth class (for instance) is by no means the equivalent of our tenth grade—indeed, at the time of the book's writing it was more like our twelfth grade, the last year before college.

Russian grading, i.e., evaluations, use a 5-point scale, with "5" denoting the top grade (equivalent to an American "A") and "1" a very seldom used worst grade (the "2" mark also indicates failure).

Acknowledgments

The American edition of this book would not have been possible without very generous help—in a variety of ways—from Tatiana Shubin, Mark Saul, Alla Yarkho, and MSRI (in particular, David Eisenbud, Jim Sotiros, and Silvio Levy).

And of course, I am indebted to Alexander Zvonkin!

Paul Zeitz
San Francisco, 2010

---

[1]This was a decision of the series editor, to avoid a pervasive sense of foreignness that is absent from the original.

Introduction

A Parent's Journal

This book is an example of the literary genre known as the "parent's journal." Children grow and many things happen to them, and their parents diligently record this in a notebook. Years later this proves to be absolutely gripping reading. Especially for the parents. No wonder, this is about their own children, and at such a tender age! And indirectly, it is about their own youth.

How often, dear reader, have you had to scan photos of children; not your own, but others? Guests arrive, pull out a stack of snapshots, and there you go! By the end of the second dozen you try to stifle your yawns but they want to go on to the bitter end. They find everything concerning their children and grandchildren irresistibly fascinating, while your only thought is how all the kids look alike!

Today, presenting this book before you, my feelings are very mixed. I would like to be an objective and impartial observer — but I can't. My wife, Alla Yarkho, is usually a severe and demanding critic. But each time she gets hold of this text, she starts rereading it again and again and is unable to put it aside. Our normal ironic attitude evaporates, replaced by altogether different emotions. This book is about our children; our son, Dima, and our daughter, Jane. The story is about their early years but it is also about their friends. However, we were undeniably much more attentive and observant towards our own children than towards others. This author must answer the harsh question: why should this book be interesting for an outsider? Why should it be of any interest, not only for our family, but for others as well?

I suppose that the answer is that this is not merely a journal, but a journal of a mathematical circle. When Dima was 3 years and 10 months I gathered three of his pals of roughly the same age (or a bit older) and started a mathematical circle. This book describes that unusual experience, and it can also be read as an exercise book of mathematical puzzles for pre-school children. But it also contains descriptions of the children's reactions, what they did and did not understand, and what kind of psychological problems and misunderstandings I encountered in the process.

Most likely, if someone wrote a book containing algebra or geometry problems, and accompanied each problem with a true story of how the students wrestled with it, it would make interesting reading. But with young children, it becomes incomparably more interesting. The evolution of their reasoning, the paths and turns taken by their intellect are much more visible, more vivid. When I started the circle I had no idea how gripping and absorbing that would be. As a result my reading for many years to come was largely composed of books on teaching and psychology; later it broadened to include subjects like linguistics, psychiatry, ethology, and behavioral genetics. I discovered a vast new world; I became richer and, hopefully, wiser — all this thanks to my children.

Pre-school mathematics is relatively simple and thus is accessible to any reader, not just specialists. This makes the potential book audience quite large: teachers, parents, grandparents, math lovers, psychologists, philosophers — you name it. Well, I've managed to convince myself that my book is interesting not just to me. Now I can, with clean conscience, recommend it to you, dear reader. (I must confess however, without false modesty, that many friends who read the manuscript version of my journal have urged me for some time to edit it into book form. Numerous photocopies of the manuscript circulated first in Moscow and later all over the world. This interest has not diminished in the past 20 years; yet another argument for me to create this book.)

Why a circle? Why a journal?

A circle, like any other form of systematic activity, is a way of imposing self-discipline. It's possible to work with children without any circle: now and then you ask questions, assign problems, and have discussions. But in the real world, this almost never works, and soon the whole project evaporates: Yesterday you were too busy, today you are not in the mood or too tired. And why does it have to be this very minute? I will certainly have time later, someday... As a result, nothing much gets accomplished.

But if you know that tomorrow at eleven sharp you will welcome four kids and will have to entertain them for thirty minutes, the situation radically changes. Whether you want to or not, you have to sit somewhere secluded and try to think of something. If you don't have any ideas you will have to borrow them from books. And when you think about something persistently, sooner or later you will have new ideas, which you would never have had had you not been duty-bound.

Or perhaps you get a new idea, but it requires preparation: you have to draw, or use scissors or to glue. To do that, you need more specific obligations than just a noble aspiration to do something "for the sake of the family."

Incidentally, kids, too, enjoy rituals in their play. If adults start interfering with their games out of the blue and pestering them with puzzles, they will get upset and will wish to get rid of this untimely disturbance as soon as possible. But it's completely different if they know that once a week, on a special day and at a special time we all get together to deal with serious things.

That was a short answer to the question, "Why a circle?"

As for the journal, I did not keep it right from the beginning, and, above all, I did not attach any great importance to our sessions. You will see that the journal starts with the 21st session. The first "20 weeks" do not represent five months, as one could think, but twice as many, because of summer vacation and other periods without sessions. You shouldn't think that because we had decided to have our lessons regularly, once a week, that we actually followed this decision to the letter.

But one day, about six months after the start, some of my friends asked me to tell them what we had been doing. I was happy to open my mouth to talk, but instead of a flood of ideas and puzzles, I paused awkwardly, discovering that I really remembered very few details. What I did remember was the general feeling of enthusiasm and overflow of kids' energy that I felt throughout our sessions. But the specific details seemed to have been lost somewhere along the way. (I felt somewhat like a person who lost his leg: he feels his leg while it no longer exists.)

I did not expect such a dirty trick from my own memory: I was upset and embarrassed. After this meeting I put down what little I still remembered, and decided that from then on, I would write some sort of summary at the end of each session. This way I would at least have a list of puzzles from which I would then be able to reconstruct the rest of the session. It is curious that already at that moment I was thinking about the rest of the session; apparently I felt intuitively how insufficient the mere list of puzzles was going to be. Very soon I made my first "pedagogical discovery:" I found that a record of just the puzzles wasn't very meaningful. It is not the puzzles, nor their solutions, that are interesting, but the process, the path that connects them. Mathematical problems for preschool kids are, objectively, trivial (inventing them, however, is not trivial). On the other hand, it can take a child several years to solve a puzzle that somebody sets him. I mean it — several years! You will see many examples. During all this time the child's mind never rests: pacing and racing, like one possessed, alert to anything that may pertain to the puzzles. This process of solution is the most interesting thing of all.

Thus my list of puzzles gradually added more and more comments, narratives, and anecdotes, and began to include not only mathematical remarks but those of a more general and sometimes "theoretical" nature, finally resulting in this journal. The next stage was feedback between the journal and the circle. When you put to paper your ideas and your thoughts, they give rise to new ideas, new points of view, new puzzles and topics. Your understanding deepens. Even the capacity to observe seems to be sharpened. Sometimes you recall something that went unnoticed in the excitement of the session, and you could have easily forgotten it, had it not been noted. This symbiosis between the circle and the journal worked grew so that it became hard to imagine one without the other.

Last but not least: My children, now grown, have read my journal. They remember many things well, but sometimes their version completely contradicts mine. At my request they added their commentaries which enriched the whole project with a new dimension. One of my friends said that it gave the journal a stereoscopic effect.

Should journals be edited?

I think — yes, absolutely. Long ago, some authors said, "These pages will never be cheapened by the printing press." This was usually insincere: they secretly believed that thrilled, grateful descendants would find their work, would be enraptured by their modesty and sincerity ("imagine that it was never intended to be made public!"), would publish it and that would bring them eternal glory. It is really simple to catch such an author off-guard: he endlessly explains to himself what he would seem to know perfectly well. As a matter of fact, it is the reader who needs all these explanations, not the author.

If, however, the journal was truly intended for the author only and then someone else read it, it could lead to monstrous distortions. Imagine the following situation: there is a person who has my infinite respect, so great that sometimes it would literally come close to worship. However, I am not blind to certain small (or not so small) flaws or funny traits of his character. In the journal "for myself" I can permit myself an ironic, mocking or even an irritated remark, without necessarily reminding myself of my great respect towards this person. ("Only don't think I do not have immense respect for him" ... don't think — who?) But if an outsider would happen to read this text later, he might misinterpret it, seeing only the sarcasm and not knowing about my respect.

Here is another, more pertinent example. I am writing about kids, or so it seems. In fact, I am only writing about one aspect of their life: namely, their relationship with mathematics. In fact, I am describing half an hour out of every two weeks of their life; it would be crazy to think that a child can be reduced in this way. Each of them has numerous interests, numerous problems, and many other talents. But when I myself read my journal, I sometimes forget about this, so it's only natural that a reader who has never met the kids personally, would understand so little about them. (I develop this idea later, but only concerning my daughter — see p. 241.) Not to mention the fact that the former kids have long ago turned into adults. Soon that will be their own kids who will read the book about their moms and dads. The journal that once pretended to be a documentary would more and more become fiction.

That would not be true to say that my journal was a strictly intimate document. It was rather a technical thing. I wrote it for myself but its contents were never secret and I was willingly sharing it with all those interested. But its technical nature created its own problems. I would not explain for my own sake the problem of the wolf, the goat, and the cabbage, or describe in detail the Tower of Hanoi.[1] Also, the original text had many repetitions, notes that needed decoding or additional explanations. (I left some repetitions as they are, especially in cases when on the basis of the same premises I came to quite different conclusions — this way it looks more authentic.)

In short, there are many reasons, both ethical and technical, why my journal needed very serious editing. That's why for many years I would refuse all suggestions to publish it "as is."

Why then it took me so long to edit it? What was I doing all this time?

Well, life is life. For starters.

Anyway, I think it's time to stop beating about the bush and get down to business.

A novice's reflections on pre-school math

When does it begin?

All of you must have seen such scenes many times: a young mother hides behind a curtain, then emerges, smiling, with a "Peek-a-boo," then disappears again. Her toddler greets each of these appearances by clapping his hands and shrieking with glee. Both are utterly happy. And both have no idea that what they are doing is mathematics.

The last phrase is not there merely to shock the reader or to stun him with a far-fetched paradox. I mean it. According to psychologists, up to the age of eighteen months, the most important intellectual problem which a child faces is to discover the law of object permanence. This means that the objects out of sight have not completely disappeared; they still exist somewhere, although we can't see them. The child discovers that such an important object as "mother," even if she has disappeared behind the curtain, is still there and will soon reappear from behind that same curtain.

As a child grows, so does his understanding of the world. A very small girl is playing an exciting game: she picks up blocks scattered on the floor and hands them, one by one, to her dad accompanying each gift with a jubilant cry: "Here!" Her Dad takes each block and she laughs happily. She has learned the word "Here" only recently and tries to use it as much as possible. But suddenly her little clumsy hands seize two blocks at once. She thinks for a few moments and then — "Eureka" — she offers them to her dad saying: "Here-here!"

---

[1]*P. Z.'s Note:* These are two classic "folklore" problems, see p. 43 and p. 286.

To paraphrase Pushkin, "It is a most fascinating pastime to follow a little one's thoughts." [1] By the age of two many things have already been mastered. A boy of two tries to wake up his dad in the morning:

"Papa, are you asleep?"

"No I am not," answers his dad rubbing his eyes. "I am in the kitchen, having tea."

His son is bewildered: this contradicts everything he knows. Just in case he runs off to the kitchen to check. His return is triumphant:

"No, you are *not* in the kitchen. You're here, you're here!"

Next time he won't be fooled that easily. But I would like to insist on this moment of independent research when he ran off to the kitchen to check. Quite intuitively I feel it to be a very important quality and wish children to preserve it as long as possible.

Counting in Japanese

Somewhat later the kid will be taught math "for real." As a rule it means that s/he will have to learn how to count. Certainly, it is important to know how to count. But adults don't always fully realize what is at stake here.

Let's try to get into the child's shoes and learn to count, but in Japanese. Here are the first ten numbers: *ichi, ni, san, shi, go, roku, shichi, hachi, kyu, ju.* The first assignment is to learn this sequence by heart. You will see: it is not that easy! When you have managed to do that, pass on to the second assignment: learn how to count backwards, from *ju* to *ichi.* Once you have done that, try and calculate. How much is *roku* and *san*? *Shichi* minus *go*? *Hachi* divided by *shi*? And now a sum for you: Mother bought at the market *kyu* apples and gave each of *shi* children *ni* apples. How many apples are left? There is just one rule: you are not allowed to translate into English, even mentally. After a bit of practice, it becomes involuntary. Sometimes we are not even aware of it.

I was able to appreciate the intellectual feat of children learning how to count only much later, when I came to live in France. I have been living here for more than 15 years now, but I still have trouble with French numerals. The French have a peculiar system for the names of the numbers between 70 and 99. After sixty-nine they have sixty-ten (70), then sixty-eleven (71), sixty-twelve (72), etc.; after sixty-nineteen there appears four-twenties (80), four-twenties-one (81), four-twenties-two (82)...and after four-twenties-nine (89) there comes again four-twenties-ten (90), four-twenties-eleven (91), four-twenties-twelve (92)...four-twenties-nineteen (99) and only then one hundred. When someone gives me a telephone number quickly or the dates of a famous person, believe me, it is not easy to catch. Fortunately, I do not have to add or to subtract.

---

[1]The great Russian poet Pushkin once said, "It is a most fascinating pastime to follow a great man's thoughts."

(By the way, this is the origin of the funny answer of a French elementary school pupil, often cited in the teaching literature: when asked, "How much is twenty times four," he answered "Four-twenties, because multiplication is commutative.")

At last you can fluently count up to *ju*. How long did it take you? A week? A month? Now you are aware of the fact this is not merely a problem of rote learning — if it had been the case, you would have made it in an hour. But if not rote learning, then what? Are you able to isolate from your experience purely mathematical problems which are always present in counting but remain hidden, unnoticed? Not that easy, is it?

But perhaps it's all for the better. Otherwise enthusiasts of early teaching, in their hurry to pull a kid up the stairs, would have rushed to explain to him what he is not yet able to understand. And he could have arrived there on his own.

Nursery school geometry

Along with counting comes basic geometry. Traditionally, it is thought that kids should learn (a bit) about geometrical figures and shapes such as triangles, squares, circles, etc., and also simple measuring. But think: if a child quite easily tells a fork from a spoon, why it should ever be difficult for him to tell a square from a triangle? In fact, this is not at all difficult! The really difficult point is understanding logical relationships and what actions can be perfomed on geometric shapes. For instance, many elementary school pupils believe that a square put sideways is no longer a square but a quadrilateral (Figure 1). On the other hand, for example, understanding the question, "What is there more of, squares or quadrilaterals?" requires exceptional logic.

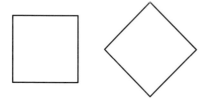 Figure 1. The left figure is a square. And the right one? Kids often think it is not: in their eyes a turned square loses the status of a square and becomes merely a quadrilateral.

From this point of view squares and triangles immediately lose their primacy: puzzles with forks and spoons as objects are no less mathematical if there is food for thought. To put it otherwise, school mathematics deals with "numbers and shapes" and this is how it should be. However, we cannot tell kids much about these objects. This, in principle, could mean that we cannot deliver to kids any worthy mathematical information. As a matter of fact, this is not true. Actually we have plenty of interesting things to show them, but we have to be careful to develop the right approach.

But what is the right approach? Well, there are as many opinions as there are people. Below I cite some of them (sometimes exaggerating, to make my point of view clearer).

Opinions

(1) *Our contemporary high-tech society requires children to be exposed to much more mathematics, even before formal schooling begins.*

Too boring! To hell with all these requirements!

(2) *It's dangerous, you know, to stuff a child's brain with such complicated stuff. All these integrals and the like!*

My God, who mentioned integrals?

(3) *Can you imagine this?! He makes little kids study probability theory! Adults with a higher education fail to understand, and kids cope perfectly well! I always said that the potential of our brain remains unknown, especially in early childhood.*

Dear enthusiastic observer, I am afraid you are mistaken: we do not study probability theory though we do observe certain probabilistic phenomena. (A person at a bus stop trying to guess which bus will come first is doing the same.)

(4) *At an early age, children usually have an excellent memory and capacity to learn new things. Furthermore, they really pay attention to what adults say. Therefore, they should be fed as much information as possible. Later, when their critical thinking skills improve, and they will not want to do things that do not make sense for them, we should give them more time for reflection and add motivation to their learning.*

I got this point of view from the internet. The author is a university professor, a neurophysiologist. Since I do not divulge his name, permit me to frankly express my point of view: this crap does not deserve a response.

(5) *I don't see why we should stuff kids' heads with this nonsense. Leave them alone; let them have a normal childhood!*

Here my opponent has raised two issues: one concerns "nonsense," the other, "normal childhood." I won't argue about nonsense; after all, this is a matter of taste. But I was doing with kids what I enjoy doing myself, and this aspect of our lessons seems to me very important.

When my articles appeared, I, quite unexpectedly, found myself in a role totally alien to my nature, namely, as a giver of advice. I got letters from parents. One of them (a mother) vividly wrote, "I've hated math since childhood. But I know that it's very important for a child's intellectual development. Could you advise me on how to do math with my son?" Fortunately I knew how I should reply in this case. I told her, "Don't do any math with your son if you hate it. Do with him only what you yourself enjoy doing, and then your engagement will be a source of joy for both of you. If you like to bake, say, do this with your son..." The only thing that worried me was that she might feel insulted by my advice; she might think that I considered her not smart enough to do math.

But I do have a quarrel with the idea of a "normal childhood." Imagine the following scene. We are sitting on the bank of a river watching a solitary wasp who makes a hole in the packed sand. When it finishes the hole, it will fly away and soon come back with enough food for her progeny, e.g., paralyzed spiders, then it will lay eggs inside the prey and close the hole. The famous biologist and ethologist Nikolaas Tinbergen demonstrated that wasps navigate by landmarks: we can put a shoe to the right of the nest and a shell to the left, and when the wasp flies away, we can move both a meter aside. A couple of minutes later the wasp comes back and, exactly as it has been discovered by Tinbergen, it lands not near the nest but a meter aside, between the shoe and the shell. This experience was welcomed with a lot of enthusiasm not only by our children but also by other kids who were on the beach. (An interesting observation is that it occurred to none of them to squash the wasp.) Well, does this sort of pastime correspond to your idea of a normal childhood? It gave Tinbergen his Nobel Prize, which could provoke enthusiastic observer #3 above to say something pompously foolish about prodigies carrying out Nobel-Prize experiments.

If I taught kids anything at all, it was the idea that they should experience their world with openness and interest. I will always remember the words of my close friend Andrei Toom, the remarkable mathematician and teacher. I cite them here not to compliment me, but rather as a beautiful description of an ideal of teaching to which one must aspire:

What you teach them is not mathematics but a way of life.

A Short History of Our Circle

I found the date of our first session quite by chance: March 23, 1980. Our lessons with the boys went on for four years, with some regularity. By then, my daughter was older and I started a second circle, with her and her friends, which went on for two years. There were a few other attempts to launch circles with other children, but none of them lasted long. I did all that side by side with my permanent job (although my heart was not in it; see p. 11). A few times I even performed as a visiting "maestro" giving a master-class.

At some point, however, I mustered up my courage and went to teach in schools. First I led a circle at Dima's elementary school; then a few similar experiences, and then I did something completely crazy: threw myself headlong into full-time teaching in a Moscow elementary school (testing an experimental curriculum, and only for a month). Previously, I was an arrogant intellectual, always ready to criticize schools and teachers and give them sage advice. But this cruel experiment on myself really opened my eyes.

But I am getting ahead of things.

An important step in this story occurred when a friend of our family, the well-known psycholinguist Revekka Frumkina (whose home workshops I had attended),[1] having read my journal, took me to the editorial office of the magazine *Znanie — Sila* (Knowledge is Power) that soon afterwards published my two papers about the circle (no. 8, 1985, and no. 2, 1986). There was also a third paper but it did not reach the sudden popularity of the first two. A remarkable children's poet and teacher, Vadim Levin, even told me once that he considered them as classics of teaching literature. Here is what happened to them afterwards: some time later both were published in English in *The Journal of Mathematical Behavior* (no. 2, 1992, and no. 2, 1993); then were published on the web on four different sites, if I am not mistaken; then were reprinted in the Russian journal *Pre-school Education* (May and July 2000), this time with commentaries by Vadim Levin; later they became part of his book *Lessons for Parents* (Moscow, Folio, 2001). Quite recently the September First publishing house came out with a booklet entitled *Home School for Kids* with the same text. Unfortunately, in some publications (especially online), the name of Levin is missing. In this way some compliments by Levin to me seem to be made by myself. It is hard to rectify the situation.

Meanwhile, it was the beginning of *perestroika*.[2] Our close friend Stepan Pachikov organized in Moscow a computer club for children; the computers were offered by the World Chess Champion Garry Kasparov. At that time (1986) it was probably the only place in the Soviet Union where schoolchildren had access to computers. I was, predictably, entrusted with a group of the youngest kids. Then followed summer computer camps in Pereslavl'-Zalessky and a winter camp in Zvenigorod. There was another computer club for children, "Zodiac." It is hard to recall everything. I was very much in demand and everybody considered me an expert on pre-school math education. Eventually, I got involved with the so-called "Temporary Scientific Team School-1" predestined to prepare a reform of the entire school system; its formal head was the academician Velikhov, but its actual leader was Alexei Semenov. Among our many activities were the textbook *Algorithmica* for forms 5–7 (ages 12–15); its authors, in Russian alphabetic order, are A. K. Zvonkin, A. G. Kulakov, S. K. Lando, A. L. Semenov, A. K. Shen'; after several mimeographed publications, the Drofa publishing house came out with several editions, starting in 1986.[3] Some of the subjects that first

---

[1]*P. Z.'s Note:* The "home workshop" was a Soviet-era gathering of intellectuals at a participant's home. These gatherings did serious work, but without incurring official scrutiny.

[2]*P. Z.'s Note:* The reforms, begun by Gorbachev, which eventually led to the dissolution of the Soviet Union.

[3]The latest edition came out in 2006: A. K. Zvonkin, S. K. Lando, A. L. Semenov, *Informatica, Algorithmica: Textbook for 6th-year students*, Moscow, Prosveshchenie (publisher); "Education."

appeared at our circle were in a slightly more complicated form than that used in the textbook. I was amused to learn that the course was chosen for teaching freshmen at an American university.

· · ·

Then my life took a sudden turn, which relates to the circle, albeit indirectly. In 1989 I changed my job after 13 years in the "All-Union Research and Development Institute for Automation of the Gas and Oil Industry." Those who lived through the Soviet period know about these places: third-rate institutes of applied research, with guardians monitoring attendance, and annual missions to a *kolkhoz*[1] to help with their work; cordial and helpful relationships with like-suffering colleagues; extremely dull and useless work (nowadays the same people do quite meaningful and practical things but elsewhere). I hated my job but there was no chance I could ever find another one. And all of a sudden I found myself in the Scientific Council of Cybernetics of the USSR Academy of Sciences, in a team introducing computer science into school curricula. I think our results were far from brilliant but at that time we were full of enthusiasm and so carried away by our work that sometimes we were literally on the verge of physical exhaustion. Ignoring the larger forces of history, in terms of my life story it is clear that without the circle I would never have gotten this wonderful new job.

I still continued mathematical research. That is, side by side with research in teaching I was also doing scientific research in the domain of mathematics. But I radically changed my direction of research. Among other things, this change was stimulated by the fact that in the above-mentioned computer camp in Pereslavl'-Zalessky I found two colleagues equally enthusiastic about my new mathematical interests: Sergei Lando and George Shabat. We started working together and are still going strong: our joint monograph with Sergei Lando was recently (2004) published by Springer-Verlag, and the Russian translation appeared in 2010.

In 1990 I first visited France. Had I still worked in my former institute, there would be no question of traveling abroad. In the Council of Cybernetics the situation was utterly different. At that time I did not yet know my colleagues in my new research field. This trip got me oriented; I found people with similar interests working in Bordeaux. I went there once, then again; then I was invited as a visiting professor for a year. Eventually, I stayed on for good as a full professor. It's a strange turn of events, that the fact that I am a professor in Bordeaux today is largely due to my starting a mathematical circle for kids years ago.

---

[1]*P. Z.'s Note:* Collective farm. Zvonkin is referring to regular "volunteer" work solicited by the government.

Acknowledgments

My readers, intelligent folks, can easily guess the first people I will thank: the children. When I was young my parents would often pester me with, "You'll understand when you have kids of your own." That angered me: What is so special to understand?! Kids of your own — big deal! Everybody has kids, so what?

How could I know at that time that having a child brings about a completely new worldview? I am sure that some people, with more vivid imagination, can intuit this without having children of their own; for such people, when they do have kids, the changes may be less violent. But in my personal universe, my children were the Big Bang, and I thank them for it.

I am profoundly grateful to all the children who participated in our circles. It is hard to imagine how much I have learned from them. But I wish to tell them one thing. Quite honestly and as best as I could, I tried to share my attention equally among them — but I am afraid I did not always succeed. I hope I did not hurt anybody. However, if any of them has any lasting grudges, I can only say, "You'll understand when you have kids of your own."

I am grateful to my wife Alla Yarkho. First, because we had children: her part of the job is hard to overestimate. Second, because it's her who thought of the circle. You will see that in fact the whole thing was as much hers as mine. I am grateful for her moral support as well as her later insistence that I should prepare the journal for publishing. It goes without saying that throughout all these years she has been a proofreader, an editor, an adviser and simply a passionate reader.

Revekka Markovna Frumkina "launched" me. Thanks to her our family enterprise became popular. Rita Markovna (as her friends call her) is a godmother of numerous interesting projects. This is one of them. And our discussions helped to clarify my ideas.

Alexei Semenov was not only my official supervisor in the council of Cybernetics, but also served as an "elder advisor" (though he is younger than me). And his conviction that my work deserved a larger audience helped persuade me.

Alexander Shen' was one of the early readers of the handwritten notebooks and often urged me to publish them. Eventually, tired of my foot-dragging, he assembled a team of high school and college students to typeset the first version of this book. Vladimir Lugovkin, particularly, did an enormous job. At this point, I had no choice but to edit the book. And again the indispensable Shen' helped me by installing the Russian version of LaTeX onto my French computer, saving me years of work.

The list of acknowledgments is far from being finished — indeed, I did not even begin properly. But if I am going to continue this way, the reader will surely skip this part. So I will have to be brief: I am profoundly grateful to all those with whom I ever discussed this book, be these discussions long or short, who encouraged me with their interest. Thank you all, dear friends!

. . .

In Moscow, on Bolshoi Vlassievskii Lane (near Arbat Street) stands a building which houses a remarkable institution that has already become widely popular among mathematicians all over the world. It is called The Moscow Center for Continuous Mathematical Education.[1] "Continuous" here means "for all ages." It comprises a publishing house, the Independent University of Moscow and its post-graduate school, and also organizes numerous mathematical Olympiads and competitions for middle and high school. So why not include pre-school children? I am happy and proud that my book was published by MCCME. Besides, in a place like MCCME, one is bound to meet old friends. One of them, Vadim Bugaenko, was responsible for the initial stages of editing this book, even though it had never been his direct duty. Later his help also proved inestimable when we worked on the second and third Russian editions, as well as the English one that you are reading now. Readers often tend to credit the author with all the glory. They sometimes don't realize how complicated and multifaceted the process of editing can be.

I am grateful to the entire team but first and foremost to Mikhail Panov who, among other things, made all the drawings. (Experts will be able to appreciate his virtuoso skills to make real pictures by means of the META-POST software initially conceived as a tool for drawing graphic images for scientific papers.)

Last but not least, I must note the outstanding role played by my American colleagues Paul Zeitz and Silvio Levy, as well as by the entire publications department of MSRI. All the gratitude mentioned above to my Russian helpers applies equally to them. Finally, I'd like to note the important role played by the American Mathematical Society (AMS) in initiating an American edition of this book.

Two Disclaimers

First: I did not create all of the puzzles used in this book. I borrowed them from many different sources, including psychology and recreational math books, and friends. I preserved some in their original form, and altered others, often beyond recognition, during the course of the sessions. I forgot some of my sources long ago; others were lost when I moved to France. For some problems I do not even remember whether they are borrowed or mine. To pay back this debt to the world, I allow everybody to use them and

---

[1] See www.mccme.ru. This website is in Russian, but substantial portions are translated into English.

pledge not to sue anybody for plagiarism. On the contrary I will be glad (and even proud) if my inventions become part of teaching folklore.

Second: my stories are not stenographic reports. They were noted from memory, and it is not always easy to discern what kids say when they all talk at the same time. I am sure to have missed or misinterpreted some things. But I believe this is more or less obvious.

Chapter 1

The First Session:
Narrative and Reflections

(The first half of this chapter is based on my article, "Mathematics for Little Ones," published in *The Journal of Mathematical Behavior*, vol. 11, #2, 1992.)

A session in action

Our circle has four members: my son Dima and his three pals Gene, Pete, and Andy. Dima is the youngest, at 3 years, 10 months old; the eldest is Andy, who's almost five.

We sit down around a coffee table. I am nervous: will I be able to handle them? To begin with, I tell the children that we are going to do some math. To increase my authority I add that math is the most interesting science in the world. Of course, this is immediately followed by the question, "What is science?"

I have to explain, "Science is when you think a lot."

Andy is somewhat disappointed, "I thought there would be tricks." At home he has been told that I would be playing math and performing tricks.

"We'll have tricks too." I cut short the introduction and get down to business.

The first puzzle: I put eight buttons on the table. Without waiting for my instructions the boys rush to count them; apparently, despite their young age, they have already been indoctrinated with the idea that "math" means "counting." When they calm down I can explain the puzzle:

"Now put on the table as many coins."

We put 8 buttons and 8 coins into two parallel, equally spaced rows.

"Which are there more of, buttons or coins?"

The kids are puzzled, they hesitate before answering:

"Neither is more."

"That means equal," I say. "Now watch what I am going to do." And I move the coins apart making their row longer.

"And now, what are there more of?"

"Coins!" shout the kids together.

I ask Pete to count the buttons. We have already counted them four times, but Pete is not in the least surprised and sets off to count them for the fifth time.

"Eight."

I ask Dima to count the coins. He counts and announces the result: "Eight."

"Also eight?" I emphasize my words. "So as many coins as buttons?"

"No, there are more coins!," the boys insist with conviction.

To tell the truth, I knew beforehand they would answer in this way. This puzzle is one in the series of tests used in experiments by the great Swiss psychologist Jean Piaget (I will speak in more detail about the "Piaget phenomena" in the next section). Piaget showed that young children do not understand things that seem self-evident to adults: if several objects are moved or rearranged, that does not alter their number. Although I knew beforehand what the kids would say, I had not prepared any reasonable response! What would you have done if you had been in my shoes? What would you have told the kids?

Unfortunately the most frequent reaction of adults is to go out of their way to "explain." "How can it be?," might say an adult with feigned surprise. "More coins? But we have not added any! We've just moved them apart, that's all! Before there were as many buttons as coins, you said that yourself. So, how can there be more coins all of a sudden?" More loudly, "Of course there are as many buttons as coins!"

No matter how you try, this teaching strategy will get you nowhere. To be more precise, it will lead to an impasse. First, don't think that your logic will convince any child. Mastering logic comes much later than the law of number conservation. Until then, logic will not seem convincing to that age group. What is convincing is your intonation, which will show the kid that once again he did something wrong. Kids do not give up easily; their common sense is hard to beat down. But if you exercise sufficient pressure you get your way: they will cease trusting their intelligence and experience and will try instead to guess what the adult wants them to say. Adults in general demand lots of weird things: you can't draw on a wall; you have to go to bed in the middle of a game; you must not ask "When will Uncle George go home?" The same thing is happening now: I see perfectly well that there are more coins than buttons but for some reason I have to say they are as many.

The acceptance of mathematics as a ritual, where you have to pronounce certain incantations in a certain order, starts in elementary school, and sometimes survives through high school and beyond.

So what to do? Should you avoid these questions if you cannot talk about the answers?

On the contrary, questions can and must be asked. It's also very useful to exchange opinions. "And you, Gene, you think the same? You, Pete? Why? How many more coins are there?" You might even give your own point of view, but carefully, accompanied with all kinds of "I think," "probably," or "maybe." In other words, you should use all your adult authority not to impose "correct" answers but to convince a child of the importance of his own reasoning and intellectual efforts. And it is even more interesting to make him discover contradictions in his point of view.

"How many coins must we take away so that there again will be an equal number?"

"Two."

We take away two coins and re-count; we have 8 buttons and 6 coins.

"What is there more now?"

"Now it's equal."

Fine. Again I move the remaining coins apart and ask the same question. Now it turns out that 6 coins are more than 8 buttons.

"Why so?"

"Because you moved them apart."

We take away two more coins; then two more. What we have at last is shown in Figure 2.

Figure 2. There are 8 buttons in the upper row and 2 coins in the lower one. What is there more of, buttons or coins?

At this moment the boys start a heated discussion. Some still think there are more coins; others suddenly "see" that there are more buttons. It's time to stop and pass on to another puzzle. Let them think for themselves.

> *I was among those who said there were more coins. At first I agreed with the others and then just repeated without thinking. It seemed correct all the previous times (at least Dad did not say otherwise), so I did not see why this time I should change my mind. — Dima*

I did not have all these ideas at once, so in my story I've gotten a little ahead of events. What I am describing now are my later reflections and future sessions. We repeated the same puzzle in different guises. For instance, once we had two armies none of which could win because they had equal number of soldiers. Then soldiers of one army moved apart, their number increased and they started to win. The soldiers of the other army, having seen that, moved even further apart, etc. (Use your own imagination to finish the story.) We also had a puzzle where the fox and the cat wanted to swindle poor Pinocchio moving apart five golden coins and saying that their number grew. I learned not to expect easy victories. No matter what I do, the kids won't master the law of number conservation for another two or three years. Nor should they! Premature instruction is no more beneficial than premature birth. Every vegetable has its season; we must not run ahead of the natural course of things, including intellectual development. (I realize that this may seem strident. But I hope to persuade you of this point of view during the course of the book.)

However, as I have said earlier, all these reflections came later. During our first session, my intuition told me to stay away from explaining things, so I merely moved on to a new puzzle.

I took six matches and made different figures. After I have composed a new figure, I asked the kids, in turn, to count the matches. And each time there are six. — No, it won't do. My style has become too dry and too formal. Let's directly observe the kids and see what actually transpired.

Each result is welcomed by a burst of laughter and delight. Andy and Gene shout that there will always be six! Dima, rather impolitely, tries to wriggle matches out of my hands: he wants to make his own fanciful figure. Pete, on the other hand, is exquisitely polite and asks me whether I can give him several matches. In a few moments, their delight turns into chaos. I have to stop them, to listen attentively to what they shout ("Why do you think there will always be six?") and not to miss new turns of their reasoning: Dima has just made a three-dimensional figure — a "well" (Figure 3).

Figure 3. A "well" made of six matches.

I invite everybody to look at it. This time even Andy and Gene are not that sure we will have six matches. It's difficult to count the matches, the well is not very solid, it collapses, we restore it, count matches, it collapses again... Finally, Dima arrives at seven. The boys are a little puzzled, but not much surprised. So seven it is, even though it's a little strange.

I must reiterate — once more — that my task as a teacher is not to dictate "the truth" to the kids, but to stimulate their curiosity. The best I hope to achieve is that in a few days (or months), one of my boys will build a well of matches and count them, because he wants to investigate. Modest — but independent — research! And if this does not happen, I'll hope that it will happen another time, with another puzzle. (Indeed, this did happen several times.) Anyway, I only say something like "how interesting!" and "amazing!" in the hope that this way it will stick in their memory.

Children have remarkable memories. I can't help telling a story that occurred much later: We were discussing the properties of three figures made of cardboard (Figure 4). First, each figure has four angles. So we can call each of them a quadrilateral. That means we have three quadrilaterals. But all the angles of two of the shapes are right. That's why they are called rectangles. One of the rectangles is special: all its sides are equal. This

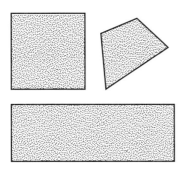

Figure 4. How many squares are there? How many rectangles? How many quadrilaterals? These questions are not easy even for adults.

is called a square. We can say that a square has three names: it may be called a square, a rectangle and a quadrilateral, and each of these names will be correct. The boys accept this information not without argument. They stubbornly try to think in terms of disjoint classes. As to their explanations, they make me think they have not yet comprehended the great law "the whole is bigger than its part." Ten minutes ago they were disputing whether dads and grandfathers were men and whether men were people. Now they refuse to call a square a rectangle: it is either one or the other. I intensively agitate for the rightful inclusion of squares as rectangles. By and by my lobbying starts to make headway. We sum up once more:

"How many squares do we have?"

"One."

"Rectangles?"

"Two."

"And quadrilaterals?"

"Three."

Everything seems to be OK, so now I can pass on to the last question (I've already mentioned it in the introduction):

"And in general, in life, what is there more of: squares or quadrilaterals?"

"Squares!" answer the boys together without a shade of hesitation.

"Because they are easier to cut out," explains Dima.

"Because there are many of them in houses, on roofs, on chimneys," explains Gene.

This is just the set-up of the story. The punchline came a year and a half later and without any prompting on my part. In summer, during a walk in the forest Dima suddenly told me, "Remember, Dad, you once gave us a puzzle on squares and quadrilaterals, what is there more of. Well, I think we did not give you the right answer then. In fact, there are more quadrilaterals."

And he rather intelligently explained why. Since then I've adhered to the principle that questions are more important than answers.

For decades, psychologists have been carrying out experiments attempting to teach children certain basic mathematical laws. Here is an example: Initially, a group of kids is tested to see whether they understand that if we squish or roll or otherwise modify the shape of a piece of modeling clay, the quantity of clay will not change. Those who do not understand are divided into two groups. One is left alone, as a control group, while psychologists start to work with the other trying to teach them the law of conservation of matter; they weigh, compare, show, and explain. Two weeks later they test the participants of both groups to see what the kids have learned. Most often than not the progress in both groups proves to be insignificant and more or less equal. As a rule, psychologists are perplexed why the kids who were taught so patiently never learned much. When I was reading about this, what startled me was the opposite: why the kids of the control group, whom nobody was teaching, managed to make some progress. After a few years of dealing with kids I think I know the answer: it happened because they were also asked questions.

Let us however return to our first session. Our next puzzle was yet another version of the same law of number conservation. Those six matches are still on the table. I put them in a row and ask to put a button opposite each of them (Figure 5).

Figure 5.   As many matches as buttons.

Then comes the standard question, "What is there more of, matches or buttons?"

"Equal."

I sum up, "That is, as many buttons as matches."

I take away all the buttons, hide them in my fist and ask how many they are. It's typical that none of the boys makes an attempt to count the matches. Why should they? The question was about buttons, so you have to count buttons. Dima, being on the most intimate terms with me, tries to open my fist, and others ask, bewildered, "But how can we count them?"

I laugh, "Of course you can't, they are hidden, but try to guess."

They toss out a flurry of wild guesses. Each shouts a different guess, only Gene's being the right one. I try to listen to him and to ask why but at this moment he retreats. His problem in general is that he is timid. When all the boys holler, he is the one who shouts the correct answer more often than others do; but the moment I calm the others and address him directly, he is embarrassed and falls silent. My problem with Andy is of a different sort. He is a very goal-oriented boy yet apparently lacks motivation at our lessons. Next time, I camouflaged the same puzzle as a war scene: instead of matches and buttons, we had soldiers with guns, then the soldiers went away leaving their guns behind, and the spy had to learn the number of soldiers, and it was he who first got the idea to count guns. He also loves games where one can win. But I don't always have enough imagination to package my puzzles appropriately, especially since it's not that important for the other boys. As for Dima, he does not fancy solving other people's puzzles but prefers to invent his own. Eventually I learn how to handle him: I say something like, "Now think of a puzzle where..." and then give my own formulation. Also, his solutions are often oddly fanciful (as the next example vividly illustrates) and it is difficult to hold him within the limits of common sense. Pete too has his idiosyncrasies. How can I cope, alone, against them? Goodness, with only four pupils I am unable to provide an individual approach. What about a schoolteacher with forty pupils in a classroom? A teacher is often compared to an orchestra conductor. But in my own eyes I rather resemble a juggler who in a minute will drop all his balls on the floor. While I am trying to speak to Gene, Dima has already pulled out cards for the next assignment ("Odd One Out") and asks, "Dad, is this the next puzzle?"

The other two wrest the cards from his hands and mercilessly crumple them without the slightest regard to the overnight parental labor. Gene is no longer listening to me but is looking sideways at them. I open my fist; we briefly check the number of the buttons and pass on to the next question.

The rules of Odd One Out are well-known. Children receive four cards with the pictures of, say, a rabbit, a squirrel, a hedgehog[1], and a suitcase. They must say which one is odd. It is amusing to watch how the kids almost always answer correctly but often cannot explain why.

"It's a suitcase which is odd."

"Why?"

"Because it is not a rabbit, a squirrel or a hedgehog."

"Really? And I think that it is the rabbit which is odd. Because it is not a squirrel, a hedgehog or a suitcase."

The boys give me perplexed looks, but insist:

"No, it's a suitcase which is odd!"

I ask whether it will be possible to find a single word to name the three not-odd objects: rabbit, squirrel, hedgehog. Pete, who is well ahead of others in his vocabulary is the first to find the word: "animals." Later he was often helpful in similar situations.

(Once I was invited to give a lesson for the children of roughly the same age, four or five years, whom I never met before. I put my favorite cards with a rabbit, a squirrel, a hedgehog and a suitcase on the table and asked which was an odd one. The kids looked at me, horrified, then one of them got up his courage and whispered: "They're equally...." Aha, thought I, someone has already put them through their paces!)

Sometimes I propose puzzles with ambiguous solutions, for example: sparrow, bee, snail, plane. The odd object could be a plane (not alive) or a

---

[1]*P. Z.'s Note:* Hedgehogs are ubiquitous in Russian children's literature.

snail (cannot fly). Figure 6 shows a puzzle in which each of the objects could be the odd one. This completely alters the nature of the problem. Now I name the odd objects one at a time, while the kids have to explain why they could be odd. Thus I hope to inspire them with the mathematically important idea that we need good explanations as much as correct answers. In other words, not only correct statements but also their proofs.

Figure 6. Instead of looking for an odd object, the kids must nominate them as odd, one-by-one, and then explain why each one is odd.

Odd One Out is very handy for teaching children to guess regularities (totally ignored by school mathematics). Sometimes it is more convenient to use eight pictures that can be separated into two equal groups according to the chosen categories; this approach was used by the Soviet computer scientist M. Bongard in his classic book *Pattern Recognition*. Sadly, you will readily agree that eight pictures are twice as many as four. How to get them? Usually Alla drew pictures for our sessions. I cannot draw at all, while she once attended art school.

Intersecting classes can be logically challenging. For example, suppose five pictures must be broken into two equal groups, each containing three pictures. One picture will belong to both groups. Example: ball, tire, rubber boots, coat, hat. Three objects are made of rubber (ball, tire, rubber boots) and three others are clothes (rubber boots, coat, hat). The common object is rubber boots. But it's difficult, conceptually, to physically divide five pictures into two groups of three each, since we can't just tear one picture in half! We use the pictorial technique of Venn diagrams to produce two intersecting circles, the common object being placed inside the intersection (see Figure 7 for a similar puzzle).

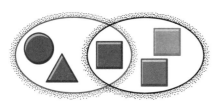

Figure 7. Here are two sets, each containing three objects. One set consists of three red objects, the other, of three squares. The red square is common to both; mathematicians say that it belongs to the intersection of these sets.

These sorts of problems clearly were a problem for Dima (or was *he* the real problem?). "This one is an uncle but it looks like a lady," he would say, pointing to a picture of a bearded old man, and place it in the women's pile. He would say that a tire was a piece of clothes because you could put it around your waist. When contradicted, he would explain that it was a car's clothes.

Some will say, "What a creative, off-beat child!" Off-beat, sure. But creative? A truly creative person can propose an unexpected, non-standard solution within the bounds of the problem. Making a well of six matches is creative. But classifying a bearded old man as a woman or insisting on a tire being a car's clothes is not. Dima often displays the first component, off-beat inventiveness, but lacks the ability to remain within the problem formulation or at least in its vicinity. It would be nice to nurture the latter without suppressing the former. But how?

We end the session with a geometry puzzle. I get out a colorful mosaic pegboard that I bought in the pre-circle days, so — alas! — I have just one. It's a rectangular array of holes that can be filled with pegs that come in five vivid, appealing colors (Figure 8).

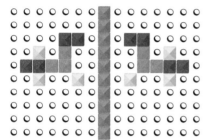

Figure 8. A mosaic pegboard. The vertical line of pegs in the middle is a "mirror", or symmetry axis. The figure on the left is made by the teacher; the pupil must make a symmetric one on the right.

Our puzzle involves symmetry. First I construct an axis, a one-color vertical line in the middle of the array and call it a "mirror." We will make figures that "look in the mirror." I construct different small figures on the one side of the mirror while the boys have to construct symmetrical figures on the other side of it. I try to vary all possible parameters: color, size, position. In later sessions, I will also change the direction of the axis: it will become horizontal and then diagonal. We check our solutions with real mirrors: is what we see *behind* the mirror the same as what we see *in* the mirror?

The boys deal with with this puzzle easily, making almost no mistakes. I can't understand why this subject (axial symmetry) causes such great difficulties in middle school.[1] We devoted many sessions to this rich and beautiful topic. We admired and drew symmetrical patterns; made symmetrical ink-blots by folding a sheet of paper into two; cut out symmetrical Christmas snowflakes; looked for "errors" in drawings containing deliberate violations of symmetry; sorted out cards containing symmetric and non-symmetric figures, etc. Other types of symmetry, (e.g., rotational symmetry) proved more difficult, but axial symmetry was a great success.

The pegboard soon became one of my favorite tools. It's a great resource for puzzles in geometry, combinatorics, logic, and discovering patterns. It even gave me a precious lesson about "what is more important for children:" The boys enjoyed the sessions and sometimes, after I called it a day, would ask me to go on. I felt smug until I noticed that they asked me to continue only when we played with the pegboard. I decided to test this: We didn't

---

[1]Specifically, the Russian 6th year, roughly equivalent at that time to 7th or 8th grade in the United States.

use the pegboard at our next session, and when I said the session was over, the boys left without further comment. I felt grave doubts: The pegboard is indeed a beautiful toy; no wonder the boys enjoy playing with it. But my mathematics is just an imposition interfering with this toy. At the next session, I decided to try the ultimate test. Once again, we use the pegboard, and once again, the boys do not want to stop. I say, "We'll end the lesson, but you can stay and play with pegboards." I receive an unanimous yell of indignation, and Pete sums up their mood with, "No-o-o, we want puzzles!"

Thus I have come to realize that kids must have fun in both intellectual and aesthetic ways. If one is missing, there is no joy. A Christmas tree without ornaments is as unappealing as are mere ornaments without a tree. The joy is in their union. I hope that one day, when my pupils are engaged in more abstract and "intellectual" mathematics, they will enjoy it more than their peers, because abstract notions and images will subconsciously blend with a "Christmas tree feeling;" the memories of brightly colored puzzles from their childhood.

By now, each kid has completed two puzzles and it's time to stop, but they want more. Suddenly I get an idea, and say, "Why don't *you* give me puzzles and *I* will do them." The kids are delighted. They make figures with a renewed enthusiasm, and I construct symmetric ones. I work industriously. Then I get another idea, and start deliberately making mistakes. Pete, ecstatic, is the first to notice. They've gotten a second wind. They watch my hands intently and greet each mistake with savage war cries. But it is really time to stop. I put the pegboard aside, thank everybody and say that the session is over.

"And when there will be tricks?" remembers Andy.

"Why, Andy! It was you who did the tricks! I hid the buttons in my fist but you could count them!"

As a matter of fact, it was not him, it was Gene who guessed how to count the buttons but Andy looks satisfied. We get up. I glance at my watch. Is it possible that our lesson only lasted 25 minutes? The boys go away and I stay to order in my thoughts, invent new puzzles, and think up new techniques and strategies. And also, to cut, glue, and paint; i.e., make the "visual aids" and "manipulatives." I have just a week to get ready for the next session.

Piaget's phenomena: reality or illusion?

Since I frequently refer to Piaget's phenomena, let's say a few words about them. The great Swiss psychologist Jean Piaget was undoubtedly one of the most influential people in his field during the twentieth centrury. During his long life (1896-1980) he wrote about 50 books and some 500 articles. In 1976 he celebrated a very unusual anniversary: his 80th birthday and his 70th year as a scientist. No kidding! He published his first paper at the age of 11: an observation of an albino sparrow in a park.

As a young student, Piaget became interested in malacology, the science of mollusks, and soon became an acknowledged expert. On the basis of his publications he was offered — by correspondence — a prestigious curatorship of a mollusk collection in the Geneva Museum of Natural History. He had to confess that he was still a high school student. By the age of 20 he was a malacologist of world renown. At this point, his interests abruptly changed to child psychology. By 30, he had written five famous monographs and was a world leader of the field.[1]

Of all of his vast work, the most famous are the so-called "Piaget's phenomena" that I've mentioned earlier. A young child does not understand that if we move a few objects (stones, blocks), their number does not change. Therefore the notion of a number remains inaccessible to him though he may know how to "count up to one hundred." Eventually he will understand the above-mentioned law of "number conservation." But we still must wait about a year and a half or even two years before he understands the same idea, but with continuous quantities: if we roll a ball of modeling clay into a hot-dog, the quantity of clay won't change; neither will the quantity of water change if we pour it from a glass into a tub. Likewise, if we have two equal quantities, and we take a bit from one quantity and a bigger bit from the other, then the first will have more material left than the second. It is hard to believe that kids do not understand what is so obvious to us!

Remarkably, Piaget's discoveries involve simple observation and do not require sophisticated equipment like rockets or lasers. Plato or Euclid could have made the same discovery. But it never occurred to them. What was needed was a person interested in cognition, able to ask the right questions, endowed with an outstanding power of observation and, willing to carry out extensive experimentations.

It is interesting, however, that Piaget's findings were strongly opposed by some members of the scientific community. Even now, decades later, some people say, "When we ask a child we use the words 'more' and 'less', don't we? Who explained to him what these words mean? The child does not understand them the way we do, it's as simple as that." This idea was best formulated by a logician friend of mine: "You did not give them the definition of the word 'more.' That's why they understand it in their way. They think that 'more' means 'a longer row.'"

How could I refute this? Indeed, I did not give them any definitions. But what kind of definition? Should I have said that there exists a bijection[2] between one set and a proper subset of the other set? That would hardly have helped: how can we be sure that if such a bijection exists once, it will exist later? I argue with my logician friend, but without conviction. I tell him about the experiments with children, how they weighed pieces of clay

---

[1]The best overview of his theory can be found, to my mind, in the book by John H. Flavell *The Developmental Psychology of Jean Piaget* (D. van Nostrand, Princeton, 1963).

[2]The technical mathematical term denoting a one-to-one correpondence; if there is a bijection between two sets then they have the same number of elements.

before and after rolling them into hot-dogs...but, so what? A child has no idea what a balance is and what it measures.

We can't escape from this vicious circle of argument. No matter what we tell the child, no matter how we formulate our questions, there will always be an intermediary link, a "signal-carrier", be it words, a balance, or calculations. And we can always blame this "interface", this "exchange protocol," claiming it to be not sufficiently precise; and therefore our interpretations differ from the child's. True, we can ask our opponents, "Why then, by the age of seven, the child answers our questions correctly though he never had any definitions?" But this won't do: in a scientific discussion we cannot ask, "Why then...?" An opponent is not obliged to prove anything — this is the burden of the proponent of the theory — of course, insofar as a proof in psychology is at all possible.

Without getting bogged down in the philosophical complexities of this, I'll share my personal point of view. After years of working with kids, I did not need any proof. I knew that Piaget was right. I observed these phenomena so frequently and under such different circumstances that I do not need to be convinced. I remember once we had visitors and were one chair short, and Dima, then aged 3, tried to make the guests change their seats to accommodate everyone. Each time there was one chair short. It was enough to see his bewildered expression to understand that it had nothing to do with the semantics of the word "more." (But I would certainly not have noticed this had it not been for Piaget.)

Psychologists have spent much time and ingenuity trying to teach children these conservation laws (or, as our opponents might say, to explain to them the exact meaning of their questions). As a rule they had no success.[1] Here is my favorite story: They selected, from a large group of children, those who seemed to have "understood everything." At least they gave correct answers to the psychologists' questions: "There is as much modeling clay as before because we did not add nor take away anything. We only changed the shape." Then the researchers took another step and they tried to *unteach* these children. The child gives the correct answer; together they weigh the piece of clay, but it becomes lighter! What happened? The mischievous experimenter secretly pinched away a small bit. And it turned out that the children who easily learned the law now unlearned it just as easily. They started to say that now there was less clay because we rolled it into a hot-dog. But the children who mastered the law of conservation before this experiment *on their own* could not be untaught. They said, "Perhaps we have dropped a small bit and have not noticed it."

OK, if it is so hard to teach kids the notion of a number, what am I trying to do? What is the point of my lessons? I said it many times and I am going to say it again: the meaning of the lessons is the lessons

---

[1]On p. 31 I'll describe a case when very modest success was achieved.

themselves. Because they are fun. Because it's fun to ask questions and look for the answers. It's a way of life.

. . .

I'll end with a few stories. The first is from my own childhood, when I was about five. We lived in Vitebsk (in Belarus, then a republic of the Soviet Union). In our courtyard, there lived an old man who liked to talk to children. I was considered a "smart boy" who knew how to count. So once he asked me to multiply three by five. I knew already that "to multiply means to add the same number as many times as necessary." So I launched myself into this perilous adventure. Three and three makes six, easy so far. Six plus three is nine; a bit more difficult, though the hardest thing is not adding but remembering how many times I did it. Next comes the most difficult step: $9 + 3$. First, it's above coming over ten; second, I must not forget how many times I have already added. Finally, at the limit of my intellectual capacities, I added 12 and 3 and said, "Fifteen."

"Good!" said the old man. "How did you do it?"

I told him.

"Why so complicated?," he asked. "You could have simply added five plus five plus five."

I was overwhelmed, and at the same time completely lost. I can add $5 + 5 + 5$ hands down! After all, $5 + 5 = 10$, which is trivial! And $10 + 5 = 15$ is also trivial! The most amazing is that you also get 15. But why!?

This mystery stuck in my mind for a long time. I was looking for an explanation, but did not find any. At school I learned that in the 6th year of school we would have algebra, and there would be formulas. Kids do not often have an idea to leaf through a textbook for the next grade. So I was patiently waiting for the 6th year, hoping to receive the long-awaited illumination. In the 6th year, I wrote the formula $ab = ba$, looked at it dumbly for some time, but no illumination came. Three years later, at the age of 15, I entered the famous Kolmogorov mathematical boarding school. The curriculum was quite advanced and soon we were learning about groups, fields, and rings. "What an idiot I was," I thought. "That was just an axiom, it is called commutativity. One doesn't prove axioms."

Eventually, I got wiser. I understood that the commutativity axiom was not invented as a whim, but because this property truly holds for the multiplication of natural numbers.

(Note that exponentiation, that is, "repetitive multiplication," is *not* commutative. If you multiply 5 by itself three times and then multiply 3 by itself 5 times, you will get two different results. On the other hand, with multiplication, i.e., "repetitive addition," the result *will* be the same.)

I don't remember when and why I finally understood that it was simply a matter of counting the same number of objects in two different ways. We can arrange stones in three rows with five stones in each row; or we can arrange them as five rows, each containing three stones, depending on what you consider to be a row (Figure 9). Thus, if you count the same number of objects in various ways, you will always get the same result! But it also means this property is not so self-evident, for otherwise it would not have taken so many years and such intense intellectual effort.

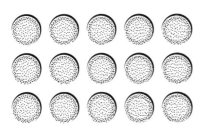

Figure 9. You see 3 horizontal rows with 5 circles in each, i.e., $5 \cdot 3$. But we can also say there are 5 vertical rows with 3 circles in each, i.e., $3 \cdot 5$. If you believe that no matter how you count you will always get the same result, the unavoidable conclusion will be that $5 \cdot 3 = 3 \cdot 5$.

The last illustration is a dialogue overheard between an elderly husband and wife. The wife plans to cook scrambled eggs but her regular pan is dirty and she does not fancy washing it right now.

"Listen," she says to her husband, "the big pan is dirty."

The husband answers, slightly irritated at being disturbed, "Well, make it in the small one."

"I am afraid there won't be enough."

Husband, thinking it over and shrugging his shoulders: "Then wash the big one."

But what about the law of conservation? Clearly it depends on the situation; suppose you gave the same couple a formal "intelligence test": if we pour beaten eggs from one pan to the other, will their quantity (a) increase; (b) decrease; (c) remain the same; (d) depend on the size of the pan? I do not doubt a minute they would answer it correctly. Which gives rise to questions that I find hard even to formulate. First, they concern the relations between formal learning and real comprehension. Second, are we in our everyday life guided by "correct reasoning" or by what is "visually obvious", and to what extent? (Have you noticed the amount of quotation marks (and parentheses!) in these last sentences? It's because I don't know how to express my idea in a brief and clear manner.)

Why read psychology books?

It is hard to convince mathematicians that psychology books are worth reading. Everything about psychology causes discomfort: terminology, the level of provability, the type of problem formulation. For example, here's an abortive conversation with a student about a series of experiments.

"For example, we'd like to know whether a two-month old baby is capable of learning."

The student shrugged and said, "Isn't it obvious? Had they asked me, I would have told them."

How can you respond to that? Indeed, it is "obvious." A French acquaintance reacted in the same way when he learned that a Nobel Prize in economics went to someone who proved that economic behavior was neither rational nor logical.

"He could have asked my doorman," remarked the Frenchman.

I felt that my student was wrong but it is only later that I found a refutation. Let's switch subjects, and ask if physical laws are the same at different places and at different moments of time. The answer *seems* to be as obvious as before. Any philosopher will tell you this must be so, otherwise they are not physical *laws*. He is correct, no doubt. But what will a physicist say? His situation is more complicated: he has to deal not with general statements but with concrete laws, say, Maxwell's equations. He will also have to concretize the vague sentence about time and space by explaining what exactly changes and in what way when we pass from one system of coordinates to another. Try to develop this idea and you will first discover the Lorentz transformations and then Einstein's relativity theory. And this is only the first step; Maxwell's equations describe electromagnetic forces but there are also weak, strong, and gravitational forces. For centuries, physicists have strived to give concrete form to the "obvious" philosophical principle of the temporal and spatial invariance of physical laws, and they are by no means finished with this task. Hopefully it will lead to a "unified field theory" (sometimes called half-jokingly "the theory of everything").

To sum up: the core of the problem is to speak not in general philosophical terms but to ask concrete questions and deal with observable and verifiable phenomena. Of course, we can't really use formulas and equations with psychology. Nevertheless, instead of asking whether a baby is capable of learning, we can ask a specific question; e.g., can a two-month baby memorize the four-bit sequence 0011? Compared to the original question, this one seems rather thin, but getting an empirical answer, even for this simple question, is not easy.

First of all, how can we know that the baby really *learned* the transmitted sequence 0011? Perhaps we can check if, to achieve some goal, the baby turns its head twice to the left and then twice to the right. But it is much more difficult to find a goal for the baby, and to make the baby want to achieve this goal. What can it be interested in? With animal experimentation the solution is simple: starvation (sorry to say that!). The weights of some experimental animals are reduced to 80% of normal, so that, while searching for food, they will be resourceful. Thank God, researchers don't treat babies in this way! What then?

In psychology, breakthroughs rarely are found by directly investigating a question, but instead through unexpected detours. Indeed, the investigation of the above problem revealed new truths. Researchers used many "attractors:" bright rattles, melodies, colored lights. Finally they found that a simple electric bulb was sufficient. As for the stimulus, it was just *the opportunity to learn!*

Here's what happened. A baby discovers quite by chance that when it turns the head to the left, a bulb lights up. Several trials suffice to support this observation, then the baby calms down, checking from time to time if the "rule" still works. At some point, it discovers that the bulb no longer lights up. The baby tries to actively look for the reason until it makes a new discovery: to make the bulb light up it now has to turn its head once to the right, and once to the left. A new cycle of verification is followed by a new period of complacency. Then the baby discovers once again that the bulb does not respond to the "rule." A new active search follows, a new solution is found, and so on, until 0011 is "learned."[1]

Thus, the principal stimulus for learning is not a prize, not a symbolic candy after school, but school itself, the possibility to learn new things. Our task is not to smother it, not to suppress this inherent urge for learning; our task is also to create a rich environment for the infant to sustain his/her interest for the world. Here, too, psychology can give us quite unexpected insights. I quote below from the book by V. S. Rotenberg and V. V. Arshavsky, *Search Activity and Adaptation* (Moscow, Nauka, 1984):

> American researchers Jones, Nation and Massad tested four groups of subjects. At the initial stage of research the first group got problems, none of which it could solve (0% of success); the second group got problems and could solve all of them (100% of success); subjects belonging to the third group were successful in solving every other problem (50% of success). After that the subjects of the above three groups and of the fourth one (the control group) were given problems which do not in principle have a solution, i.e., the researchers tried to develop the so-called 'learned helplessness'. At the final stage all the subjects got solvable problems of average difficulty. In this way the researchers wanted to learn the efficiency of the previous stage. What came out was that only the subjects of the third group had developed immunity against the learned helplessness. They were the best in solving the final stage problems. No meaningful difference was observed between the first, the second, and the control group. The most interesting result here seems to be that both 100% failure and 100% success were similarly inefficient in increasing the resilience of the subjects in the face of the later failure.

Similar results have been obtained in experiments with children, with puppies, and with baby rats. It gives you food for thought, doesn't it? I am still upset I have not told all that to that student I argued with.

---

[1]The experiment is described in T. Bower's *Development in Infancy*, W. H. Freeman and Company, San Francisco, 1982 (2nd edition).

We all wish our kids to grow up bright and alert, don't we? What should we do to achieve it?

Urie Bronfenbrenner, in his book *Two Worlds of Childhood: US and USSR* tells about a project called "The Thirty-year Experiment." Its goal was to mainstream mentally retarded children living in a special home, to help them achieve independence. The experiment consisted of many stages, but probably the most heart-rending was the initial one. Each child was given a surrogate "mother"; these were mentally deficient women who lived in the same homes. Special tests carried out two years later showed that the children's intelligence increased 20–30% on the average, while the intelligence of the control group decreased. I was most impressed by the fact that these mothers were clearly unable to "teach" anything to these children. All they could do was to cuddle them, swaddle them, kiss them, and in general to "mother" them. And it happens that, at least at a certain age, emotional links and parental cuddles are much more important for the child's development, including here — and I would really like to emphasize this — their intellectual development than any other forms of teaching or activities. Parents should not forget about it!

I don't want to write a psychology book (especially since I'm not exactly the greatest expert). But I want to return to Piaget's phenomena one more time and describe an experiment, the only one that partially succeeded in teaching the law of conservation. I have in mind "cognitive conflicts" of Jan Smedslund (described on pp. 374–5, in the book of John Flavell mentioned above; the italics are mine.)

> If, for example, a given subject was inclined to think that elongating a plasticine ball augmented its quantity and that subtracting a piece from it diminished its quantity, the experimenter would do both at once .... Such a procedure was intended to give the subject pause, *to induce him to vacillate between conflicting strategies*; thence, he would be expected slowly to veer towards the simpler and more consistent addition-subtraction schema ...

Notice that nothing was "explained" to the children, nor verified by means of a balance. They succeeded to "teach" four kids out of thirteen, and there was no way to "unteach" them later.

I know I am inclined to jump to conclusions without solid bases or else to contradict myself (just a few pages ago I insisted that it was not our goal to teach a child the conservation law, and here I am trying to explain how we can do that). Never mind! What I want to underline as the basis of my teaching is the following: make them pause; make them hesitate between two mutually contradictory strategies. An opposing viewpoint is that intelligence is a capacity to rapidly solve brain teasers. Once more, at a risk of pretentiousness, I propose that our goal is to raise children to be *homo deliberans* ("reasoning man"). See later for concrete examples.

Why do we need theories?

I am holding in my hands a remarkable book with a boring title: *Mathematical Simulation in Ecology: Historical and Methodological Analysis.*[1] The subject of this book seemingly has nothing to do with our discussion. But it really crystallized my thinking about the importance of "theories."

Among other things, this book deals with the classical Lotka-Volterra equations. The initial idea is rather simple. There are, for example, populations of foxes and rabbits; as foxes eat rabbits, the population of rabbits diminishes, and foxes do not have enough food. Now it is the population of foxes that diminishes; hence the life of the rabbits becomes less dangerous and they multiply. The foxes have an abundance of food, their population increases, in turn diminishes that of rabbits, and so on. This model is rather easily interpreted in terms of differential equations. Luckily, these equations can be solved explicitly (which is rare in this subject) and yield nice cycles and oscillations if both populations are considered as functions of time.

The theory is ready; now we must test it empirically. In fact, empirical observations, e.g., measuring two populations (not necessarily of foxes and rabbits but of any two species, one of each eats the other) do not give satisfactory results. No surprise, considering how many extraneous factors interfere with the populations. Any attempt to isolate these factors and take them into account is too complicated. One can carry out the experiment in the laboratory, with all parameters controlled, using species (like yeast) which are much easier to deal with than animals. But even in these cases, there has been no thorough statistical treatment (the experiment was made in the 1930s before mathematical statistics was well developed), so it is difficult to come to definite conclusions. Once researchers even found oscillations in the populations of hares and lynx near Hudson Bay. The problem was that the cycles were going in the wrong direction, as if hares were predators and lynx were prey. The article was sarcastically entitled, "Do hares eat lynx?"

In a word, we have failed to experimentally prove this model. What should we do? Should we just abandon the model? Certain philosophers — science critics — are of this opinion. But the authors of the book are not philosophers, they are working researchers, and they come to the opposite conclusion. In the attempts to prove (refute, specify, develop, modify) the Lotka-Volterra model, numerous useful measurements were taken and valuable experience was accumulated. We cannot express it in simple equations, but nevertheless ecologists know a lot more today than at the end of the 1920s. They would not have known where to begin, had not they got this initial impetus. They would have remained on the level of general declarations like "in nature everything is interrelated."

---

[1]Authors are V. N. Tutubalin, Yu. M. Barabasheva, A. A. Grigoryan, G. N. Devyatkova, E. N. Uger.

What we must not forget is that an author of a theory invests so much in his creation that he starts to believe it as if it were Holy Gospel. Being a dilettante, I can juggle theories, even contradictory ones, can invent theories without (or almost without) foundations and refute them the next day. There are psychological models in which I have full confidence, like Piaget's phenomena. There are others which I think are rubbish, among them the so-called "theory of step-by-step formation of mental actions" once so popular in the USSR, or Piaget's theory of infant language acquisition.[1] But if we approach theories without dogmatism, they all are worth consideration since they all provide us with food for thought, and in my case, with ideas for inventing new puzzles for kids.

In the same ecology book, I read the following parable. A group of tourists visited islands on the coast of the White Sea. They've heard that somewhere in the vicinity there is an island with a lake of fresh water abundant with perch. It is possible they are already on this island. But how to find the lake? It's not easy to wander the marshy, hilly, Karelian forest. They need a *theory*! The water from the lake must find a way out: it may be an outgoing spring and there may be a path along the spring. They walk along the coast and indeed find a spring and a parallel path. So far so good! They go up the hill by the path along the spring. Soon, however, both the path and the spring disappear. "We climb up a steep hill from which we can see nothing but forest. For some time we wander blindly and all of a sudden find a path which brings us to a lake." What's more, it is full of magnificent perch! The moral of the story: we need theory not to correctly reflect reality but *to begin doing something*, and then we'll see. (Though, as the authors write elsewhere, the right theory is better than the wrong one.)

It's high time for me to stop babbling and begin doing something; time to return to our circle.

---

[1]See the remarkable book by Steven Pinker, *The Language Instinct: How the Mind Creates Language*, Harper Perennial, 1994.

Chapter 2

The Boys' Math Circle, Year One

As I mentioned above, I started the circle in March 1980, and did not take notes until February 1981. The first 20 sessions are thus lost for ever; the journal begins with session 21. The session titles are not full descriptions. Each session usually had several activities while the title describes only one, generally a new idea or a noteworthy incident or sudden turn of events.

Session 21. The Möbius band

> Wednesday, February 4, 1981, 10:30–11:00AM.
> Dima, Pete, Gene, Andy.

Activity 1.

I cut a sheet of paper into four strips and together we glue them into four Möbius strips.

Explanation for non-mathematicians: If you take a strip of paper and glue its ends "normally", you'll get a cylinder (see Figure 10, left). But if before gluing you first twist one of its ends through a half turn (180°), you'll get a different shape, the so-called Möbius band (Figure 10, right). A cylinder has two surfaces, an inner one and an outer one, and you can paint them in different colors. The Möbius strip has only one surface, and if you begin to color its inner "surface" you will soon find yourself on the outer one.

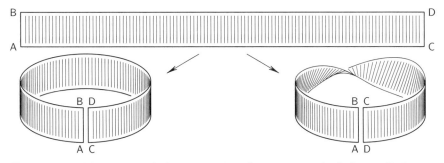

Figure 10. Two ways of gluing a strip of paper: on the left a cylinder, on the right a Möbius strip.

For myself I glue a cylinder (for comparison). Two ants compete: whose house is more unusual (or something else)? On Dima's Möbius band, I trace the ant's progress on one surface and then show how it gets onto the "other" one. On Gene's band, I trace the ant's path on the boundary and show how it gets to the "opposite" boundary. [I should have done it more slowly and let them see for themselves on their own bands that there is only one surface and one boundary.]

Next, I cut along the middle line of the cylinder, and then do the same with a Möbius band, each time asking them to guess what we'll get. Then I do the same with the newly cut objects, again asking them to guess. [It would have been better, when cutting a second time, to not go along the middle line but instead to cut along a line a third of the way from the boundary. This way the linking of the two components would be more spectacular.]

I show them a ball and explain how it is consists of two halves, glued together; explain that the boundary of the halves disappears. Then show how to make a torus of two rubber tubes (it won't have a boundary either). Tell them what will happen if we glue together two Möbius strips along their boundaries (there will be no boundary but it will be possible to pass from the outside to the inside). It makes absolutely no impression on them. I tell them about milk that was inside but then found itself outside.[1]

"So what? It spilled," say the boys. [I should have told them that the milk never spilled over the edge as there was no edge.]

Activity 2.

What's the metro fare (bus fare, tram fare)? What entrance turnstiles do we have in the metro? (They only accept five kopeck coins — no tickets). What kind of coin machines are in the bus? (Five kopecks in assorted coins, then a ticket).[2] Now we have to get 5 kopecks in as many ways as possible. (Coins are laid out in different piles. To be able to compose 5 kopecks in all possible ways, one needs $1 \times 5 + 2 \times 3 + 4 \times 2 + 11 \times 1$ kopecks).[3] The boys were less successful in doing this than I had expected — they did not understand the question; made mistakes while counting; repeated the combinations; were stuck with a group of coins; could not find the right coin because they always sorted the same pile: "I keep getting one-kopeck coins!"

---

[1] *P. Z.'s Note:* An excellent Russian source for topology activities, translated into English, is *Intuitive Topology* by V. V. Prasolov (American Mathematical Society, 1995). This book is volume #4 in the "Mathematical World" series; all volumes are recommended.

[2] I am afraid the readers have forgotten — or never knew — the public transport fares at the time: 5 kopecks for bus and metro, 4 kopeks for the trolleybus, and 3 kopecks for trams.

[3] *P. Z.'s Note:* Using 5-, 3-, 2-, and 1-kopeck coins.

> *I think I saw that Gene "kept getting one-kopeck coins" be-*
> *cause he was sorting out the wrong pile. I did not know*
> *whether I should tell him and was so distraught by this idea*
> *that I did not notice I could not find the right coin for exactly*
> *the same reason. — Dima.*

[I should have started with the tram fare, then moved on to trolleybus and bus fare. And it would be even better to start with a telephone booth (2 kopeck coin).]

Session 22. What is bigger, the whole or its part?

Saturday, February 14, 1981, 10:35–11:20 AM.
Dima, Pete, Gene, Andy.

Activity 1.

A question to Dima: "What is there more of, hares or animals?"
"Animals."
"Why?"
"Because *besides hares* (my italics) there are also parrots, wolves, cats, dogs, etc." I suggest, "Because hares are also animals."

A question to Andy: "What is there more of, geese or birds?" Andy explains that there are more birds because they live everywhere — in India, in Georgia and even on the North Pole. He borrowed the pattern of Dima's answer (that there are many different birds) without mentioning the central idea of "besides." I say that there are also very many geese and tell them where they live. Is it possible there are still more geese than birds? Andy says he does not know.

A question to Gene: "What is there more of, men or people?"
Gene thinks there are more people but cannot explain it. Dima gives the right answer, "Because men are also people. They are double people." (We discuss whether grandfathers and fathers are men.)

A question to Pete: "What is there more of, flies or insects?" "Flies." "Why?" "Because they fly everywhere." "And insects do not fly everywhere?" "No, they don't." "Are flies also insects?" "They are." (We discuss the fact that not all insects fly.)

Dima was the only one who gave the right answer. But Activity 4 below (see p. 39) showed that he, like the others, did not fully understand this concept of class inclusion.

Activity 2.

We continue answering questions (for the third time) about boys and girls who wear or do not wear glasses. I ask four more questions, one for each participant.

The kids get cards with pictures of boys and girls, some of them wearing glasses. They are asked whether statements like "All the kids who wear glasses are boys," or "There is a girl without spectacles," etc. are correct. These sorts of questions can be asked about any card, which makes the activity easy to revisit.

Pete has noticed that he and Gene got the same pictures. Alla remarked that the statements were also similar: "All the girls wear glasses" and "There are no girls without glasses" are equivalent. Andy has more trouble than the others and keeps talking about boys even though the questions concern girls. I think this is because he was absent at the two previous sessions when we did this activity. The only one who coped with the problem independently (without my help) was Dima. But his question was easier: it concerned all the children, not boys or girls separately.

Once again, we discuss the problem of the empty set. For example, is it correct to say, "All girls wear spectacles" when there are no girls pictured on the card? The kids, naturally, say that it would be wrong.

"OK, then show me a girl without glasses."

"But there are no girls at all!"

"That's why I say that those who are here wear glasses."

"But there are none!"

"I don't say there are any..." And so on.

An amusing scene at the start of the activity: As soon as I laid out the cards, the boys start shouting in English: "Blue! Yellow! Brown! Grey!"

I take this opportunity to ask (also in English), "Is it a boy or a girl?"

"It's a boy!" (Andy was joking).

"No, Andy, that's not true, it's a girl."[1]

Activity 3.

The boys each get different cards, with pictures of shapes similar to that of Figure 11. They have to guess which shape is missing. Andy is the first one to guess. I ask him how he did that, he explains. Upon which the rest also solve the problem, except Dima who gives the wrong answer. (Gene seems to have solved his puzzle independently of Andy's prompting.) I show Dima his mistake.

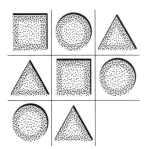

Figure 11.   Which shape is missing?

---

[1]The boys had English lessons with Alla and sometimes we used the same cards.

"Look, here each row contains all the three shapes, while in your drawing there are two squares in the row and no triangle." We discuss the general principle of the pattern and Dima corrects his drawing.

A new round with similar cards, but this time the missing shape is not in the lower right corner but in a more difficult spot (e.g., the center). Then they get cards with only 4 shapes out of 9 with the task to fill in the empty squares (Figure 12). All four perform impeccably.

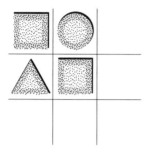

Figure 12. Fill in the missing shapes. Each row and each column must have three different types of shapes.

Activity 4.

I show the kids a cardboard triangle and ask what it is called, and why. Then lay out a quadrilateral (with sides of unequal length), a rectangle, a square, a pentagon. The boys name them.

"How do you tell that it's a rectangle?"

"All of its angles are right."

(Some time before I read to Dima the book *Geometry for Kids*,[1] so he already knew about right angles.)

"Can it be called a quadrilateral?"

"No."

"Why not? Count its angles."

"Four."

"Right, so it is also a quadrilateral.[2] It has two names: a rectangle and a quadrilateral. A rectangle is a quadrilateral, but a special one, with right angles."

I ask the same question about the square. "Can it be called a quadrilateral?"

"No."

"Why not?"

"Because it's not longish," says Dima.

---

[1] We had three remarkable books, all brilliantly illustrated: V. G. Zhitomirsky, L. N. Shevrin, *Geometry for Kids*, Moscow, Pedagogika, 1975; L. L. Sikoruk, *Physics for Kids* (my favorite), Moscow, Pedagogika, 1983; E. P. Levitan, *Stars and Planets for Kids*, Moscow, Pedagogika, 1986.

[2] *P. Z.'s Note:* The Russian words for many of these shapes convey less ambiguity than their English equivalents. Triangle, quadrilateral, rectangle, and pentagon sound, respectively, to Russian ears, "three-angular thing," "four-angular thing," "right-angular thing," and "five-angular thing."

A similar discussion follows: I explain that a square can have three names and each will be correct. "And now tell me, what is there more of: squares or rectangles?"

"Squares!"

"Why?"

"Because they are easier to cut out," says Dima.

I give up.

[I should have laid out all the three figures and asked them to count the number of squares, rectangles, and quadrilaterals.]

The next shape I present is a non-convex polygon with eight sides (Figure 13). Gene is the only one to count the number of angles correctly; the rest do not take into account the concave parts.[1] I explain that they must count them too. Dima asks, "But are these also angles? They are holes... angular holes."

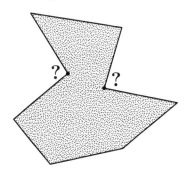

Figure 13. A polygon with eight angles? Or not?

I distribute similar irregular quadrilaterals. They must draw a line with a pencil, cut the shape along it and get (a) two triangles; (b) two quadrilaterals; (c) a quadrilateral and a triangle; (d) a pentagon and a triangle.

Andy is the only one to do them all flawlessly. The rest make a few mistakes, and sometimes copy from each other. Dima suggests an unusual solution for (b): he cut out a quadrilateral inside another one (Figure 14), which remained a quadrilateral, albeit with a hole.

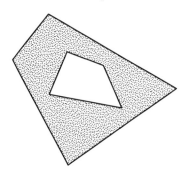

Figure 14. What is this? A quadrilateral?

---

[1]*P. Z.'s Note:* A convex shape is one such that the line segment joining any two points of the shape lies entirely inside the shape. In contrast, a concave part of shape violates this; for example a solid circle is convex, whereas the letter "C" is not; it has a "concavity."

I am about to tell him that his solution is wrong, but stop myself just in time, feeling that such an original idea has to be encouraged. Dima, thus inspired, continues along this path and proposes a similar solution for (c), cutting out a triangle within the quadrilateral. Then he tries to solve (d) in the same way but fails altogether.

At the end of the session, the boys almost get into a fight for scissors (there are only two); besides, the activity has taken up quite a long time, so I stop the session without fully discussing (c) and (d).

Andy says he wants to take his shapes home, and it goes without saying that the others follow his example.

Session 23. The Tower of Hanoi

> Saturday, February 28, 1981, 10:40–11:15AM.
> Dima, Pete, Gene, Andy.

Activity 1. Oral questions on transitivity.

I ask Andy, "A boy likes ice-cream more than nuts and nuts more than oranges. What does he like more: ice-cream or oranges?"

"Ice-cream."

"Why?"

"Because he started to eat it before."

"Because he was allowed to do that before?"

"Yes."

Dima's turn: "Grandfather has more money than dad and dad has more money than mom. Who has more money: grandfather or mom?"

"Grandfather."

"Why?"

"I know that grandfather earns more than mom."

"How do you know?"

"I just know, that's all."

"But you know it from the problem or from life?"

"From life."

For Gene: "A pine is bigger that a fir and the fir is bigger than a birch. What is bigger, the pine or the birch?"

"The pine."

"Why?"

I don't remember Gene's answer, for at this moment Dima cuts him off saying, "Because the pine is the biggest and the birch is the smallest. And the fir is the mediumest." We discuss whether it is the same in reality. The boys gesticulate.

(Oh yes, I remember, Gene said, "The pine started to grow before the birch.")

It may be that they understand my "Why?" as a demand to explain, "Why did it happen this way...?" It is not the logical fact that interests them but rather an explanation why it happened this way.

To Pete: "A saucepan holds more water than a kettle and the kettle more than a jug. What holds more water, the saucepan or the jug?"

Dima interferes again, and together the two boys give a correct explanation.

[Next time I should try implausible conditions: Jane[1] is bigger than Dima and Dima is bigger than dad. Who is bigger, dad or Jane?]

Activity 2.

Once again, I lay out three shapes: a square, a rectangle and a quadrilateral. We recall their names, and I ask them to count the number of squares (one), rectangles (two) and quadrilaterals (three). Pete is the only one to answer the last question correctly. Now I sum up:

"What is there more of, squares or quadrilaterals?"

Their answer has not changed:

"Squares (because there are plenty of them in the houses, on the roof, in the chimney, etc.)"

I do not explain anything, but ask whether squares are quadrilaterals. They answer, "Yes."

Activity 3.

I have picked out 16 objects (a multiple of 4, because we have 4 participants) from the "elementary school mathematical kit:" 2 blue circles, 2 yellow squares, 3 red squares, 4 red triangles, 5 green triangles. I place a circle (a rope with its ends tied together) on the table. Each boy gets a shape and has to put the red ones inside the rope circle and the not-red shapes outside.

I remove the rope circle and put another one on the table, exactly similar. Now the task is to put triangles inside the rope circle and other shapes outside it. Again nobody makes any mistakes (except Andy — once).

Now I put both rope circles on the table but they do not overlap yet. The boys have to do both assignments simultaneously. After the first round I slip a red triangle to Dima. Without thinking he puts it with the red shapes. I draw everybody's attention to the conflict of the assignments. [Rushing again! I should have waited until they finished and then discuss it.]

Andy says, "Is it done on purpose?"

"Of course it is. Before it was just warming up, the real problem begins now: you have to think of something so that the triangle could be simultaneously here and there."

---

[1]Dima's younger sister, who is 14 months old.

Dima tries to make a bridge between two ropes with the triangle. I give a hint: "Perhaps we could shift the ropes in some way?"

Andy gets it: he proposes to overlap two rope circles (apparently Dima got it too, but did not have time to say it). The problem is solved and is easily completed (each boy gets a red triangle since there are four of them). White ropes and bright-colored shapes look beautiful on the black table. I tell them so. Andy says, "That was my idea!"

Dima says, "No, it was mine!"

I try to say that red triangles belong to two categories but get no reaction.

Activity 4. The Tower of Hanoi.

Each boy gets his copy of the puzzle and I explain its rules.

This puzzle is renowned as a real gem of computer programming. You can use it to teach 5-year-olds, but graduate students can also find it challenging. Here is description from a recent *Wikipedia* article:

> It consists of three pegs, and a number of disks of different sizes which can slide onto any peg. The puzzle starts with the disks neatly stacked in order of size on one peg, the smallest at the top, thus making a conical shape. The objective of the puzzle is to move the entire stack to another peg, obeying the following rules:
>
> (1) Only one disk can be moved at a time.
> (2) Each move consists of taking the upper disk from one of the pegs and sliding it onto another peg, on top of the other disks that may already be present on that peg.
> (3) No disk may be placed on top of a smaller disk.
>
> The puzzle was invented by the French mathematician Édouard Lucas in 1883. There is a legend about a Vietnamese temple that has a large room with three time-worn posts in it, surrounded by 64 golden disks. The priests of Brahma, acting out an ancient prophecy, have been moving these disks, in accordance with the rules of the puzzle. According to the legend, when the last move of the puzzle is completed, the world will end.

A problem for older children is to estimate, at least approximately, when "the world will end." [Hint: To move a tower of n disks, we need $2^n - 1$ operations. Let one operation take one second. How much time do you need to move a tower if $n = 64$?]

It is difficult to follow all the boys' moves, and they constantly break the rules. Dima has already done this puzzle twice, so he finishes first and never breaks the rules. At the end when the others were at a loss, they watched his sure and quick moves with bated breath. Pete seems unable to understand the rules and keeps breaking them even when Dima, Natasha[1] and I try to help him. Dima's suggestions anger him.

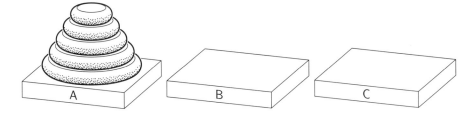

Figure 15.   The Tower of Hanoi: the initial position.

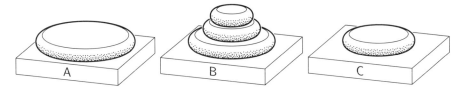

Figure 16.   One of the intermediate positions. At the end, the tower must completely move either to B or to C.

Gene understands the rules, but is very hesitant. He moves the two upper disks but then is stymied, not knowing what to do next. Natasha, Dima and I helped him. He gets angry with Dima; tells him he failed because of his interference. Dima in turn mocks him and says that he helped Pete so that the latter could finish before Gene and Andy; that everybody would go for a walk and Gene would stay behind. I had to reprimand him rather sharply.

Andy, whom I failed to watch, has moved his tower very quickly, much more quickly than I could have. I asked him to repeat his moves, but he realized that he must have done something wrong and refuses categorically. He says he solved the puzzle once and would not do it a second time.

I said, "I am afraid you have broken the rules." "When?!" — asked Andy insolently, knowing I couldn't catch him since I had seen nothing. But then Lyuda gave him away. Andy became very upset. Lyuda tried to console him, started to show the correct way to do the puzzle and eventually solved it herself. After Pete had finished, Andy said,

"Pete got too much help." He obviously forgot that he himself had failed altogether. He too mocked Gene.

My shortcoming is that I react to their behavior as if they were adults, not young children. In theory I am well aware of the principle "criticize the

---

[1]Natasha is Gene's mother. Lyuda, mentioned below, is Andy's mother. Parents were almost always present at the sessions, since they had to bring their kids and take them home a half hour later. On the one hand, that made me feel rather uncomfortable; I was never the undisputed leader, and had to hold my feelings in check. On the other hand, it helped to enhance my reputation; before the circle, other parents had no idea that math lessons could be so interesting and inventive.

behavior, not the child," but in practice I miss the mark. The worst thing is that it puts me in a funk, and my mood affects the general atmosphere much more than their little idiocies.

Session 24. A bit of topology

Saturday, March 7, 1981, 10:35–11:10.
Dima, Pete, Gene.

Activity 1. Transitivity questions with improbable conditions.

I ask Dima, "Once upon a time, there lived a girl by the name of Jane, a boy by the name of Dima, and their dad. Jane was bigger than Dima ('Oh!') and Dima bigger than dad. Who do you think is bigger, Jane or dad?"

Dima laughs, but correctly answers, "Jane is bigger, she's the biggest. She's bigger than Dima, and Dima himself is bigger than dad."

I ask Gene, "Once upon a time, a worm, a bike, and a plane decided to see who could run faster. It has turned out that the worm runs faster than the bike and the bike runs faster than the plane. Who do you think runs faster: the worm or the plane?"

Gene gives the correct answer but not before wiggling and giggling and falling back on the sofa. I ask him to hurry up; Natasha tries too, but to no avail. It appears he was confused by the fact that the plane does not run, but flies.

To Pete: "Once upon a time there lived three boys: Dima, Pete and Andy. Dima was older than Pete and Pete was older than Andy. Who is older: Dima or Andy?" Pete answers and explains correctly.

[Remark: One can speculate that such questions may be examples of "cognitive conflict" according to Smedslund (p. 31). The kids have to choose between two opposite explanations. If an ant is heavier than a dog and a dog is heavier than an elephant, it is possible to conclude who is the heaviest proceeding from (a) life experience (an elephant is obviously heavier as it is very big while an ant is very small); (b) transitivity, i.e., from the problem formulation. Perhaps humor stimulates intellectual development, because it creates a sort of a cognitive conflict. However, it's a bit of a stretch, because the kids understand very soon that they should answer "inversely."]

Activity 2. Topological classifications.

I remind the boys of the "odd one out" game. I explain that today we won't have one odd card, but instead they will have to divide the cards into two equal groups (in passing I ask how much is 8 divided by 2).

The categories are the following (opposing pairs):

(1) Convex — non-convex (this is not a topological property but a geometric one); all shapes are homeomorphic to a circle;[1]
(2) One shape — two shapes;
(3) Two shapes, one inside the other — two shapes, one outside the other;
(4) Eight topological circles, four of which have two "antennas;"
(5) Eight circles, four having two "antennas" and the rest with three "antennas;"
(6) Two similar shapes linked by either two or three "bridges."

Puzzles #3 and #6 turned out to be the most difficult, puzzle #5 was quite difficult, and the rest were solved in no time at all.

The real problems were not mathematical. As soon as I laid out the cards, the boys tried to grab up as many as possible, without waiting for instructions, sqabbling and crumpling the cards. I was getting worked up, and most important of all, we couldn't analyze the cards. Finally I had to impose strict order, and forbade them from touching the cards until a solution was proposed and I approved it.

The easy puzzles (1, 2 and 4) were mostly solved by Pete. He and Dima were the most active participants but Pete found the solutions faster. Gene was left out. Dima invented a lot of fanciful "explanations" and did not always keep in mind the puzzle guidelines (for example, instead of dividing cards into two groups of four, he proposed two and six).

Gene solved the more difficult of the puzzles (5 and 6), when the others were at a loss. I should say that he also worked well with "one odd out." It was not easy to be patient enough to listen to his solutions (as soon as attention is focused directly on him, he falls silent), or to protect his cards from Pete and Dima.

Dima gave a solution to puzzle #6 that differed from what I had in mind. He categorized the shapes as "straight-lined" or "curved." I couldn't argue with this approach. But then, he opposed to any attempts to find another solution of the puzzle, so that I had to chide him, telling him that the circle was for everyone, not just for him alone.

In puzzle 3 I had to hint at the solution. I said that all the classifications that they proposed (especially Dima) were too complicated, while I could explain the difference in two words. One word will determine what we put in the first pile, and the second word will determine what goes in the second pile. Then I said the words: "inside" and "outside."

---

[1]*P. Z.'s Note:* Informally, we say that two shapes are *homeomorphic* if one can be continuously deformed into the other, with a one-to-one correspondence of points, no cutting, ripping, etc. The canonical example of homeomorphism is that between a coffee mug (with a handle) and a donut. Shapes that are homeomorphic to a circle would include ellipses, polygons, etc.

Activity 3. The Tower of Hanoi (2nd time).

Dima finished first. Gene (after about five hints from me) finished next, and was very happy; he jumped and kicked his legs. Pete again relied on Dima's hints (for some reason, he can't cope with this puzzle); he made only the first five and last two moves independently.

> *I tried to stop him so that I could say later that I did everything for him. — Dima.*

I had planned one more activity, concerning sets and subsets, but ran out of time. It was just as well; otherwise we would have done too many activities with cards.

Session 25. The boy in the elevator

> Saturday, March 14, 1981, 10:40–11:00.
> Dima, Pete, Gene, Andy.

The session lasted only 20 minutes, as Gene was late and I had to leave at 11 o'clock.

Activity 1.

A little boy lived on the 15th floor of an apartment building. His mother let him take the elevator alone. But the way he used the elevator was somewhat odd: when he went down, he went all the way to the ground floor, but when he went up, he only took the elevator as far as the 7th floor, and then he took the stairs. How can you explain that?

"It was his habit," explains Andy.

"He was working out."

And so on.

"But when he grew a bit, he started to take the elevator to the 9th floor, and then took the stairs."

"I think he became lazier," says Dima.

"But the puzzle doesn't say whether he was lazy or not, or whether he was working out or not. It just says that he was little."

Andy sums up, "It was his habit, that's all."

I suggest they think it over later. [I hoped it would be easy for them to solve the puzzle using their own experience, but no such luck.]

Activity 2.

I place chips of 4 colors, 13 of each color (one big one and 12 small ones) in a cup and begin a story: "Once upon a time there were four armies: red, yellow, blue and green. These are their generals (big chips) and the rest are soldiers. Let's form the armies!"

We make four columns, the generals at the front. The columns are not of equal length, and quite spontaneously the boys start to discuss which one is bigger. Andy occupies an interesting intermediary position. First he says that there are more soldiers in a longer column (he considers only the length of the column), but when I stretch the shorter row and make it longer he keeps saying that there are still more soldiers in the first row.

With my typical lack of flexibility I cut the discussion short and continue telling them the puzzle.

"These armies were fighting all the time until they were sick and tired and so they decided to make peace and to have a big feast. They put tables (I lay out cardboard squares), each for four soldiers, one soldier of each color. But the rule was that each table had to have a different seating arrangement, otherwise peace would not be stable and everlasting."

I place the generals, and the boys immediately grab small chips and start to place them. (I had, of course, envisioned a more orderly procedure.) Consequently, the search for identical (and hence, forbidden) seating arrangements is difficult. Pete is the first to discover them. Whenever two identical positions are found, the boys immediately change one of them without thinking that it could now be the same as another table's.

Sometimes (not without Natasha's help) there is confusion about the rules; permutations obtained by rotation are identified.

[Remark: All in all, $4! = 24$ arrangements are possible, but it's too much for the kids. I chose 12 chips only because there are either 3 or 4 participants and there should be equal numbers of chips.]

Addendum.

On Tuesday, Alla asked Dima to take the elevator to the 15th floor. He wasn't able to reach the button, which made him recall the puzzle and find the solution. The same thing happened to Andy; he did not even need a hint as he lives on the 13th floor.

> At the session it did not occur to me to imagine the boy entering the elevator, reaching for the button etc. In fact, I did not try to imagine myself in the boy's shoes. — Dima.

Session 26. Intersecting classes

> Saturday, March 21, 1981, 10:35–11:00.
> Dima, Pete, Gene.

Activity 1. Classification with intersections.

(1) I display a set of 5 cards (showing a butterfly, a crow, a plane, a train, a ship) and ask the kids to choose the ones that can fly. Then we put the cards back into a pile and this time I ask them to choose cards that show means of transport. They argue about the plane. Dima thinks it should be left with flying objects (to make disjoint classes), but Pete insists that it belongs with means of transport, Gene sums up,

"It's common to both!"

I praise Gene for having found the exact word and ask them, without really hoping to get a good answer, what problem it resembles. Suddenly Dima gives the correctly responds,

"Red triangles."

Happily surprised, I praise Dima and take out the ropes. Gene tries to put the card with a plane on the two ropes (as Dima did once before) but Dima and Pete say it is wrong and place the cards correctly. Then they quickly place the following sets in two classes without waiting for me to name them (I thought it would be necessary).

(2) An egg, a fish, a mushroom, a fir-tree, flowers. They quickly declare, "These are things we eat, and these are all things that grow." Pete immediately puts the mushroom in the intersection.

(3) A pigeon, a magpie, an ostrich, a giraffe, a lizard. I blunder; instead of an ostrich I lay out a card with a crane and furthermore, call it a stork. Publicly admitting my mistake, I have to turn the card over and just declare it "an ostrich." Alla uses this opportunity to tell us about the corncrake, a Russian bird that also cannot fly. But when migrating, it can walk hundreds of kilometers.

[Generally speaking, it's not a good idea to determine classes by negation ("cannot fly") but I was limited by the choice of cards. Next time I'll ask Alla to draw the pictures I need.]

(4) A little girl, two little girls, a little boy, a man, an old man. I encounter an unexpected difficulty: Dima immediately puts the picture of an old man in the intersection with the remark, "Though it's an uncle he looks like a lady."

[The man in the picture is bald and has a big beard.]

After many attempts Pete solves the problem.

Activity 2.

The boys get cards with pictures (a flower, a pencil, the letter "A," etc.). Some cards depict only one object, and others show a few objects. There is also a card with the empty set (there is nothing on it). We put the cards on a large sheet of gray paper. The boys have to draw arrows to show the relation "this is my part" (i.e., subset). My principal problem is that it upsets me to see how the boys treat our neat new beautiful cards: they try to draw their magic marker arrows right on the cards and despite all the precautions and several warnings smear a few of them.

Dima is the first to draw an arrow from a set to an empty set but it does not occur to him to draw similar arrows from other sets.[1] Though the kids coped well with the task I had a general impression that they did not clearly understand what they were doing.

---

[1] *P. Z.'s Note:* Note that the empty set is a subset of any set.

Session 27. Pegboard quadrilaterals

Saturday, April 4, 1981, 10:35–11:10AM
Dima, Pete, Gene, Andy.

I think that Andy is sick and tired of our lessons. He is a boy who likes competition and winning, but that happens rarely in our circle. It would be stupid to force him to attend, but on the other hand I can't just stop inviting him. I must do it with tact. I hope that Lyuda is more aware of this situation than anybody else.[1] And today he was mostly responsible for almost spoiling our session.

Activity 1.

Before we started, the kids were very noisy, and to calm them down I suggested that they count to ten and backwards in whisper. However, I blundered by saying that he who spoke most softly would win. As a result, when the counting was over, instead of being calm and focused, they started to argue about who had won.

Activity 2.

Once again, classification with intersecting categories. Since the kids already knew what it was about I immediately put two ropes on the table and started to explain, "You remember we have already done this sort of puzzles, first with red triangles and then with cards...," but then Andy cut me short saying, "No, I don't want to do what we have already done, it's boring."

"Ok, if it's boring you don't have to do it, just watch us," I replied.

Then Pete also said it was boring. (Only a week ago he told his mother that he liked math even more than drawing and English. His reasoning was unexpected: we play during English and drawing lessons, while at the math sessions we do serious things. Love is like a rebellious bird....[2])

Not knowing what to say, I tell him what I told Andy. Dima, my only hope, thought a bit, and said, "For me it's also a bit boring but I will do it anyway."

Without waiting for Gene to express himself I hurried to begin. "Well, here's a set of cards for Dima and Gene...." Then Andy saw that cards were not the same as the last time, and shouted, "OK, I'll do it," trying to grab all the cards.

Pete also shouted, "I'll do it too!," but my mood was irrevocably ruined. I was vexed, the more so that Andy did not let the others have cards, was fighting with Gene and continually distracted everybody with stupid jokes.

We only had time to see three sets (I had prepared eleven!):

(1) A ball, a tire, rubber boots, a coat, a hat (three rubber things, three pieces of clothes; rubber boots as the common element);

---

[1]Lyuda, Andy's mother, is a music teacher.
[2]From the opera *Carmen*, by Georges Bizet.

(2) A ball, a tire, rubber boots, a rattle, a toy clown (three rubber things, three toys; a ball as the common element);

(3) A ball, a tire, rubber boots, a steering wheel, a car body (three rubber things, three car elements; a tire as the common element).

On the whole the boys did worse than the last time. Dima always has the same problem: he cannot stay within the puzzle's rules but his creative impulse lacks order. In this case he insisted that "tire" was also a piece of clothes because you could wear it on a waist. We tried to dissuade him, whereupon he declared, "All the same it's a piece of clothes because cars wear it."

The boys couldn't solve the first puzzle and I had to show them the solution. In the remaining two puzzles Dima placed the cards correctly, but both Pete and Gene had explained the correct solution in words before.

Activity 3. Problems on the pegboard.

A puzzle for Dima: Make a triangle (done). For Andy: make a square (done). For Gene: make a rectangle (done). For Pete (I warn him that this is the most difficult task): Make a quadrilateral, but not a rectangle. Pete makes a hexagon; I ask them to count the angles; Dima says immediately there are only two angles and shows them (they are indicated in Figure 17).

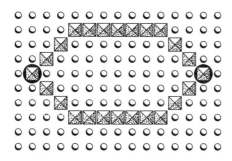

Figure 17. Is it true that this shape has only two angles?

"Wrong!" shouts Gene and starts to count the angles, but Dima has already understood which angles to count, he pushes Gene aside and counts six angles. Now Dima has the same assignment that Pete had and again he produces quite an unexpected result (Figure 18):

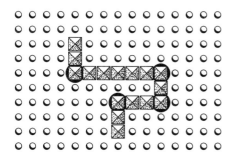

Figure 18. An unexpected "quadrilateral".

"This is a quadrilateral," says he, "because it has four angles," and shows them. I say this is a very interesting solution but that we need a closed quadrilateral. Then Andy gets the same assignment and makes an irregular hexagon. At last Gene finds the correct solution and makes a parallelogram with an angle of 45° (Figure 19).

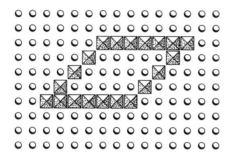

Figure 19. A parallelogram with an angle of 45°.

Here our session ends but Pete won't go: he asks me to solve *his* puzzle: He makes a shape and I must make the same but turned by 90°. I do what he asks and he leaves quite satisfied.

Session 28. We start probability theory

Saturday, April 11, 1981, 10:40–11:15
Dima, Gene, Andy.

Activity 1. Classification with intersecting categories: continuation.

I lay out the same two ropes and say, "Look, Alla drew new pictures for you," with a slight emphasis on the word "new."

I am not the only one to change the tone. Andy, seemingly coached by Lyuda, asks much more politely, "Why do we always do the same puzzles?"

I answer pitilessly, "Did you do all the puzzles last time?"

Andy bites his lip and falls silent without looking at me. I add, "We just want to learn how to do these sorts of puzzles."

I take their word that this time there will be strict order, everybody will do his puzzle in turn, and nobody will interfere until the puzzle is done. If only I had, from the start, stuck to this primitive but indispensable school rule: Discipline first! This could have prevented many problems.

(1) For Dima: a pencil, a pen, a typewriter, a vacuum cleaner, a sewing machine (3 writing tools, 3 household appliances; the typewriter is the common element).

"This is what we write with," says Dima, but for some reason puts a sewing machine in the intersection.

"Do we write with this?" I ask.

"Yes, we do."

"And what is this?"

"A sewing machine. Oh, it is not for writing, but stitching!"

Gene tries to correct Dima but the latter, defiantly, places the cards in a silly way. After a long discussion, together we get the cards into the proper places. The kids find it difficult to formulate what "household appliances" have in common. I help them and we recall other appliances that could fit this class (meat grinders, washing machines, refrigerators, etc.) and the second one (chalk, paint brushes ...)

(2) For Andy: an hourglass, a wristwatch, an alarm clock, a ring, a necklace (3 clocks, 3 objects that people wear; a wristwatch as the common element).

Andy names the classes correctly, "These are clocks and this is what people wear," but for some reason he puts the alarm clock in the intersection. We discuss his solution and I ask whether we wear an alarm clock. Again, Gene corrects Andy. Dima interferes, starts to rearrange the cards and after three or four tries, arrives at the correct solution.

This time it is Gene who, defiantly, declares that this solution (his own!) is wrong, and everything is again confused. Quite unexpectedly it is Alla who interferes this time; she has found a new solution: clocks and "round objects," with the alarm clock in the intersection. Generally speaking, it's not bad to show that several different solutions are possible, but unfortunately this division (into "clocks" and "round objects") was meant for the next assignment, so Alla's solution was inadvertently a hint.

(3) For Gene: an hourglass, a wristwatch, an alarm clock, a plate, a drum (3 clocks, and 3 "round objects;" an alarm clock as the common element). Gene immediately names the classes correctly but hesitates to put the cards into the ropes. When he finally does that, he puts the hourglass in the intersection. However, he explains that it is round when seen from above. I have to agree but I also convince him that we must put the alarm clock in the intersection. After that we discuss what will happen if the wristwatch is also round (in this case the set of clocks will be a subset of the set "round objects").

Activity 2. Steps toward probability theory.

I put two yellow cubes and two black ones into a opaque sack and say that it is a dark cellar containing a pair of yellow shoes and a pair of black ones. To go places, you have to put on a matched pair; you can't wear shoes of different colors. But the cellar is dark, so you have to get shoes one by one without seeing them. The boys take turns pulling out cubes, keeping track of how many cubes they removed in order to get a matching pair. [It would have been better to provide them with chips with figures on them.]

We discuss how many removals (1) cannot make a pair; (2) can make a pair but not necessarily; (3) always make a pair. During my explanations Andy is obviously bored and distracted and Lyuda (for the first time) reprimands him (apparently to get him "ready for school").

After the session was over, Jane (our little daughter) was carrying cubes into my study and putting them on the floor while I picked them up and put them on my desk. When there were 6 cubes on my desk and 3 on the floor, Dima said, "Ah, there are three left in the other room." It has turned out that during the session he managed to count the cubes (12) and now has computed the value of the expression $12 - (6 + 3) = 3$. It's interesting that I never do arithmetic with him, but only answer his questions from time to time. He learns on his own. He will be five in a month.

Session 29. Total failure

Saturday, April 18, 1981, 10:30–10:45
Dima, Pete, Gene, Andy.

Classification with intersections (the end)

Today's sets are:

(1) A window, a drinking glass, eye glasses, a ring, a belt (3 glass objects, 3 things that people wear; eye glasses as the common element) [cf. #4 below];

(2) A grand piano, a violin, a drum, a plate, an alarm clock (3 musical instruments, 3 round objects; the drum as the common element) [cf. #3 and #5 below];

(3) A grand piano, a violin, a drum, a sofa, a wardrobe (3 musical instruments, 3 pieces of furniture; a grand piano as the common element);

(4) A window, a drinking glass, eye glasses, a cup, a mug (3 glass objects, 3 utensils for drinking; the drinking glass as the common element);

(5) An alarm-clock, a plate, a drum, a spoon, a kettle (3 round objects, 3 pieces of kitchenware; the plate as the common element).

The boys do all the puzzles without mistakes. In the fifth puzzle they propose another solution: since a kettle is also round if seen from above, there will be two objects in the intersection: a plate and a kettle.

When I am on the point of passing to the next activity, Andy asks, "And when math will be over?"

I answer that it is already over for those who are not interested and that he can go and play if he wishes, since I never force anybody, etc., etc. But I speak haltingly, and I think it is clear that I feel discouraged. After a little confusion, while I am preparing a bag with colored cubes Andy makes up his mind and says, "All right, I'd better go and play," and off he goes into the children's playroom, to join our little Jane, Pete's sister Sandy and Andy's cousin, also named Sandy (so sick and tired he is of math that prefers the company of three little girls!).

Without saying a word, Pete follows him. Gene mumbles something like, "I've done all the problems," and also runs away. Only Dima wants to continue (probably because of our recent conversation concerning his conduct at an English lesson, when I told him how important it was to be willing to learn.) He is on the verge of tears when I tell him, "Later."

> *I was on the verge of tears not because there would be no lesson but because I was sorry for my Dad (he was so sad!) and because I was trying to console him but he did not pay attention. — Dima.*

Anyway, Dima is not our greatest concern at this moment. We are busy solving "pedagogical" problems. And they concern not just the kids but me as well. Alla is well aware of my emotional involvement with these sessions, and she needs all her tact to try to console me. And I am torn between two extremes: give up, screw the lessons or... what? Alas, I have no idea what to do. Lyuda is also in an uncomfortable position. On the one hand, she wishes to protect Andy from our anger; on the other hand, she does not want to hurt our feelings.

After long discussions (as a group, and also one-on-one), we decide on the following plan:

(1) Continue without Andy.[1] On the following day I talked to Lyuda, saying that I did not see much sense in forcing Andy to do things he did not enjoy, that he would have plenty of that at school, let him pass his few remaining months at his ease; besides, he would only miss 3 or 4 sessions, big deal! As a matter of fact, all that was true: that we should not force kids, and that they will have plenty of that at school. Also, he was to start school in September, and our circle was for pre-school kids.[2]

My only regret is that I had to say all this after all that happened, rather than before, which made my sensible words seem a little hypocritical. I was not in the best position to negotiate; it was obvious to all that my feelings were hurt.

(2) Not to scold the boys under any circumstances.

(3) Take a break, hoping, in part, that they will ask for math lessons (this sometimes did happen earlier, even with Andy). For a while I stubbornly repeated, "I won't do lessons until they ask me."

It's hard to think of something more stupid. Kids live in the moment, and never think about what will take place at 11 o'clock on Saturday morning. And if nothing takes place, they certainly won't notice.

Our moratorium lasted three weeks.

---

[1] Our depiction of Andy in this journal is not the complete picture, because I did not record the first 20 sessions, during which he was as active and engaged as the other boys.

[2] A year later Pete and Gene also started school but we continued until Dima started school, one more year later.

(4) Make the next session completely different from the previous ones (suggested by Rita Markovna[1]).

> *I would have appreciated more if it had been the same as always. I don't remember whether I missed the circle but if I did what I missed was the usual pattern, not a new one. Anyway, I was disagreeably surprised when we settled down not in the sitting-room but in the hall. — Dima.*

Looking back at this episode I am really surprised by my overreaction. It was as if I put myself in the role of a revolutionary who wished to make people happy. But rather than welcome me with open arms, the people continued to practice their vices. And I was almost ready to cut off heads. . .

Session 30. Pouring water

Saturday, May 9, 1981, 10:10–10:40AM
Dima, Pete, Gene.

We experiment with pouring water (the law of conservation of matter). This session takes place in the hall, so as not to spill water on the carpet, but also for a new, fresh atmosphere. Our equipment consists of two pots containing colored water (one colored yellow, the other blue), two mugs to pour water, two empty milk bottles, two narrow glasses, one wide glass, and four wineglasses. I warn the kids to be careful not to break glassware.

Question 1. I pour an equal quantity of blue and yellow water into each bottle. The kids see for themselves that the quantities are equal. Then I pour all the yellow water into two wineglasses and ask which color there is more of. Dima, surprisingly, gives the right answer ("equal again") and even the right explanation,

"Because it's the same water; it's just been poured into two wineglasses. Nothing was added or taken away."

I do not give up easily and pour out the yellow water into three wineglasses, then into four (Piaget had subjects who changed their point of view when the numbers of utensils changed). But Dima holds fast: it's the same quantity of water.

I turn to Pete, and ask, hopefully, "What do you think?"

Alas, Pete is of the same opinion, Gene too. I am discouraged and embarrassed. First, my plan to use the Smedslund's idea of cognitive conflict (p. 31) won't work, since the kids already understand the law without my help. Second, the session that I pinned so much hope on now is in danger of collapse: in five minutes, I have just about exhausted my lesson plan. I am dreading asking the next question. If they give another correct answer, that will mean another failed session, and what am I to do then?

---

[1]R. M. Frumkina (see pp. 10 and 12). We often discussed things with her.

Question 2. I pour some water into the wide glass and ask them to pour the same quantity into another, narrower glass. Pete fills the narrow glass up to the same level (Figure 20).

Figure 20. The kids think these two glasses contain the same quantity of water.

My heart calms.

I ask what will happen if we pour water from the wide glass into another narrow glass (empty). Will there be more or less water? They say there will be the same quantity.

"So we'll have the same quantity of water in the two narrow glasses?"

"We will."

I pour the water from the wide glass into the narrow one. The boys are very much surprised to see that the quantity of water in the two narrow glasses is different but they quickly understand why. We discuss at length how the width and height affects the quantity.

We spend some time pouring water into different utensils. The kids understand that if we want to pour the same amount of water into different containers, we must first pour it into identical ones and then pour the water from one of them. Besides, we need to pour water into identical containers in order to check where there is more water.

A little confusion happens when we correctly pour the same amount of water into a narrow glass and into a wineglass and, coincidentally, despite different width, obtain the same level (Figure 21).

Figure 21. These two utensils do contain the same amount of water despite different width, but this is pure chance.

Later, when we pour equal amounts of water into a bottle and a wineglass and, in order to check whether the amount is really equal, want to pour water either from the bottle into an identical wineglass or from the wineglass into an identical bottle, Gene suggests that we compare the level of water by raising the bottle at the height of the wineglass bottom (Figure 22).

Figure 22. To check whether we have the same amount of water in the bottle and in the wineglass, we raise the bottle so that its bottom is on the same level that the wineglass bottom.

He explains quite correctly that the bottle and the wineglass have the same width. This leads me to improvise another question. I put a narrow glass on an overturned mug (Figure 23). The bottom of the glass and of the wineglass are thus on the same level.

Figure 23. Once more the same mistake: the amount of water seems to be the same. But this time the mistake is quickly corrected.

Now I ask to pour the same amount of water into the glass and the wineglass. Gene does it, and makes the same mistake as Pete did before. But as soon as I take the glass off the mug, he immediately understands that he has made a mistake and corrects it.

The final question also concerns bottles and water though it has nothing to do with conservation of matter. Each boy gets a sheet of paper with a picture of two milk bottles. One of them stands up normally (vertically), and the other is inclined. The water level of normal bottle has been marked; they have to draw the water level of the inclined bottle (Figure 24).

Figure 24. Show the water level in the inclined bottle.

Pete immediately makes a correct drawing. Gene looks at Pete's drawing and does the same (it is not important that he spied on Pete: if his drawing is correct, then, according to Piaget, he already formed the corresponding mental image). Dima's drawing is incorrect; the water level is parallel to the bottom.

> *I wanted to guess the right answer rather than imagine water in the inclined bottle. Besides, I think it was difficult for me to balance the horizontal drawing with the vertical bottle. — Dima.*

We pour water into the bottle, incline it and show it to Dima. He tries to correct his drawing but this time he draws the level vertical and then even concave (Figure 25).

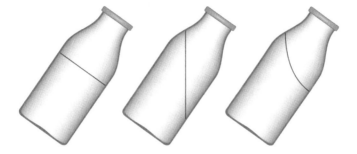

Figure 25. Attempts to draw water level in the inclined bottle.

(Not long ago I was scooping water from the bathtub and Dima asked me why, even though I always scooped in the same place, there was no hole and the water surface remained flat.)

> *If somebody asked me if we could get a hole this way, I would say no. What I did not understand was why should one scoop water if not to make a hole. But if Dad thinks it is possible to make a hole in the water by scooping it, he will probably do it. I believed Dad more than my own experience. — Dima.*

I don't explain anything and call it a day with a story about Little Roo, who was sick. Roo hated cod liver oil, but his mother Kanga, under doctor's orders, had to get him to drink a glass of it every day (I show them the narrow glass). Then Kanga had an idea to pour the oil from the narrow glass into a wide one. Little Roo thought that now there was less oil (it made half a glass, its level was lower) and agreed to drink it. And that's how he got better.

According to my meagre observations, introverted children are more inclined to logical reasoning, while extroverts have more success at geometry. I would say Dima and Gene are introverts, and Pete and Andy are extroverts (these are just my opinions from casual observation, not psychological testing).

It's typical that Dima often spills liquid (tea from a teacup, water from a jar when he paints, etc.) because he does not check that the fluid level is horizontal. We are angry at his awkwardness and inattention, the reason is probably "mathematical."

Session 31. Probability theory, again

Saturday, May 16, 1981, 10:35–11:00
Dima, Pete, Gene.

Activity 1.

I say, "Dima and Gene surely remember the game we played together but since Pete was absent then, I will explain it once again."[1]

I tell them about a man who was looking for a pair of shoes in a dark cellar and put four pairs of small plastic cubes into a sack: two yellow, two red, two blue and two black pairs. We take turns pulling out cubes until we get two of the same color. Each child takes a chip with a figure indicating how many "shoes" he had to remove before getting a pair.

I take a turn and get four cubes of four different colors. We discuss the fact that now, no matter what cube I remove, it will make a pair. Pete was lucky: he was the only one to get a single-color pair with just two cubes removed.

Activity 2.

The same story, but this time with a three-legged man. We put into the sack three yellow, three blue and three red "shoes." The goal is the same: to pull out blindly a complete set of shoes, three cubes of the same color. (Natasha tries to "help" me and suggests that these are not shoes but a hat and two mittens but I insist on my version.)

When it's my turn, once again I get the maximal result: 6 cubes, three times two colors. Again I take this opportunity to discuss that no matter what my 7th cube is, I will get a same-colored trio.

Activity 3.

After we've all had a turn, I take away the sack and put the cubes on the table.

Working successively with three, four, five and six cubes, we discover that we can get both complete and incomplete sets.

---

[1] *P. Z.'s Note:* The underlying concept used in these activities is the famous and extremely useful *pigeonhole principle*, which states that if you have more "pigeons" than "holes," then at least one hole must contain at least two pigeons. For example, if a sack contains two cubes of each of four colors, then *any* set of five cubes ("pigeons") must include two of the same color ("holes").

Then I propose to do the same for seven cubes. After a few trials, the kids say that seven will always force at least one complete set. I supplement their experimentation with something like a proof.

Activity 4.

While discussing the previous point, I take out a sheet of blue paper and we place on it our chips labeled 0, 1, and 2 ("impossible" to get a set). Then on a green sheet of paper we put 3, 4, 5, 6 (a set is "possible, but not certain"). Finally, 7, 8, 9 (we "certainly" get a set) find their place on a red sheet of paper (Figure 26). An interesting detail: these synesthesiae (associating blue with impossibility, red with certainty, and green with possibility) were suggested quite independently by Alla and me, which means that they were chosen "correctly" in a certain sense. Something like "cold," "warm," "hot."

Activity 5.

I tell them that a thermometer measures the temperature ("warm or cold") and I have invented another, "magic" thermometer which measures "hope for success." I show them pictures with a thermometer with zero height of the liquid column ("impossible"), with a maximal height of liquid ("certain"), as well as three other thermometers showing different degrees of expectations. We discuss which of them shows greater or less hope. Now let us see what our thermometer will show in the problem of the three-legged man. I take out a sheet of paper (a punch card) with a picture of ten thermometers (under each of them there is written a digit from 0 to 9) and ask the kids to draw on each thermometer the level of expectations as to pulling out three shoes of the same color. Unfortunately, Dima has a dentist's appointment, and I am in a hurry to finish the session. So I show them myself (and draw the liquid columns) what will happen for the levels 0, 1, 2 (probability zero) and 7, 8, 9 (probability 1) and leave them only figures 3, 4, 5, 6. The boys flawlessly show the level of expectations rising with every figure, and we discuss this fact together (Figure 26).

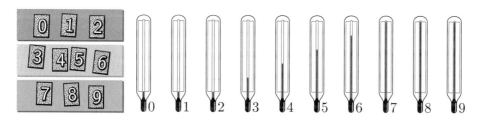

Figure 26.   A thermometer measuring the expectation of pulling out three cubes of the same color.

[I should have shown them a real thermometer and explained how it worked. I am not sure they know.]

With this, our session is over and Alla and I rush to get Dima ready.

Session 32. Diplomas

Saturday, May 23, 1981, 10:40–11:15
Dima, Pete, Gene.

Concluding session.

I tell the kids that today is our last session of the school year and that they must try to do the assignment as carefully as possible.

Activity 1.

We recall and note on a separate sheet of paper the symbols of addition ($+$) and equality ($=$). We also do and write down several sums.

Activity 2.

This assignment is borrowed from a Bulgarian primer. Each boy gets a sheet of paper divided by straight lines into small irregular cells (about 20 cells all in all). Each cell contains a sum, e.g., $3 + 2$ (no sum exceeds 7). The boys are to do all the sums, writing each answer in pencil.

I check their sums, erase their mistakes, and ask them to redo the erased cells.

Dima writes the figures 3 and 4 backwards: Ɛ Ꮞ. So I have to write big figures and put the paper in front of him.

Pete finishes the first and without a single mistake (though he has missed a couple of cells). Dima is the second; he has made a mistake but has found it himself. For some reason he is puzzled by the sum $0 + 2$: he hesitates and thinks it will probably equal 0. Gene works more slowly than the others but also makes only one mistake. It is hard for him to add $2 + 5$ and $3 + 4$ but I give him counting sticks and that helps. Dima and Pete have already finished and are distracting him by suggesting answers.

While the boys work, Pete's father takes pictures.

Activity 3.

The next assignment is to find all the cells with the sum 7 and color them with a red magic marker. Again I ask them to work carefully. I advise them to first draw red dots in the right cells, then we check them together (each has missed a few cells, and I point them out), at last they start to color. They all draw a big red "5."[1] Although they have finished, they don't realize what it is until I show them the colored sheet of paper from a distance. Dima is amazed: how come they have made a five?

---

[1] This is equivalent to an "A" in American schools. See p. xiii for more information.

Diplomas.

I show the kids my University diploma and explain what it is, what it means and what is written on it. I also show them the attached report card containing my grades and explain what it is. After this we begin an official ceremony for the presentation of diplomas. To make our diplomas, we bought ready-made Diplomas of Youth Mentors, and cut off the margins to eliminate the slogan "Workers of the World, Unite!" Then we glued a picture with three intersecting sets and a graph with multicolored arrows over the hammer and sickle, left the word "Diploma" and replaced the words "Youth Mentors" with "Mathematical Circle." Then comes the text:

> *This diploma is awarded to Dima Zvonkin*
> *for his year of mathematical studies*
> *that made him very intelligent.*
> *May 23, 1981*

(The others have the same text.)

I explain that the five they have drawn is their grade for the year and that this sheet is their report card.

Dima asks, "Why did we all get fives?"

"Because you all worked well during the school year. Besides, I think that you have really earned it today: if you had done the sums incorrectly and colored the wrong cells, you would not have got five."

This last remark starts an animated discussion; they have only now understood that the result depended on their correct solutions. Then they read in turn what is written in their diplomas. They seem to really believe that they have become intelligent. I congratulate them with the end of the year and Katya takes pictures of them with their diplomas. Then they start bragging,

"I've got a five!"

"Me too!"

"Me too!"

"I'm intelligent!"

"And I'm intelligent!"

"And I got a five!"

Until Dima declares, "There's nothing to brag about, because we all have the same thing."

A few more problems

Here is a brief list of problems, without commentary, that I was able to recall from the first 20 sessions (which were not mentioned elsewhere).

Determine the number of objects in a set without counting them.

(1) Construct a staircase of blocks (Figure 27). Ask kids to put consecutive numbers on each step, checking along the way for each column that the number of blocks corresponds to the figure.

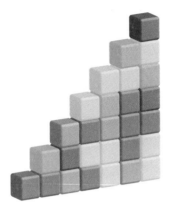

Figure 27.   A staircase of blocks.

(2) Construct another column of bricks. To determine the numbers of bricks in it, line it up against the staircase.

(3) One boy takes three bricks twice, another boy takes two bricks three times. Who has more bricks? Discuss why they have the same number of bricks.

(4) Similar to #1: Make a row of bricks with consecutive digits labeled on them. The number of bricks in another row is determined by comparison.

(5) We want to send letters but lack envelopes (try to re-distribute letters among the envelopes, only to discover that there still not enough of them).

Combinatorics.

(1) Arrange different sequences made of a triangle, a square and a circle (i.e., construct the different permutations).

(2) The same with four colors.

(3) The same with four objects (two circles and two squares).

Classification.

Given a 4×4 table, with rows labeled by shapes: a square, a circle, a triangle, a semicircle. The columns are labeled by the colors red, blue, yellow, and green. Put each object (e.g., a blue square) into the right cell.

Universal quantifier.

A few figures are laid out on the table. Is it true that: (a) All triangles are red? (b) All blue shapes are circles? (c) No shapes have holes?

Order.

(1) Roll three balls into a tube in this order: red, blue and yellow. In what order they will roll out of the tube?

(2) Partial order: In what order do we put on different articles of clothing? (Use pictures.) Specifically: What can you put on before putting on a coat? What must be put on before putting on a coat? What can be put on last? What can be taken off first? What can be taken off only after a coat is taken off? What can be taken off both before and after a coat is taken off? What must be taken off before a coat is taken off?

(3) To get to work, I first take a bus, then a trolleybus, then the subway, then a tram. In what order will I take them on my way home?

Symmetry.

(1) Draw a straight line on a sheet of paper and call it a "mirror." On one side the teacher draws a fanciful curve. The pupil must draw its symmetrical image. The result can be checked with a real mirror. You can show kids pictures of flowers, butterflies, etc., and ask them to draw in the "mirror line."

(2) A more complicated version: the curve crosses the line. It can also be multicolored.

(3) The same assignment can be done on a pegboard.

Rotation.

(1) The teacher draws a figure, the pupil must draw the same figure but "horizontal" instead of "vertical" (see Figure 28). You can manipulate cards with pictures before rotating them in different directions.

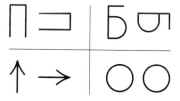

Figure 28.   Shapes rotated 90°.

(2) Variations: use a pegboard; rotate counterclockwise.

Miscellaneous.

(1) Find the pattern and continue the sequence (Figure 29).

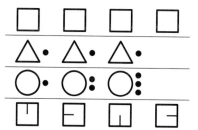

Figure 29.   A sequence goes from left to right. Guess the pattern and continue it.

(2) The children are given pairs of pictures (Figure 30). For each pair draw
the elements that make them different, that is, the elements present in
one picture and absent in the other.

Figure 30.   Draw the elements which make the pictures in the pair different.

(3) A figure of red and yellow pegs is made on a pegboard. Make a similar
figure replacing red pegs by yellow ones and vice versa.

(4) A figure is made on a pegboard. Make the same but upside down.

(5) A diagonal divides a rectangle or a parallelogram into two congruent
triangles. (A paper parallelogram is cut along the diagonal line and
then the two triangles can be superimposed on one another.)

(6) An assignment similar to activity 3 in Session 22 (p. 38) but now, all
figures use three colors.

(7) A triangle has three angles. One angle is cut off. How many angles
remain? (The answer is four: if we cut off an angle from a triangle it
will become a quadrilateral.)

(8) For the last "dancer" (Figure 31) indicate the color of the skirt and
the position of the arms. The skirts can be of different colors from the
beginning, or we can ask kids to color them (in each line and in each
column all colors must be different).

Figure 31.   Add the missing dancer.

(9) Kids are given a picture with shapes of different colors, such as Figure 32. How many are there of the following shapes?
  (a) Circles?
  (b) Red (blue, yellow, green) shapes?
  (c) Polygons?
  (d) Non-convex shapes?
  (e) Quadrilaterals?
  (f) Rectangles?
  (g) Red (etc.) polygons?
  (h) Shapes (all in all)?

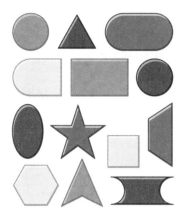

Figure 32. Shapes of different colors.

How to draw a cube?

The following story was almost lost. My notes were on a stray piece of paper, undated.

One day Dima told me, "I know how to draw a cube. Someone has shown me."

"How?" By way of an answer he made a standard picture of a cube in "axonometric projection" (Figure 33, left), though I read somewhere that it was more typical of children to draw in reverse perspective (similar to that seen in Russian icons). I started to pester him with questions.

"What's that?"

"It's the upper side."

"And where is the lower one?"

"You can't see it."

"Why can you see the upper side and can't see the lower one?"

"Hmm...Indeed..."

Dima was lost in thought. Then he added, "And you can see this side but can't see that one." He took a cube, a sheet of paper and started to think it out. It took him no less than an hour. After which he came to see me, "Dad, I got it." And he showed me what you can see on the right half of Figure 33 (a cube in reverse perspective), and explained where were its upper and lower sides, and left and right ones.

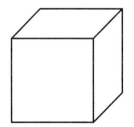 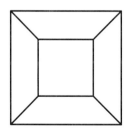

Figure 33. Left: this is how adults draw a cube. Right: a drawing more typical of children (a cube in reverse perspective).

I said, "Well done!"

Certainly I've shown some dogmatism in this story. Once I think that a child should not be artificially drawn to a higher intellectual level, I'd rather pull him down if someone else has dared to do it.

We shouldn't overly exaggerate the importance of one or the other. But what am I proud of is that Dima spent an hour on independent research to discover how we actually see a cube and how it should be drawn.

I hasten to add, however, that the Russian academician B. V. Raushenbakh[1] says that there exist several systems of perspective, each with its own merits and disadvantages. Reverse perspective is no worse and no better than classical Renaissance perspective. The former is better suited to the depiction of nearby objects, while the latter is better adapted for objects far away.

---

[1] In his books *Prostranstvennye postroeniya v zhivopisi* (*Spatial Constructions in Painting*), Nauka, Moscow, 1980 and *Sistemy perspectivy v izobrazitel'nom iskusstve* (*Systems of Perspective in Art*), Nauka, Moscow, 1986

Chapter 3

Children and $\binom{5}{2}$:
The Story of One Problem

This chapter is based on my article "Children and $\binom{5}{2}$", published in *The Journal of Mathematical Behavior*, vol. 12, #2, 1993.

I suppose my readers have already noticed that in our sessions devoted, for instance, to probability theory, there are no definitions, no formulas, and not even arithmetic. I use the term "probability theory" for lack of a better one. Without these traditional mathematical ingredients, what are we really talking about?

Before answering this question, let's ask another one: where does probability theory come from? What is its source? Clearly, like many other sciences, like arithmetic itself, probability theory emerged from observations of certain real-world phenomena, namely, random, unpredictable phenomena. And it is exactly these kinds of observations—fundamental to the formation of science—which are worth making together with kids. Well, not all of them, of course, just the simplest ones. Besides, kids are making them on their own; e.g., when they play games with dice. What we can do is just make the probabilistic nature of their observations slightly more evident, as well as introduce them to the fact that a probabilistic world is also quite varied. We can show them, instead of a dice, an irregular polyhedron, and they will see that this way the game becomes "unjust": some scores happen more frequently than others. Or you can propose a game where they have to add the scores on two dice. Here too the kids will sooner or later notice that they get 7 more often than 2. With these kinds of activities the only limits are our imagination and the capacities of kids. If they have understood something, if something has stayed in they head, this is excellent. If not—no problem, then we just "played together."

To paraphrase the same idea: what we are interested in is not science[1] itself as a ready-made product of the previous generations, but rather the observations that precede it and that once gave an impetus to its emergence.

---

[1]*P. Z.'s Note:* The Russian word for "science" used here (наука) has a somewhat broader meaning than the English word, and includes mathematics, as well as other scholarly investigation.

This chapter looks at just one example. Chapter I was devoted to a single session; here I focus on a single problem. Just one problem, but much to think about!

A combinatorial puzzle

Our problem comes from combinatorics. At one time, this subject was studied in the 9th year of ten-year schools (i.e., for 16-year olds). Later it was considered too difficult (remember the frightening binomial theorem!) and removed from the curriculum. But all the difficulties lay in the fact that the high-school students start with the formulas without having the preceding "palpable" experience. I insist on the word "palpable" because a necessary preliminary stage would be manipulating real physical objects in order to count them; this is what combinatorics is about — counting various combinations of objects. However, in a theoretical presentation objects are lacking; you have to imagine them, as well as their combinations. It would have been much better if we could have started by counting real objects such as bricks or chips, but who would ever think of doing this in a high school?

We sit down around our pegboard. The assignment is to make chains of "beads" using five pegs, two of which will be red and the rest blue. This can be done in several ways. Our task is to sort out all the ways to do it and to avoid repetition.

Technically speaking, these sequences are called *combinations of two elements from a set of five*. In the Russian tradition the number of these combinations is designated by C_5^2. English-speaking countries use the notation $\binom{5}{2}$ instead. The value of this number is equal to $\frac{5 \cdot 4}{2} = 10$.

Of course, the kids have no idea of all that and will not learn it at our sessions. They just make bead chains, in turns, one after another. We check each chain together: is it a new one or was it made earlier? Sometimes we disagree. For instance, does Figure 34 depict one or two different solutions? In fact, there is nothing to dispute: we can just *decide* that these solutions are either the same or different. This way we'll have two different problems, both worth solving. It turns out that it's easier to solve the problem where these solutions are considered to be different, so I propose this interpretation.

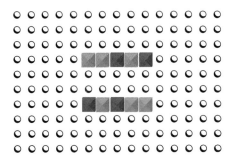

Figure 34. Are these chains of beads different?

Eventually we arrive at 10 solutions (distinct chains).

The main question in combinatorics is how many solutions there are. But the boys are nowhere near ready for this. At this point, they don't see the difference between "this is impossible" and "I cannot find any more" and are absolutely sure that I will be able to find the eleventh solution, the twelfth one, and as many as I wish. Consequently, I cannot leave them to their own devices. The kids worked haphazardly, without any system. In contrast, I am a model of organization: I sort out the solutions in a strict order. I put the first (leftmost) red peg in the first place and the second one in the second, third, fourth and fifth position in turn. When this sequence is exhausted, I put the first peg in the second position, etc. Do you think the kids are impressed? Not in the least! The only thing they comprehend is that I have also failed. (I could easily undermine my authority...) They can distinguish one solution from another, but are not yet able to distinguish order from disorder. We must postpone this problem and attack it again in, say, six months. (And it might be nice, meanwhile, to teach them to put their toys away where they belong. Perhaps order with toys is related to order in reasoning!)

Equivalent problems

After six months or so, the problem comes up again. Of course, I change its outward appearance. Each kid gets a sheet of paper on which there are drawn several rows of five connected circles (uncolored "beads") (Figure 35).

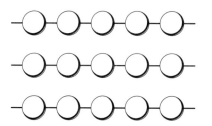

Figure 35. These beads are drawn on a sheet of paper. The children have to color two circles out of five so that the beads are different.

I have prepared more than a dozen such rows of "beads," in case of mistakes and repetitions. The task is to color two beads in each string, leaving the remaining three empty. He who finds the largest number of solutions will be the champion. And one more detail, insignificant at first sight. I hand out different colors of magic markers, but later, discussing the solutions, ignore this fact altogether: two circles can be colored by any color whatsoever. Children do not always understand which detail is important and which has nothing to do with the question and so I try, as best as I can, to emphasize purely combinatorial nature of the puzzle. I remember, with another group of children, instead of five circles, I drew five squares, another time five triangles, etc.

After a few minutes of independent work (and it was evident that it was harder to solve a puzzle on paper than with the pegboard, even though the kids were six months older), they noisily exchanged results and opinions. Now everybody has 10 solutions.

"Do you remember a similar puzzle we had once?"

How easy it is to be trapped by substituting my own point of view for the kids'! What does it mean — similar? I take it for granted that a similar puzzle concerns combinations of two elements out of five. The kids think, however, that a similar puzzle was when they drew something with magic markers. I hate prompting them, but this time I have to. The boys gladly grab the pegboard, make beads and even think of comparing the pegboard and paper solutions. Someone remembers that the previous time we also had 10 solutions. This gives rise to their first doubts:

"Perhaps, it's really impossible to make more?"

I smile an enigmatic smile and pass on to our next assignment.

I have discovered a gold mine. Or, it would be better to say, a new Proteus. This puzzle can be couched in an amazing variety of forms and can be revisited almost indefinitely. Here is another version. Each participant gets a sheet of graph paper marked with 3×4 rectangles. (Before I can get to the problem, we first argue briefly whether these regions are square or not.) The boys have to draw all possible paths from the lower-left corner to the upper-right one, under one condition: the moves can only be up or to the right (Figure 36).

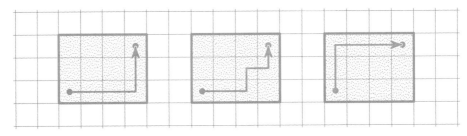

Figure 36. Find all possible paths from the left lower corner to the right upper one.

If you don't see the immediate connection between this puzzle and the previous one, be patient: you will understand it soon!

The work hums along. My "mathematicians" have obviously matured; they make fewer mistakes and find all 10 solutions quite rapidly. (I am afraid another trap awaits us: soon the boys will get used to the fact that the number of solutions in all combinatorial problems is 10. Once — not today — one of them called it "the problem about 10." I must take preventive measures and propose a puzzle with a different number of solutions.) At last I get to the main question: *How many steps upwards and how many steps to the right must be made in order to get from the left lower corner to the right upper corner?* Alas, it does not work. For me, a step is any passage from

a cell to the adjacent one, but the kids think this is any straight segment.[1]
First we need to agree on the definition of "step." This done, I am sure
the answer will now be obvious. Nothing doing! I am bewildered and have
to think it over after the session. Indeed, only my thoughtlessness could
make me think that this question was easy. The coordinate representation of
vectors, i.e., the fact that when we add vectors we also add their coordinates,
is based exactly on this fundamental idea: that the number of horizontal
and vertical steps is the same for all paths. I vividly remember being struck
by this back in high school. This property of vectors can inspire an entire
series of puzzles and could even help us to make a first approach to negative
numbers, if reverse steps are allowed and denoted with the symbol of minus.
(Unfortunately, I did not follow through with this.)

Meanwhile, we count steps: it turns out that each path contains exactly
three steps to the right and two steps upwards. At the next session, we solve
a "new" puzzle: we write sequences of letters UURRR, URURR, URRUR,
etc. — each containing three letters R and two letters U (U for a step upwards
and R for a step to the right; see Figure 37).

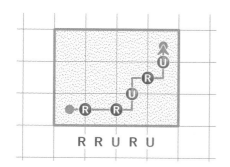

Figure 37. A move to the right is
denoted by R, a move upwards by U.

You should have seen the excitement of the kids when I draw their
attention to these symbols! They demand that the sheet of paper with
five-letter sequences be cut into ribbons and start comparing them to the
corresponding paths, pushing one another aside. I sit and watch them, then,
as if by chance, try to introduce another idea.

"We can probably find more solutions, the eleventh, twelfth, ...?"
Gene answers,
"No, we have 10 here and 10 there".
"But perhaps they are different? Here we have 10 solutions, and there
10 other solutions?"

But by this moment all the paper ribbons are fixed and we see this is not
the case: both groups of 10 solutions match beautifully. Or, in mathematical
terms, they are in one-to-one correspondence. But it was worth doubting
the result to better appreciate it afterwards!

With this enthusiasm, we can probably move a bit forward.

---

[1]*P. Z.'s Note:* For example, in the second path of Figure 36, Zvonkin would count
three right steps and two up steps — indeed, this will be true for all paths — but the kids
would count two of each.

"Tell me, boys, can we denote our steps to the right and upwards with other letters? Not with U and R but with others?"

"Sure, any letter will do!"

"Which, for instance?"

"For instance, A and B", says Pete.

"Or hard sign and soft sign[1]," says Dima.

"Or," I say, "we can denote a step to the right by a plus sign and a step upwards by a comma."

"Ho-ho-ho!," they chuckle.

"Or," I go on impassively, "we can denote a step to the right by a white circle and a step upwards by a colored one."

"How?"

"This is how." I take the path that you can see in Figure 37, choose the corresponding five-letter string RRURU and draw nearby beads from Figure 38. In the ensuing pause — a pause before the explosion — I still have time to link the circles, which makes them look exactly like in the second version of my puzzle. They have recognized it! There is no doubt: the insight is accompanied by joyful howls and dancing. On the table everything becomes a mess and it is impossible to go on. It's time to end the session. Now I can step back, take a month off, and propose different types of puzzles. Let them get accustomed to this idea, let it take root. Besides, the kids may be sick of this type of puzzle.

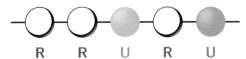

R   R   U   R   U

Figure 38.   Draw a white circle instead of R and a colored circle instead of U.

Denoting...

We're approaching the finish line. On the table there are five empty match-boxes and two balls. We have to put the balls into two boxes, leaving three boxes empty. And we want to do this in different ways. (Figure 39).

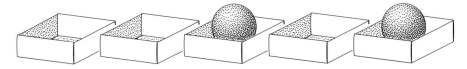

Figure 39.   Put two balls into five boxes in different ways. The main difficulty now is to remember all the versions we have had, since they are no longer in view.

The work starts quite briskly but soon, after several trials, an animated discussion breaks out as to whether we repeated a solution. The boys ask me to be their judge but I pretend not to remember. This situation is, of course, intentional: I could have easily prepared enough matchboxes and

---

[1]These are two letters in the Cyrillic alphabet.

balls to provide several rows of five boxes; this would have led us to the same puzzle as before. Now, with a limited number of boxes, we have to compare each solution with those we have already found but which exist only in our heads. How to proceed?

Actually, not every kid will think of a way out. The point is that we shall need a symbol to *denote* each empty box and another symbol to *denote* a box containing a ball, and we shall have to note all the solutions using them. But behind this modest word *denote* is hidden an immense idea born and grown side-by-side with human civilization, namely, the largely mysterious history of writing: the evolution of pictograms into hieroglyphs, and these latter into alphabetic writing, and so on.

Mathematics has been engaged, from the very start, with developing systems of notation, first for numbers, then for arithmetic operations, then variables, and then for more and more abstract entities. As late as the twentieth century, the study of sign systems has occupied an independent discipline, semiotics.

In Chapter 5, we'll return to a more detailed discussion of this. Here I'll just remark that at our sessions, I've always tried not just to solve puzzles, but to formulate, at least for myself, more general goals. One such "meta-problem" is to introduce the ideas of semiotics. We often discussed the fact that numbers were denoted by figures, speech sounds by letters and musical sounds by notes. We also spoke about other semiotic systems, like road signs. So this idea is not entirely new for the boys. That's why they propose now to *draw* the solutions. At the beginning they try to make realistic sketches — apparently they are yet at the stage of pictograms. But this is not that easy technically, so we pass to the stage of hieroglyphs: the sketches become more abstract, an empty box is represented by a square and a box with a ball, by a square and an inscribed circle. I suggest that in the second case they simply draw a circle. Another difficulty lies in the fact that the kids are unable to draw accurately, so their squares and circles often look similar. I make another suggestion: to draw a crisscrossed circle. After implementing all these suggestions one of our solutions looks like Figure 40.

Figure 40. The first, second and fourth boxes are empty; the third and the fifth contain a ball.

"Why crisscrossed?"

"Why not? You can denote it the way you like," I shrug my shoulders to hint at the idea that a semiotician would formulate like "relative independence of the sign with respect to the signified and its (limited) arbitrariness."

It has happened that the resulting puzzle is more difficult that the previous ones in one aspect: each new solution is to be compared not with other solutions but with their representations. This time the boys find only nine solutions and after a few failures conclude there are no more.

At last comes the moment of triumph that I have been waiting for and preparing for so long. Pete exclaims, poking his finger at the sketch,

"Look! R, U, R, U, R!"

Dima, very excited, jumps up, "Yes, Dad, I was going to tell you!"

"Then there must be another solution," echoes Gene.

"Let's bring the solutions of that problem and see which one is missing," says Dima.

As always with kids, no sooner said than done: he is off to my study to fetch the list. But he does not need to go far. "Coincidentally," the envelope with the solutions turns out to be right here, on the table.

> *I was extremely disappointed that I "did not need to go far."*
> *First, I ran off to another room for nothing; second, I under-*
> *stood there was no real discovery and that Dad had prepared*
> *everything beforehand. — Dima.*

We discuss which version — with letters, with paths or with beads — is more convenient for our purposes, and choose beads. While we lay out stripes of paper with "beads" on them, there is a little confusion: one stripe was accidentally rotated by 180°. Consequently, one of our previous solutions is lost and another one, symmetric to it, is represented twice. This almost derails us.

> *I wanted to say the stripe was turned but didn't, as I thought*
> *it was probably not important. — Dima.*

Somehow all the boys are sure that the missing solution will be the last one. But the fact we find it as the fourth solution does not discourage them in the least. They place balls representing this solution, tell me how to draw the 10th one and then match the remaining beads with other sketches. I finish the session feeling absolutely triumphant.

Today's events were really important. We didn't just solve a puzzle. We reduced it to another, isomorphic one, which had already been solved. This is an extremely important mathematical idea, and isn't it miraculous that it was possible to demonstrate it to six-year-old kids? And on top of this, they were able to discover it on their own!

Proof

Our circle zooms along with dizzying speed. Hardly have we sorted out one great idea, when another, no less great, is knocking at the door. Why do we always have ten solutions? The question seems to arise quite naturally. Is it true there is no more? Or have we just failed to find more? How to prove there are only ten of them?

In other words, we are approaching the idea of *proof*: The central — in fact, formative — notion of mathematics which sets it apart from all other intellectual disciplines. The concept of what is and what is not a proof had been evolving throughout centuries and became what it is only at the turn of the twentieth century. Mathematicians of preceding generations would have accepted as convincing the statements that would nowadays be indignantly rejected by any school teacher. Actually, we are dealing here with a very odd phenomenon. Why would abstract reasoning, often completely beyond any common sense, make any statement more convincing to us? A very intelligent high school student once asked his teacher,

"It's perfectly obvious that the angles at the base of an isosceles triangle are equal; you can see it in examples. Nevertheless, this fact has to be proved. On the other hand, it is not at all obvious that voltage is equal to current multiplied by the resistance. Yet this fact is never proved; it is only demonstrated by experimentation. Why?"

Such intelligent questions are rare. Most often than not, pupils perceive proof as a ritual: "This is how you are supposed to act in mathematics." This brings to mind a historical anecdote from the eighteenth century. A nobleman dabbling in mathematics says to his teacher, "Who needs all this ambiguous reasoning? We are both noblemen, give me your word of honor that the theorem is true, and it will be enough for me."

But doesn't the same occur when we read a textbook of history? No proof, just "theorem formulations:" it happened there and then. Period. And the "word of honor of a nobleman" — in this case, the textbook author — is enough for us to believe it. As a matter of fact, a mathematician's everyday activities do not radically differ from those of a historian. It would be an illusion to believe that a mathematician finds a proof and stops at that, because in the overwhelming majority of cases he produces incorrect proofs. But he is aware of the fact that the same method will do to prove another, obviously false statement and so he perseveres, looking for errors and contradictions, and trying to discover a new road to the truth. He *is discovering new territory.* And he will stop only when all the parts of the puzzle fit. A historian or any other researcher is also looking for the same kind of harmony. But in the textbook we will merely see the shortest way from A to B. The moment the student swings from this shortest way, "turns to the right one traffic light too early," he finds himself in a completely unknown place and has no idea how to get out. Not so with a real expert: he has perfect mastery not only of the shortest way but also of the entire neighborhood, since he has been studying it thoroughly for a long time.

But let's not wander too far afield; we must get back to our kids. There's a paucity of material for introducing the idea of proof to little ones, but there are some possibilities. For example, "odd one out" puzzles with different possible solutions, where it is important not only to give the correct answer but also to explain it. Or puzzles like this: prove that we see with our eyes and hear with our ears, and not vice versa (proof: close your eyes and you can't see; plug your ears and you can't hear); prove that clouds are nearer to the earth than the sun (proof: clouds cover the sun); prove that we think with our head and not with our stomach. I personally do not know a convincing proof for the last puzzle[1] but at our session I proposed the following: cut off a man's head and he will stop thinking. The boys did not agree but none said this proof would also be valid for the stomach.

Well, what could be a proof for our combinatorial puzzle? Clearly, it must be an *ordered* enumeration of possibilities, i.e., a kind of enumeration that will make us certain no version has been lost. A year ago the boys were unable to understand this idea. Have they become more mature by now?

Let's return to the discussion cut short in the middle of a sentence. So, how can we be sure that there are no other solutions besides those 10 already found?

Dima says, "We must try for many years and if we don't find any, then there is none."

I argue, "And if still there is one?"

Gene is pessimistic, "I won't be able to find more."

Pete asks me if it is true that I don't know the number of solutions or I do know but ask them just for the sake of talking. I confess that I know exactly how many solutions there are. Now the boys cease to understand what is it that I want. At this moment I am saved by Dima who utters vague phrase — I don't really catch its meaning as I am thinking about something else, but I focus on the words "the first box from the left." I hasten to interpret these words in the necessary direction. This is what we are going to do: take the first ball and put it in the first box from the left. Where we can now put the second ball? Obviously in one of the remaining boxes: the second, the third, the fourth or the fifth one. Thus we obtain 4 solutions. Having exhausted all the solutions with the first ball being in the first box, let's now put it into the second box. Again we'll have 4 positions for the second ball: we can put it into any empty box. Now put the first ball into the third box, and so on, and so forth. In other words, we'll get 4 solutions 5 times, that is... 20 solutions! What do you think of that? The boys are utterly bewildered, and I end our session as quickly as I can.

This time I am sure I've hit the bullseye! They will certainly puzzle over it, trying to understand why, to get the correct answer, that 20 must be divided by 2.

[Damn it! What a shame. My excruciatingly honest son (of today) compels me to admit that I've stretched the truth a bit in this story. It was just wishful thinking. At the time, I was terribly upset that I had not had this idea during the session! In reality I did explain to the boys why there would be 10 and not 20 solutions and why, having put the first ball into the second box, we did not have to put the second ball into the first box. But what a pity to waste such a beautiful story!

After the session we had a long argument with Dima. I didn't take notes, so I don't remember what we were talking about but Dima does.

---

[1]Apparently no such proof exists. Quite recently I learned that ancient Egyptians, when making a mummy, neatly preserved for future life all the internal organs except the brain which they threw away as completely useless.

> *At first Dad's systematic enumeration did not convince me. Either at the end of the session or after it I asked him,*
> *"But what if you still missed one?"*
> *"Which one?"*
> *"I don't know. One of them."*
> *"Well, in which box is the first ball?"*
> *"I don't know. In any box."*
> *"Let's say in the second."*
> *"OK, in the second."*
> *"But then the second ball can be either in the 3d, in the 4th or in the 5th box, and we have already enumerated them."*
>
> *At this moment I felt (though perhaps I was not ready to recognize it) that indeed the 11th version would be hard to squeeze through: no matter where we put the first ball, it will always turn out that we have already enumerated all the possibilities. — Dima.*

Perhaps after all there was no reason to be upset. My reasoning, even as such, was hard to understand, and I would have made it harder by piling one difficulty onto another.]

Physics and logic

I would like to relate another one of our discussions with Dima which occurred when he was 5 years and 9 months old. Looking back, I find it odd that I could discuss such serious subjects with such a little boy. Nevertheless, it is documented in my journal. (For some time already I have been entering here not only our sessions but other related stories.)

The discussion starts with a sudden and somewhat unusual question: Does God exist? As a rule I try to avoid a direct answer to this question (besides, I don't know the answer), thinking that he will decide this for himself when he grows up. This strategy has not been successful, since I am not his sole companion: someone has already told him that "there is no God because nobody has seen him." As usual, I steer the discussion to suit my goals and say that if this is the case, how can he convince me that a *dream* exists: nobody has seen it, has he?

Dima tries several tentative approaches,

"What is your dream?"

I answer I don't have any.

"But what do you wish more than anything?"

I say that I wish nothing.

"But you do wish me to grow up intelligent?"

This is a sort of moral pressure but I remain adamant: I say I do not wish anything at all, period.

Dima falls silent and thinks; then he asks the question that made me want to tell this story: He asked me how it is possible, at all, to convince another person of something?

"There are different ways to do that," I say. "For instance, in mathematics, we use *proofs*."

"What do you mean?" asks Dima.

I remind him of our recent puzzle with 10 solutions and of our attempts to systematically enumerate them, to be sure we hadn't missed any.

"And in physics, we do experiments."

"Ah, I get it." (By this time we had already looked at L. L. Sikoruk's *Physics for Kids* and done some of the experiments in it.)

"For instance, what do you think: which objects fall down faster, heavy ones or light ones?"

"Of course heavy ones."

"That's what you think; and someone else will say that all objects fall with the same speed."

"No, no, this is not true!"

"Why not?"

"But if we take a stone and a sheet of paper, the stone will fall faster."

"So, to convince this person you will have to make an experiment, won't you? You will take a stone and a sheet of paper and will see which one will fall faster."

"Yes."

"Now let's do another experiment."

I got the idea for this from a friend. First we take two sheets of paper and they surely fall down with the same speed. Then I crumple one sheet of paper into a ball. I am going to ask Dima which sheet will fall faster but he stops me,

"Now this one (he indicated the paper ball) has become heavier."

"Why!?!"

"Because it will fall down faster."

So this is how things are. For a physical experiment to convince you, your logic must be mature enough to be aware of the inadmissibility of circular logic. No conclusions can be drawn from experiments without logic. Which one is primary and which one is secondary? Frankly, I have no idea. I suppose they grow up together in a kind of symbiosis.

There is no stopping me now. We go on dropping all kinds of objects we can lay our hands on: a button and a heavy sheet of drawing paper; a button and a weight; a hollow plastic cube and a wooden cube of the same size, etc. Dima is clearly bewildered by the results. He even ventures a hypothesis that a button is heavier than a sheet of drawing paper, but then gives it up in view of its obvious absurdity.

"Well, it means sometimes light things fall down faster and sometimes heavy things do."

He is almost ready to be satisfied with this quasi-theory but then — eureka!

"I got it, Dad! That's the air that does not let it fall!"

"Does not let who?"

"The sheet of paper is big and the air does not let it fall down, and a button is small, and the air stops it less."

"Good! And if there were no air, what would happen?"

"Then they all would fall down with the same speed!"

"Right! And what happened when I crumpled the sheet of paper?"

Dima chooses his words to give me a correct answer but I am too impatient and answer in his place,

"The air does not stop it."

Dima corrects me, "Yes, it still does, but it's going to stop it less."

I have already shared with the reader one of my guiding principles: never impose your own point of view on a child, even by a hint. But the hierarchy of principles contains another principle, even more important: never follow your principles blindly. Perhaps now is a good time for flexibility. And with an obvious hint at the "only correct answer" I indicate again the crumpled sheet of paper and ask,

"Does it really become heavier?"

Dima laughs a knowing laugh, as if wishing to say, "It's hard to believe I could say such a stupid thing!" and says,

"Of course, not! Maybe only a tiny bit heavier."

In the evening, when I am noting this conversation into the journal and thinking it over again, I remark a thing that has escaped me before. What we have done together is not a physical experiment properly speaking. An experiment is a question we ask nature, *an answer to which we don't know.* In our case Dima knew all the answers beforehand. Strictly speaking, it was not necessary to really throw a weight or a button — the child's personal experience of the surrounding physical world is enough to predict correctly the result of this experiment. We may say that none of these experiments has given him new information — if we limit ourselves to facts. What was new was comparing and arranging known facts. As a matter of fact, we have made the same systematic enumeration of logical possibilities that we had earlier performed for the balls in the matchboxes. This situation shows once more why questions are so important in teaching. They help a child to compare the experiences that once existed separately, on different shelves of memory's bookcase.

· · ·

During the summer, we rented a country house not far from Moscow, and one day Pete came to visit us. The boys talked about their recent visit to the zoo where they were shown monkeys. I interrupted, telling them that they were not shown monkeys, they were shown to monkeys. This naturally provoked a heated protest, but they did not immediately find the right argument.

"We were looking at them."

This was easily countered with, "You were looking at them — big deal! They were also looking at you."

Their second argument was more solid: "We can walk wherever we want to, and the monkeys can't."

But I still refuted them with, "No, you don't walk wherever you want to. You can't go inside the cage. And the monkeys can't go outside the cage. There are bars separating you, and you walk wherever you want to on one side of them, and the monkeys do the same on the other side."

We were arguing this way for some time until Dima exclaimed with delight, as if he had caught me red-handed,

"Hey, Dad! We're doing math again!"

Quite an interesting evolution: at the first session of our circle the kids rushed to count buttons laid out on the table. That was how they saw mathematics then. Now it has become a sort of logical game, Lewis Carroll-style.

$$\cdots$$

It's a shame that I've robbed the following chapter of its tastiest morsels. But first, I wanted to present the material with a new perspective. I was not sure that the reader could have followed the evolution of the combinatorial puzzle if it had been divided amongst several chapters. Second, the events at the beginning of the chapter belong to the "undocumented" period and would have otherwise remained off-screen. I hope there are still items of interest left in the chapters to come.

Chapter 4

The Boys' Math Circle, Year Two

Session 33. Geometric similarity

Saturday, September 19, 1981, 11:05–11:50.
Dima, Pete, Gene.

The first school bell.

As a rule, the boys don't arrive at the same time. While waiting for one to show up, the other two start playing, then the third one joins them and it's hard to tear them away to start the session.

The solution to this problem comes out of the blue. We had a broken doll with a very melodious bell inside. When I ring this bell, its soft, beautiful tone mesmerizes the boys, who stop playing and come quietly. Sometimes they ask me to let them ring the bell.

And thus, the bell rings, and I congratulate the kids on the start of the school year and tell them that at school on the first day they always celebrate the first bell.[1]

Activity 1. Oral questions.

(1) Two brothers come outdoors with their bikes[2] and ride away on five wheels. How is this possible?

To my surprise, the boys don't come up with the right solution for a long time; instead they invent bicycles with four wheels. Then Dima gets the right idea.

> *As a matter of fact, I got this idea immediately but I did not want to say it out loud because I never saw anybody riding a tricycle outdoors. So I thought my idea wasn't good and together with the others proposed a solution with a unicycle.*

---

[1] *P. Z.'s Note:* The first day of school, in early September, was an important day in the Soviet calendar, and is still celebrated in Russia, sometimes with a formal bell-ringing ceremony.

[2] *P. Z.'s Note:* This problem is language dependent. The English word "bicycle" would tend to imply two wheels, whereas the Russian word for bicycle, велосипед, pronounced "velosiped," does not specify the number of wheels.

> *Then I remembered that unicycles only were in the circus and this was even less probable than a tricycle outdoors, so I told my first solution. – Dima.*

(2) A simplified version of one of Smullyan's "monkey tricks:"[1] I show a closed fist and say, "I have two coins that total 6 cents, but *one of them is not a penny.* What are they?"

[The solution is that while one coin is not a penny, the other is.]

Again, the result is discouraging. First the kids can't figure out how to get a sum of 6 cents. When Dima proposes at last a penny plus a nickel, they have long ago forgotten the second condition. I remind them that one of them is not a penny.

"Of course," says Dima, "it's not a penny, it's a coin." I open my fist and ask, "Is it true that one of them is not a penny?"

"It is."

"Which one?"

The boys point to the nickel without surprise. I give up.

Activity 2. Operations on sets.

Two big cards A and B each contain images of sets of objects. Five smaller cards contain depictions of the sets $A \cap B$, A, B, $A \setminus B$, $B \setminus A$, $A \triangle B$.[2] The activity is for them to recognize these sets. For instance, "Find the card which has the things in picture A but not in picture B," or "Find the card with the things in both pictures A and B," etc. The boys answer rapidly and without mistakes. It's somewhat hard to express verbally the difference between union and intersection. In both cases you have to say "find objects that are present in both pictures."

Dima says, "I can't see why all these things are in the same picture." That is, he does not understand why these particular objects are in the same place. I explain that there is no reason whatsoever.

Activities for future use.

(1) An active version: instead of choosing among the cards prepared by me, the boys have to draw the sets themselves (using simple symbols as set elements).

(2) Same thing, but with a set of objects laid out on the table in two rope circles (as set elements we may use numbers, and objects on the table might be chips with numbers written on them).

---

[1]*P. Z.'s Note:* Smullyan, Raymond, *What is the Name of This Book?*, Prentice-Hall, 1978, p. 15. Zvonkin's actual formulation involved one- and two-kopeck coins.

[2]*P. Z.'s Note:* $A \cap B$ denotes the intersection of sets A and B; $A \setminus B$ is the set of elements of A which *are not* elements of B; and $A \triangle B$ is the set of elements which are in A or in B but *not* in both sets.

Activity 3. Geometric similarity.

I draw several pairs of similar-shaped figures on graph paper, one scaled twice as big as the other (Figure 41).

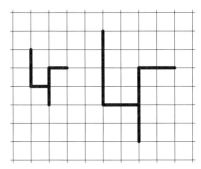

Figure 41. Similar figures, one twice as big as the other.

I explain that we will use the pegboard. I construct figures on the pegboard and ask the boys to construct similar figures that are twice as big. They have no trouble, but I suddenly realize that I haven't really thought things through. Here are two wrinkles (these didn't occur to the boys):

(1) Quite naturally they replace each peg by two pegs, but what is to be done with corner pegs? The boys double them as well, but the result depends on where they have started (Figure 42).

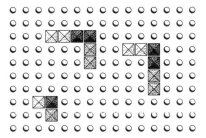

Figure 42. How to double the corner on a pegboard?

(2) The pegs (points) can be organized into "constellations" with "lines" in different ways. For example, Gene and I perceived the the 8-peg shape of Figure 43 in two different ways. His interpretation was on the right, and he started to double that one.

I honestly admit these issues to the boys and say that next time the same assignment will be done on graph paper, avoiding ambiguity.

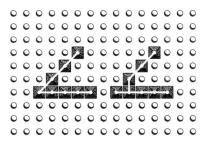

Figure 43. On a pegboard we only have "points" but to double a figure they have to be mentally linked with lines; this mental operation could be done in various ways.

Activity 4. "More likely, less likely" (a game of chips).

I say, "And now the last activity."

The boys cut me short, "Why the last one? We want more!"

Oh, sweet sounds! After the terrible blow I received when they had deserted me, I need so much to be reassured!

Our game board is a rectangular grid of cells drawn on graph paper; 7 rows and 15 columns. Below the cells the numbers from 1 to 15 are written. There are four players (including me). Each player gets three chips of the same color, one big and two small. We put the chips in the first horizontal row. Then each throws two dice, adds the number of pips (collateral training in arithmetic!), and moves the corresponding chip one space ahead. The chip that first reaches the upper (seventh) horizontal row wins, getting two kopecks if it is the big chip that wins and 1 kopeck if it's the small one.

The goal is (a) to remind the kids of the existence of improbable events (sums 1, 13, 14, 15 are impossible to get), and (b) to demonstrate experimentally that among probable events there are more or less probable ones (for example, a sum of 7 is more likely than any other).

We play twice though the kids ask for more. They do not guess that there are impossible sums but when I ask why the chip in cell 1 never moved they explain it (Dima is the first to give the correct answer). Then I ask what other sums are impossible and again they give the right answer. We do not discuss the relative probabilities of different sums as we have little time left; I decide to do this at the next session. After the first round, Dima says that he wants to put his chip on 6 (it won in the previous round) but he puts a small chip on it. Gene wins in both rounds, with his chips first on 6 and then on 7.

Session 34. An uneventful session

> Saturday, October 3, 1981, 11:05–11:35.
> Dima, Gene.

Pete has scarlet fever, so we have already missed one Saturday. We don't want a month-long gap, but nor do we want Pete to fall behind (besides, it's more fun to have three pupils instead of two), so we decide to conduct just one session in the middle; this way we'll have two gaps of a fortnight each. The next session will thus take place on October, 17.

Activity 1. Oral questions

(borrowed from V. A. Levin), of the sort: a man has an arm, a hen has a ...? I asked a few questions haphazardly.

Activity 2. Geometric similarity ("doubling" figures).

This time we use graph paper. I draw a figure like the one in Figure 44 and the boys are to draw one twice as big.

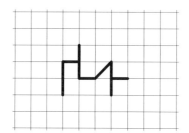

Figure 44. Draw a figure twice as big as this one.

In general they do fine, though they make mistakes from time to time. I gave them pencils with an eraser, which they use. Dima makes three figures, Gene two.

Activity 3. Repeat of the previous probability game.

Dima wins the first round (on 5), and I win the second round (also on 5).

This time we discuss more thoroughly which events are impossible, which numbers are more profitable and even why they are so. I show them that the numbers 2 and 12 can each be obtained by only one combination of pips, while other numbers can be obtained by several combinations. We decide to make a table next session (actually, that will be a table of addition up to 6), as well as play the same game once more. If we continue this way, in no time we'll be able to calculate probabilities!

Session 34. Almost calculating probabilities

Saturday, October 24, 1981, 11:10–12:00.
Dima, Pete, Gene.

Dima was sick on October 17, so our gap was three weeks instead of two.

Activity 1. Oral questions.

The same type of questions as at the last session (mentioning that Pete does not know them). This time I use the entire list of examples given by V. A. Levin in the journal.[1]

Activity 2. Operations over sets.

I give the boys two pictures. The first one contains images of a square, a cross, a circle, a star and a crescent, the other one, of a triangle, an arrow, a cross and a crescent. The boys have paper and pencils and have to draw the intersection, both differences, the union and the symmetric difference of the two sets.

---

[1]Characteristically, I don't have the slightest idea of what journal I am talking about. The reader must remember that at no moment I was thinking I was a researcher of early childhood development; I was doing all this "by guess and by God," without any system.

The boys are doing well. As for me, I have the same difficulties in formulating the puzzle as before: everyday language distinguishes poorly between set unions and intersections. "The things in both pictures" — is this the union or the intersection? Because of this ambiguity, the boys often give opposite answers.

While drawing the symmetric difference, Pete first drew the union and then crosses out the intersection and shows with an arrow that it should be discarded.

Activity 3. Rectangles.

Among other things, I ask how many rectangles there are in Figure 45.

Figure 45. How many rectangles?

Of course the boys say there are two. I show that there are three. This idea can be developed further.

Activity 4. A game of chips, and almost calculating probabilities.

We play the game of chips once again. Gene wins (on 7). At a certain moment in the middle of the game, when the chips form a wedge (as in Figure 46), I direct the boys' attention to this fact and say, "You see that the closer to the middle, the more the chip has moved forward."

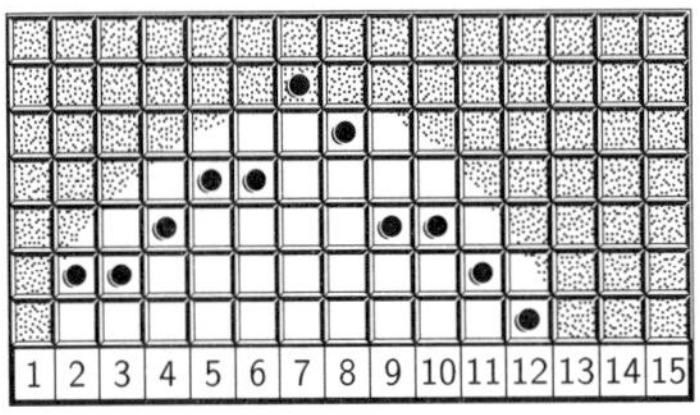

Figure 46. Disposition of chips during the game.

After finishing the game we start making a table; we note all the possible results of a dice roll and count the sums (Table 1).

	1	2	3	4	5	6
1	2	3	4	5	6	7
2	3	4	5	6	7	8
3	4	5	6	7	8	9
4	5	6	7	8	9	10
5	6	7	8	9	10	11
6	7	8	9	10	11	12

Table 1. Addition table up to 6.

The kids have guessed the regularities almost immediately and dictate the contents of the table without any calculations. When the table is ready I mention that we have not actually calculated, but instead guessed the sums, so it would be interesting to check whether everything is correct. To do that, we verify several cells and see that it is.

While making the table Pete observes that the same numbers form rows parallel to the secondary (southwest to northeast) diagonal. We discuss this fact and I ask, "Which number is the most frequent and which row is the longest?"

The boys answer in chorus,

"Six."

This means that they have also taken into account the numbers outside the demarcation line of the table (i.e., not only sums but also addends).

> *I was just going to ask whether we should count them as well but it was too late. — Dima.*

I should have foreseen such an outcome and use as table entries not figures but images of the die sides, as in Table 2.

	·	··	··	::	::	::
·						
··						
··						
::						
::						
::						

Table 2. We should have put the sums in a table like this one, then the question which figures we should take into account would not have arisen.

So I have to make this line bold and to explain that inside the table we have sums of points on two dice and at its edge the number of points on a die, and they should not count these latter. By and by we have sorted everything out and even guessed how many times the sums $2, 3, 4, \ldots, 12$ occur. For the results see Table 3.

Sum	2	3	4	5	6	7	8	9	10	11	12
# of occurrences	1	2	3	4	5	6	5	4	3	2	1

Table 3. Sums of points on two dice and the number of occurrences of each sum.

At last I say, "Now you know which sums occur more often and which occur less often. Where would you now put your chip if you could choose?"

Dima replies by placing the big chip on 7 and the small ones on 6 and 8. I tell him that he nailed it!

Session 36. A game of three dice

Saturday, October 31, 1981, 11:05–11:50.
Dima, Pete, Gene.

Activity 1. A chain game

(Inspired by V. A. Levin). I explain the rules: Each player must say a word in some way related to the previous one, by association, subject, resemblance, contrast, even by a rhyme. This is the chain we get:

> *record player – needle – thread – spool – pool – water – bottom –*
> *sand – stone – stumble – walk – jump – swim – bubble – film –*
> *soap – potato – sunflower oil – margarine.*

I also play with them while Alla takes notes.

Activity 2.

Again we have two sheets of paper; one (A) contains the numbers $1, 3, 5, 7, 9$; the other (B) has $4, 5, 6, 7$. I put down our 10 numbered chips. The first assignment is for everyone: select just the numbers we need (i.e., the union), and put aside the rest. Then I ask Pete, Dima, and Gene in turn to pick $A \cap B$, $A \setminus B$, $B \setminus A$. After these three sets are picked up and isolated, I put a rope ring in the form of a Venn diagram (Figure 47) and place the chips inside.

Figure 47. Intersecting sets.

We discuss the fact that the first rope corresponds exactly to the first sheet of paper and the second one to the other sheet of paper and that it is therefore natural that the common part contains common figures, and "here" (I indicate) there are only figures that are present in A but absent in B, and so on, and so forth.

[We should have done the same with small cards from the very first assignment on operations over sets, those with images of a cat, a vase, an apple, etc.]

Activity 3.

I say, "Today we shall play a new game and throw three dice. Tell me what will be the smallest sum of points we can get."

"Three!"

We discuss why.

"And the biggest sum?"

"Three times six!"

We count how much this makes. I get out a game board with the numbers from 3 to 18 marked in big cells (Figure 48).

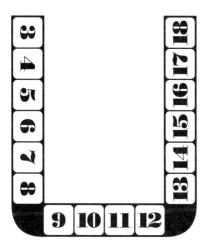

Figure 48.   A board for the game of three dice.

To make it look nicer I colored the left side (3–8) yellow, the lower side red, and the right side green. I made the winning side red on purpose (see Session 31, p. 61) and avoided blue. I am not sure, however, about the synaesthesia of yellow. The rules: Each player sits down opposite one of the sides (the boys immediately sit down, Gene on the left, Dima at the bottom, and Pete on the right); each gets an equal number of chips (9, in this case); at each move each player bets a chip; then we throw the dice, and he who "owns" the number equal to the sum of the dice gets all three chips. The game is over when two of the players are completely "busted" (when the third one gets all the chips).

I say, "Gene owns 6 numbers (i.e., 3–8), as does Pete; Dima, however, has only 4."

"It's OK," says Dima.

> I was in a hurry to start playing so I did not listen attentively
> to what Dad was saying. Before we started the game (but
> after I said "It's OK") it dawned upon me that I had less
> numbers than the others and I could thus lose. But then we
> started to play and I forgot about it. — Dima.

We throw dice in turn (me too); the player who does it must calculate the sum. It's interesting that the boys do these calculations, which are rather difficult for them, willingly and repeatedly, yet in other situations they slack off.

The game goes on and on without any end in view. So we decide that we note how many chips each has and continue next time. *Gene has 2 chips left, Pete 11, Dima 14.*

[A good problem for me: find the expected duration of the game as well as the probability of an "anomaly," i.e., the bankruptcy of the player who sits in the middle.]

Session 37. How many rectangles?

> Saturday, November 14, 1981 , 11:05–12:00.
> Dima, Pete, Gene.

We missed the previous Saturday because of a holiday.[1]

Activity 1. A chain game

(brain exercise):

> *pictures – paints – brushes – tree – root – weed – water –*
> *ice – skates – to skate – a man – boot – Italy – map –*
> *wall – house – hole – hamster – animal – eye – spectacles –*
> *magnifying glass – glass – frame – bicycle – wheel – tire –*
> *brake – train – smoke – chimney.*

It's interesting that even now, 20 years later, I can recall which associations came to Pete. "Boot – Italy!" You can immediately recognize a child from a liberal arts family.

Activity 2. Set intersection.

(not done at the previous session) We have two big pictures and small cards (see Activity 33-2). The small cards contain unions, intersections, and differences of the sets from the big pictures. I lay out two intersecting rope rings and ask the boys to place the cards so that we shall have picture A inside one rope and picture B inside the other one. That is, when everything is done correctly, we shall have inside the ropes only cards $A \setminus B$ (to the left), $A \cap B$ (in the middle), and $B \setminus A$ (to the right). As to the remaining cards, we shall only need them "for reference."

As usual at the start, the boys dash about, fight over the cards, grab them from one another, and place them helter-skelter. Then some order is established and we start to work more systematically. During our discussion, it's clear that Dima is in the dark; Gene is difficult to judge as he limits himself to a few sentences. Only Pete immediately places the right cards in the right places.

---

[1]*P. Z.'s Note:* Zvonkin is being ironic here. The holiday in question is the October Revolution anniversary of the former Soviet Union (which took place on November 7 due to the change in calendars).

After we obtain the correct solution we check it thoroughly and discuss the meaning of set union.

Activity 3. Find all the rectangles.

The boys get sheets of paper, each with a rectangle divided into four parts by midlines (Figure 49). They must find and shade all the rectangles (there are 9 in all).

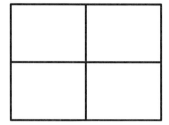

Figure 49.   Find all nine rectangles.

The kids do well, with hardly any mistakes. Gene is the first to find an "original" solution: he shades the big rectangle before shading all the smaller parts and he also shades a vertical shape composed of two parts. After I praise Gene for this, Dima proposes an even stranger "solutions:" first he shades an angle (see Figure 50, left) and then a rectangle formed by a "missing" line (Figure 50, right).

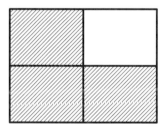 

Figure 50.   These solutions are incorrect, yet ... the left figure has six angles, but all are right angles! Why isn't it a "rectangle?"

I reject both solutions: the first one is not a rectangle (we count angles, there are six of them!); as to the second one, I explain that there could be an infinite number of such solutions. When all the versions are exhausted, I try to prompt them with the idea that there are no more, but fail. So then I explain it myself, adding that this is the most interesting part of the puzzle: to explain why we have found all possible solutions and know there are no more.

Activity 4. Finishing the game (of three dice).

Gene, Pete, and Dima get 2, 11, and 14 chips, respectively, and we go on with our game. Gene soon goes bust. Now Dima and Pete each bet one chip per turn so the winner gets two chips instead of three. (When the sum lands on Gene's numbers, we ignore it.) The game speeds up since now

Dima's advantage becomes clearer. Gene participates by throwing dice and counting sums. When it becomes clear that Pete will soon lose, Dima tries hard to roll a sum that lands on Pete's numbers. This gives me another opportunity to remark that the outcome of a random event does not depend on our will. At last Dima wins. I ask,

"How has it happened? Dima has won, it means he has got more sums than you, but he only had four numbers while each of you had six."

We start to discuss this fact. The boys rapidly arrive at the conclusion that some numbers are more profitable than others and even explain that this is so because "there are more combinations." We turn to examples and discuss how many combinations give a sum of 3 and how many sum to 10. But the more we discuss, the less they pay attention. This is a good place to end the session, although Pete wants to play with the pegboard.

Session 38. Losing my grip

Sunday, November 29, 1981, 17:20–17:50.
Dima, Pete, Gene.

One of the least successful sessions. Again we missed a Saturday because I worked at the office all week long and had a tutoring job Friday evening,[1] so I was too tired and had no time to prepare. On Saturday, November 28, Dima had a dentist appointment, so we missed that day, too. That is why we decided to have a lesson on Sunday, at 5 PM. Gene, however, had not showed up, and no one answered the telephone. I decided he wasn't coming at all, and suggested that Dima and Pete play the 3-dice game again. But in the heat of the game Gene appeared, I stopped the game, Dima and Pete whined, and I got annoyed. At the beginning of the lesson Dima, as it often happens to him lately, did not sit upright: he swayed from side to side, then almost lay down on the table. I rebuked him twice, then lost my temper and said,

"One more crack, and you're out of here!" (we had had similar conflicts at lunchtime).

Dima turned gray and fell silent. I was also unhappy: I felt I had been unfair (in tone if not in words). Besides, I was worried about promoting negative associations with mathematics. I tried my best to change my mood before our first activity. I drew a deep breath, and paused, but it did not really help.

---

[1] We start to forget the realities of life in those days. I used to go to my job three times a week, the remaining two days were so-called "library days" (I had the right not to come to the office). But sometimes, especially by the end of the year, there was urgent work to do, e.g., writing annual reports. And like many others in my situation, I gave private lessons to make ends meet.

Activity 1. The game "how do you link them?"

(again borrowed from V. A. Levin). I give the first and last members of a chain; they have to supply an intermediate link, which is a homonym. For example, a solution for the middle element of the chain[1]

$$foot \rightarrow ? \rightarrow pen$$

could be *ball*.

The kids don't understand the example, and are unable to solve similar chains: *drum* → ? → *sugar* (answer is *beat/beet*), or *belly* → ? → *garbage* (answer is *waist/waste*). They fall silent. Everybody is bored.

Activity 2. Cutting a non-convex quadrilateral with one straight line

What are the possibilities when you cut a non-convex quadrilateral with a single straight line?

It turns out that there are 15 different configurations in all:

(a) Two triangles (3 ways);
(b) Three triangles (1 way);
(c) A triangle and a quadrilateral (6 ways);
(d) A triangle and a pentagon (3 ways);
(e) Two quadrilaterals (2 ways).

First we draw different polygons and count angles. As usual, Dima's "polygon" does not close. I explain that such a figure is not called a polygon but my explanation is muddled and I can't think of a simple synonym for "closed."

Then I ask whether we can call a figure formed by four arcs a quadrilateral (Figure 51: it does have four angles!) and explain that we can't.

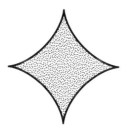

Figure 51. This curvilinear figure usually is not called a quadrilateral.

Next, I give the boys a non-convex quadrilateral (Figure 52) made of cardboard. A metal stick plays the role of a straight line, and the boys show different ways of cutting a quadrilateral and I sketch them.

---

[1]*P. Z.'s Note:* For obvious reasons, we have replaced the original Russian examples with English words, so that you see a few examples of this interesting game, even though it did not work with Zvonkin's students.

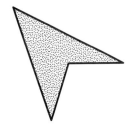

Figure 52. A non-convex
quadrilateral.

At first I can't make the boys calm down and listen to the assignment. They snatch the quadrilateral from one another, try to draw right on it and when I take the pencil away they try to scratch on the quadrilateral with the metal stick.

Then suddenly they get in the groove, understand the gist of the problem and become very inventive in proposing different ways of cutting. They work without repeating themselves and correctly determine what kind of shapes they get. They're lively and engaged.

At this moment I get a phone call from A. V. Ch. He is someone for whom I feel a deep respect, and though he asks me very politely whether I can talk, I do not have the guts to say I can't. The kids wait for me for 10 minutes, idle and bored, whereupon their moms let them go outdoors.

Session 39. Back on track

Saturday, December 5, 1981, 11:20–12:20.
Dima, Pete, Gene.

In contrast to the previous session, this one was one of the best, which is evident from its duration. Besides, I was obviously very excited to try out, for the first time, a project that I'd been working on for a long time: the programming language *Kid.*[1]

Activity 1. Find a proof.

(1) Prove that we hear with our ears and not with our eyes.
(2) Prove that we see with our eyes and not with our ears.
(3) Prove that clouds are nearer than the sun.

Dima is the first to answer them all. I won't elaborate further since I've already discussed this activity.

Homework: prove that we think with our head.

---

[1]*P. Z.'s Note:* In Russian, малыш ("malysh").

Activity 2.

My friend Stepan[1] and I invented a programming language for pre-school children (I think *Kid* is an appropriate name). Since certain stages of its development were connected with early sessions, unnoted in my journal, and since the language itself requires a separate description, we will take a long digression here.

A short excursion into the past.

1. During one of the first 20 "lost" sessions (perhaps #15) I constructed a tower of wooden blocks on the table (Figure 53) and asked the boys to build a tower of the same height but on the floor.

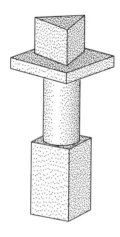

Figure 53. This tower is built on the table. How to build a tower of the same height, but on the floor?

When Dima was only 3 years old, I asked him to do the same thing on the stairs of the dacha we rented in the summer. At that age he understood this to mean building a tower whose top would be on the same level as of the previous tower. Now he knew, as did the others, that height was translation invariant. So he constructed a tower of roughly the same height and then grasped it at the top and bottom and tried to compare it to the tower on the table. Unfortunately for him — and to my secret joy — his tower kept collapsing.

After his third failure, I introduced a new rule: no touching or moving towers! A momentary pause followed and then Dima exclaimed, "I got it!," and constructed a tower on the floor using exactly the same blocks as the first tower.

I did not expect such a solution but despite my usual rigidity, I praised the boys (indeed, I never specified what elements should be used to build a tower on the floor).

---

[1]Stepan Pachikov, a close friend, later a founder of the Moscow Children's Computer Club and the software firm ParaGraph. Currently, he lives in the USA.

"And now another assignment, a bit more complicated," I said. "Build a tower of the same height but using different blocks," and I gave them multicolored plastic blocks of standard dimensions.

This time the pause was longer. I hated to finish the activity with failure so, despite my principles, I gave them a hint. As if by chance, I put a piece of string on the table and said,

"Go ahead, think it over."

They immediately snatched the string and started manipulating it, but actually had no idea how to use it. Mostly they stretched between the tops of the two towers. Then I brought a stick and said, "Perhaps this will be more useful."

But it wasn't. They did the same thing: placed it between the tops of the towers, getting an inclined line. I had to give them another hint:

"What's taller, the stick or the tower?"

The stick turned out to be higher than the tower but it had a scratch exactly at the level where the tower reached. This at last gave them an idea for building a tower on the floor that would reach this same scratch.

2. I had a good idea for representing the process of building of a tower as an *algorithm* (Figure 54).

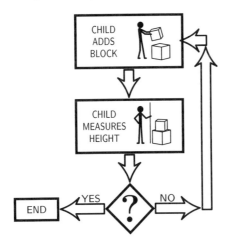

Figure 54. An algorithm for building a tower of the required height. The cards did not contain any text; I explained their meaning. As for the words "yes," "no," and "end," the kids were already able to read them.

I began by asking the kids to build a tower once again. This time they worked quickly and flawlesly, which among other things demonstrated their good mastery of the subject.

"Now," said I, "let us think what actions we make and in what order." And quite naturally got the following answer.

"We put several blocks one on top of another, then take measurements, then add or take away a block."

(Indeed, their error never was more than a single block.) A real pain in the neck, I began to drone on about a necessity to divide the problem into the smallest possible steps, e.g., put only one block and not several, etc.

Then I showed them cardboard cards with the following images (made by Alla):

(1) A rectangular card: a boy adds a block.
(2) A rectangular card: a boy measures the tower on the floor.
(3) A diamond card: a big question mark (which means the silent question: are they of the same height?)
(4) A smaller rectangular card with the word END in block letters.
(5) We also cut out a set of cardboard arrows: several small ones and a big one; on two small arrows are written words YES and NO.

I showed all this stuff to the kids and asked in what order these actions were to be performed. They were already familiar with these sorts of questions since earlier they had the following activities:

(A) Determine the order of morning activities (getting dressed, washing oneself, waking up, having breakfast, skating, gym, stretching in bed, etc.) – borrowed from Tamás Varga's book *Flowcharts, punch cards, and probabilities*.[1]

(B) Determine in what order you put on things when you get dressed (slip, T-shirt, socks, shoes, shirt, trousers, sweater, coat, scarf, cap).

The first set has a linear order, or a "program without branching," but the second set has a partial order, i.e., a non-deterministic algorithm.

Thus, with the tower puzzle, the kids ordered the sequence of actions correctly. When we had to return to the step "a boy places a block," I produced, with a flourish, a long arrow and we had the flowchart of Figure 54.

3.   Now, with hindsight, I'm unimpressed with the above. It has at least two drawbacks: first, the verification of the condition is not well implemented; second, the operation of measuring the second tower, the one on the table, has somehow disappeared (it should have preceded the first instruction in the flowchart). Another drawback is even more important: the whole scheme seems unnatural. The boys understood perfectly well *what* I was doing, but not at all *why* I was doing it, nor why I did it this way. And their actual behavior was different: they put several blocks one on top of another and then measured once or twice.

Nevertheless, this provided me with a new idea of inventing puzzles on algorithm construction and with a few principles that persisted into the final version.

Principle 1. An algorithm must be described using flowcharts, rather than a "written" programming language (or natural language, for that matter). The boys cannot read or write, except for the simplest words.

Principle 2. Flowcharts are not to be hand-drawn (the kids' drawing skills are too shaky) but instead, presented with cardboard cards. (The

---

[1]Tamás Varga, *Matematik I. Flußdiagramme, Lochkarten, Wahrscheinlichkeit*, Klett-Cotta, Stuttgart, 1988.

most cumbersome consequence of this principle is the need to cut out many arrows of different lengths.)

Principle 3. Show operators and logical conditions on cards not with words but with simple and clear images. It is even better if these are symbols.

Besides, it was an aesthetic joy putting out white cards on a black polished table surface!

However, it took me long time to think of a new puzzle in this direction. I got all sorts of ideas: going up in an elevator, drawing balls of two colors from a sack and distributing them into two urns. But these were processes that either did not yield to algorithms or were uninteresting and unnatural. The idea of an algorithmic language seemed utterly unattainable: If I am unable to think of a single puzzle, a whole class of puzzles is even less possible to invent! I was also somewhat discouraged by the idea that for each puzzle I would have to make new cards and drawings.

4.   After numerous discussions with Stepan about modern programming in general and toys with built-in programmed chips in particular, I came to understand the most important roadblock faced when trying to create a programming language for kids.

The language needn't be universal, that is, it has to be specialized. All the languages I knew specialized either at working with numbers (FORTRAN, ALGOL) or data (COBOL) or texts and lists (LISP, SNOBOL). There also were universal languages that could do all of this (PL, ALGOL-68).[1]

But these language "domains" (numbers, lists, etc.) are neither interesting nor intelligible to kids (of these domains, numbers are the most accessible, but even to understand the meaning of puzzles that can be treated with algorithms, the kids need to be at least 5 years older). So the main difficulty is to come up with a domain (of application for a language) that is suitable for children. The language itself is secondary.

Two days after a telephone discussion during which I formulated this problem to Stepan, he called me back to describe an ingeniously simple solution: the domain should be objects moving in a maze drawn on a graph paper. He also proposed that we start with a rectangular room as the simplest version of a maze.

Whereupon each of us, quite independently, invented the same language, even down to nearly identical symbols, proving, to my mind, its natural character.

The programming language *Kid*

In 1981, there already existed a programming language for children, namely, *Logo*. Like *Kid*, *Logo*'s objective was to control the movements of an object

---

[1]Don't forget that I was writing this in 1981.

(a turtle). However, *Logo* was much better developed and, more important, was an existing software product. For this reason, today our invention seems rather like a wooden bicycle. I even hesitated to include it in this book. But then I decided that it would be a pity to discard a whole bunch of puzzles as well as the enthusiasm our project had generated first among us, the adults, and then among the kids who were naturally carried away by our excitement. Besides, back then we didn't even know about *Logo*, and not only did we not have computers, we didn't even dream of having them. Also, if you think about it, the invention of wooden bicycles is not that stupid. (This subject is surely worth discussing someday.)

I turn now to the description of *Kid*. I will first describe the core language and then possible extensions.

1. The moving object: I glued a wooden arrow—the "robot"—using Dima's construction kit (Figure 55). The robot fits into a cell of size 8×8 cm.

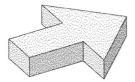

Figure 55. This wooden arrow is the "robot." It moves in a checkerboard room.

2. The room: Drawn on a big sheet of paper, a rectangle of 5×7 cells. Of course it can be modified to suit the problem.

3. Executable commands ("verbs"): For the moment, just these four: "take one step forward," "turn right," "turn left," and "turn 180°." They are shown in Figure 56.

Figure 56. The executable command cards are made of white cardboard. Each side is 3 cm.

4. Logical conditions: Again, just four: "wall is in front," "wall is to the right," "wall is to the left," and "wall is behind," as shown in Figure 57. (Most of our programs use only the first one.)

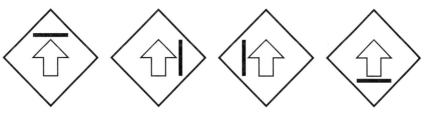

Figure 57. Logical conditions are cardboard diamonds with diagonal length 6 cm.

5. Arrows: We need arrows of many lengths in multiples of 1.5 cm. Some of the 3 cm arrows are labeled YES or NO. Note that each of these words should be written on the arrows in four ways: from head to tail, from tail to head, and vertically upside and down (in Figure 58 you can see three out of the 8 types that we needed).

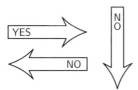

Figure 58. Three out of the eight types of arrows; they attach to the logical condition diamonds.

6. Begin and End: Each program begins with a semicircle with the diameter on the bottom and ends with a semicircle with the diameter on the top. Up to now we have only used semicircles with the words BEGIN and END (Figure 59). Later, we will put input and output information in these semicircles.

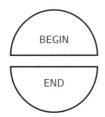

Figure 59. The entire program is bracketed between these two semicircular symbols.

7. Subprograms: We have not used them so far, but in the future we may do the following:

(A) We maintain a notebook which will contain all the active programs (each on a separate page). Each program is *numbered.* The verbal formulation of the task will be written on the same page, as briefly as possible and in block letters, so that the kids who can read could do it.

(B) If we need to use a program already noted as a subprogram, we'll include a new symbol: a big 6×6 cm. square, framed by two semi-circles; the big square will merely contain the *number* of the subprogram (Figure 60). If we have input and output data, it will be handled by the semicircles.

Figure 60. This is what subprogram #1 looks like. The notebook will explain what it does.

The form of this "subprogram" symbol must emphasize that it is an entire program, with its own beginning and end (hence the semicircles) which performs not one action, but many (that's why the square is *big*!). Correct proportions are essential so that the flowcharts layout looks right.

8. Counters: Very soon, we hope to enrich the language by introducing counters (integer variables). Stepan suggests that its symbol should look like a container that can hold balls. We have not yet decided how to denote a counter in the flowchart. I am adamant in refusing operators of the type "$i = 1$." I first thought of denoting a counter by a triangle with a letter; in a flowchart, reaching triangle A will mean "put one ball in container A." Stepan thinks it will be better to instead draw a shape resembling an actual container that can hold balls. This is a good idea, but all the glass jars we have at out disposal are cylinders, which in a graphic representation is another rectangular shape. Currently, I am inclined to try a card on which is drawn a jar with the letter A, a ball and an arrow showing where to put the ball. If we need to subtract a unit from the counter it will be easily depicted in the same manner (a ball taken out of the jar; earlier I thought I would turn the triangle upside down). Both versions, old and new, can be seen in Figure 61.

Figure 61. Two possible versions of a counter increment card (left) and its decrement counterparts (right).

The introduction of counters requires new logical conditions such as "$A = 4$," "$A > B$," etc. But first we should introduce the symbols $=, >, <$ to the kids. Our programming language does not intend to make use of any other arithmetic operations (not even addition).

· · ·

Now we can at last come back to the session whose description was interrupted in mid-sentence.

When I put the box with all the cards and arrows on the table I am completely swamped by questions. Eventually, I am able to explain the following:

A robot is a mechanical person. It can do various things, but in contrast to a person it has no mind, so it only does what it is told, and no more; it is perfectly obedient.

I show them what the robot can do. They have trouble distinguishing between turning to the right, to the left, or by 180°. I put them in a row and do some military maneuvers, which reveals that they are not sure either about the difference between right and left. However, when the same orders are executed by the robot, there are fewer mistakes, because the arrow indicates the direction.

I explain that the robot does not have eyes (mechanical eyes can be made but this is very difficult), so it can only feel with his hand whether there is a wall nearby. We take a diamond logical condition card and start checking with various positions of the robot whether the condition is true. Dima very pertinently says that the condition "wall to the right" is also true when the wall is on the other side but the robot (the arrow) is turned in the opposite direction, as compared to the diamond card (Figure 62). This is curious, as it means that he understands that "left" and "right" is invariant (with respect to rotation of the robot) yet he still can't remember which is which.

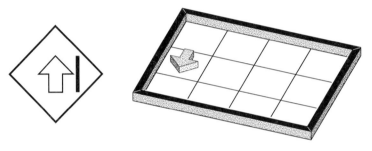

Figure 62.   The wall is to the right of the robot.

Finally I can formulate an assignment for the robot: Go as far as the wall and stop.

Pandemonium ensues. Someone grabs the robot and starts taking steps with it; another one lays out cards in the cells of the "room;" nobody understands anything whatsoever; someone pesters me about why we need such a long arrow.

With great difficulty I restore order and explain that the flowchart must be laid out not in the room, but on the table; that the sequence of actions must be shown with arrows and that we should begin with "Begin" and end with "End."

Then they create the flowchart of Figure 63; what they have in mind is, informally, the following course of actions: "Begin and go on until the end." I demonstrate that with this program the robot sometimes reaches the wall, sometimes doesn't, and sometimes even gets its nose smashed.

Then Dima shouts, "OK, I know, we need as many of these things (he indicates the card with one step) as we need steps, I'll tell you how many – one, two, three... we need five!"

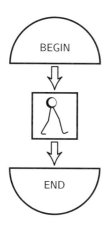

Figure 63. The first (wrong) version of the program to "go as far as the wall and stop." This program instructs the robot to take only one step and doesn't even check if there is a wall in front.

And again I make the same pedagogical blunder as always: what I should have done was to develop this idea calmly and without haste; cut out paper squares, draw little men, and make all the charts they proposed. Then the idea of a loop would have evolved as a true discovery. But partly from inertia and partly because I am afraid that I don't have enough of the "take one step" cards, I merely wave aside this idea on the grounds that the program will be different for different cells, and also too big if the room is large.

Then we investigate the possibility of using just a single "step" card by coming back to it with arrows. It turns out that in this case the robot always collides with the wall and gets its nose smashed.

What we do then is that I blindfold the boys in turn and ask them to do exactly what the robot must do, that is, go as far as the wall and stop. But before they start, I carry each of them around the room blindfolded, and spin them around, so that they do not know where the wall is. I ask them to note that, before starting to walk, each of them stretches out his hand to check if there is a wall in front. We conclude then that the first action must be to check whether there is a wall in front. The program is ready.

In conclusion each of the boys makes the robot walk in the room strictly according to the flowchart (and when someone starts to mess around, I emphasize that robots, in contrast to humans, are *absolutely obedient*).

Session 40. First encounter with Dienes blocks

Saturday, December 12, 1981, 11:10–11:55.
Dima, Pete, Gene.

Activity 1.

Domokos Szász[1] brought me a set of plastic shapes from Hungary. Each piece has four distinct attributes: color (red, blue, yellow, green), shape

---

[1]A Hungarian mathematician, specializing in probability theory. He was a graduate student work in Moscow. I am indebted to him for this gift forever.

(circles, squares, and triangles), size (big or small) and presence or absence of a hole: $4 \cdot 3 \cdot 2 \cdot 2 = 48$ in all. They are called Dienes blocks.[1] Our first activity uses them.

We start by discussing the different attributes. Here's the puzzle: Make a chain of pieces so that each piece is different from the preceding one by a single attribute (while three other attributes are the same).

The boys make few mistakes, and immediately correct any mistakes that they do make. Soon the chain is as long as the table.

Activity 2.

At this moment I'm inspired to try something like Levin's "how do you link them:" I put two pieces on the table that differ by all four attributes, and say these are the beginning and the end of a chain to be linked following the same rule as before. To my surprise, this puzzle does not present any difficulties either: the kids do each action correctly, at every step diminishing the "Hamming distance"[2] by one.

Afterwards Gene suggests that we take away the previous long chain and link the remaining ends by a short chain, like a moment ago. We do it. Then Dima suggests that we link the ends of the two resulting chains (to make a quadrilateral). Done as well.

"It's a square," they say.

I explain this is not a square, but a quadrilateral, since its sides contain different number of pieces (the ends of the original chains do not differ by all four attributes). Then I show how to make this quadrilateral into a circle. For some reason they love the circle! Dima wants to draw a diameter inside. But I stop him.

They argue about what to do next. I try to explain that if we play through all the different Dienes block games, we won't be able to do any more later. But they really want to do more with them. I am about to agree when Pete asks, "Can we get the *robot* later?"

I say yes. This starts another round of debate. Some who were eager to play with the Dienes blocks agree to switch to the robot, some who agreed to call it a day, now want to continue with the blocks since they don't like the robot. Gene says he doesn't like the robot because it's difficult. (Later, it turns out that he did quite well with the robot, so he's probably just repeating what his mom said.) I say that it's hard to decide, because there are three of them and each wants something different so we have to elect

---

[1]Zoltán P. Dienes is a leading advocate of "active" mathematical education, i.e., education based on *concrete* activities. Today the Dienes blocks are universally known and easy to obtain. Dienes also created manipulatives for understanding place value; these are also called Dienes blocks. The manipulatives described in this book are sometimes called Dienes *logic* blocks.

[2]*P. Z.'s Note:* Hamming distance is used to compare two strings; it is equal to the number of positions at which the strings differ. For example, the Hamming distance between "GAUSS" and "GAUDY" is 2.

one person who will be the boss and he will decide. Everybody agrees that I must be the boss and we move on to programming.

Activity 3.

Today the puzzle is to go to the wall and turn your back to it. The results are stunning.

Dima says, "Dad, make the same thing for us as last time!"

I don't have time to answer: Gene and Pete grab things from the table. Dima, afraid he will be left empty-handed, follows suit.

In a flash the three of them construct a flowchart (not for the old problem, which was Dima's idea, but for the new one). At first it contains two mistakes but they immediately correct them: (1) they forgot two "return" arrows after a "step" to the "wall in front?" diamond, but then Gene remembers and puts them in place; (2) Dima wants to attach a third arrow to the diamond, leading to a "turn 180°" command, as in Figure 64; I ask why the YES arrow does not lead to anything and in what case will the third arrow be "active," but before I have time to formulate my question properly Pete interrupts, "It should be here", and shows the correct place for the turn command.

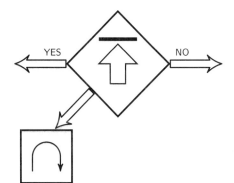

Figure 64. An example of "illegal" use of a logical condition diamond. It's not clear when we should follow the third arrow: when it is neither YES nor NO?

After this each boy implements the program by following the flowchart with his finger and making the robot walk in the room.

I forgot to say that at the beginning the boys wanted once more to walk blindfold around the room. I said we would do it if necessary, but otherwise, why should we?

They whined, "But we want to...."

But nobody remembered this later when we started to work.

Session 41. More of the same (robots and Dienes blocks)

Saturday, December 19, 1981. 11:10–12:00.
Dima, Pete, Gene.

Activity 1. A Hungarian game.

I remind them about last time, the chain where each piece differed from the previous one by one attribute and suggest that we now make a chain where each successive piece differs by all four attributes.

The assignment goes on smoothly (with a few inevitable mistakes). In the middle of the work Pete remarks that big and small figures alternate. We discuss why (the attribute "size" has only two values, big and small) and discover that the same happens to holes (figures with and without holes alternate) and for this reason all big figures don't have holes while all the small ones have them. I propose that we remove all the unnecessary pieces (big ones with holes and small ones without) to be able to find what we need more easily. That helps us to finish the assignment in no time.

On Dima's suggestion we construct above the first chain another one, almost the same, but where figures without holes are replaced by those with holes, and *vice-versa*. Dima notices that horizontally we've got "the new assignment" and vertically "the old assignment" (that is, only one attribute changes).

The composition of chains looks so beautiful that I can hardly convince the kids to destroy it. Dima is especially stubborn. I manage to placate him only after we decide to cut out similar decorations for the New Year tree.[1]

Activity 2. A problem for the robot: Go to the wall behind you, and stop with your back to it.

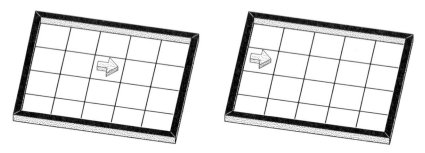

Figure 65. The robot must walk from the starting position (left) to the final position (right).

I show the boys the initial and final positions of the robot and ask them to do the task "manually," that is, to take the robot and make all the necessary actions (steps, turns, etc.; see Figure 65). To my surprise, only Gene does everything correctly (turn around, take two steps, and turn around again). Pete and Dima do God knows what; they walk sideways, zigzag, make a lot of unnecessary turns, go backwards, etc., and they don't end up in the right place. I don't know if they were inventing a new assignment (Dima's

---

[1]*P. Z.'s Note:* New Year's was the Soviet answer to Christmas, complete with a tree and a Santa figure, "Grandfather Frost."

favorite pastime) or didn't understand mine. I need to be very patient as I repeatedly correct their mistakes. Finally, I ask Gene to explain how he did it correctly, but for some reason he messes up everything. It seems that they've forgotten what the puzzle was about. We have to start from scratch.

> *As a matter of fact, the real problem was that I did not want to make a simple program but rather a very sophisticated one, so that it would work but the robot would run across the field like crazy. However, I had to settle for very simple programs, and even these were not easy to construct. Only a few months later did we manage to write a really "good" program — it brought the robot into the corner — but not even Dad could understand why it worked. — Dima.*

At last, everything is straightened out and we start programming. We try numerous versions, testing each to see whether it works. Each time when the program enters an endless loop it provokes tremendous laughter and general delight. Finally we create a program that works and achieves the desired goal, but not from every initial position; it first takes a step and *then* checks whether there is a wall in front (thus if the robot in the initial position has its back to the wall, after turning around and trying to take a step it will smash its nose). I remind the kids of the proverb "look before you leap," and say you can't just take a random step, that before each step you must check if the wall is in front. However, this does not immediately fix things; what follows instead is a series of meaningless versions. Finally we develop a correct program. We end with a new tradition: each boy executes the program from an initial position of his choosing. And the session is over.

Session 42. Snowflakes

Saturday, January 2, 1982, 11:10–11:55.
Dima, Pete, Gene.

A New Year session.

Strange as it may seem, I hadn't planned for this session to have any kind of holiday connection (it just didn't occur to me). New Year's just crept up on me, and I didn't think about it until the session was over. Had I realized it sooner, I would have planned something more special.

Activity 1. Magic squares.

Pete brings his very first newspaper, *Pionerskaya Pravda*. The issue contains a puzzle: a 4×4 table of three-digit numbers, which are to be rearranged to get a magic square with the sum 1982.

I say that this is a very difficult puzzle, but take this opportunity to tell them what a magic square is.[1] I bring an album of Dürer, find the engraving *Melancholia* and explain that Dürer was both an artist and a mathematician. I show them the magic square in the picture. We start to verify that it is "magic" and compute several sums of rows, columns and a diagonal.[2]

Two numbers in the engraving are illegible (I haven't noticed this before). I suggest that the boys deduce their values. No one thinks to subtract the sum of the three numbers that we know from the row total (34) in order to obtain the unknown one. Instead they use trial-and-error, but manage to guess the number after one or two attempts.

Activity 2. Central symmetry.

I remind the boys that we have already seen symmetry with respect to a straight line ("mirror"). There is another kind of symmetry, with respect to a point (the "center"). I take a sheet of graph paper, mark the center with a point and then draw dots, circles, lines at various places and then their symmetrical images. Some of the boys join me. Dima, as has become customary, eschews my diagram and creates his own center,[3] and starts drawing a curved line and then another one, centrally symmetric to it. But his drawing skill is shaky and it is difficult to tell how well he is doing. With effort, I convince him that this independent project is too difficult and that he must first learn how to manage easier problems.

Then I challenge him to transform a triangle, and he draws an axially symmetric figure; he forgets to turn it upside down to get a centrally symmetric image. I show the correct solution (Figure 66) and we discuss it.

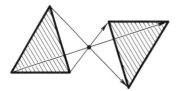

Figure 66.   An example of central symmetry.

Next, I show the boys pictures from Hermann Weyl's *Symmetry* and from a collection of papers, *Patterns of Symmetry*.[4] We look for axially symmetric and centrally symmetric patterns and I remark that the more symmetrical a figure is, the more beautiful it will be. We come across a snowflake. Dima, quite surprised, asks, "Are these snowflakes?"

---

[1] *P. Z.'s Note:* A *magic square* is a square array of numbers such that every row, column and the two diagonals have the same sum.

[2] *P. Z.'s Note:* Dürer's *Melancholia*, which includes this magic square can be easily found online.

[3] Indeed. Even my thesis problem was my own rather than suggested by my doctoral adviser. — Dima.

[4] *Patterns of Symmetry*, Marjorie Senechal and George Fleck (editors), University of Massachusetts Press, 1977.

I say they are, but very much magnified.

The boys decide to go outdoors with a magnifying glass to examine snowflakes (unfortunately, it was not possible that day as the snow was packed down).

> *Later, Pete and I would catch and scrutinize fresh snowflakes. — Dima.*

At last we start making a centrally symmetric figure on the pegboard (taking color into consideration, of course). Just then I should have thought of constructing a snowflake! Instead we construct a purely centrally symmetric figure without axes of symmetry. The kids work nearly flawlessly. Gene's father, Boris, joins in.

When the session is over and the boys have put on their coats, I tell them about how Kepler wrote the mathematical monograph *A New Year's Gift, or On the Six-Cornered Snowflake* as a New Year's gift to a friend. And only then does the idea of a special New Year session occur to me! We could have cut out paper snowflakes...

Session 43. On certain properties of addition

Saturday, January 9, 1982, 11:20–12:00.
Dima, Pete, Gene.

I start by saying that yesterday, at their English lesson, each of them got a plastic snowflake. I show them Dima's snowflake and say that today, our lesson will also be dedicated to the New Year.

Activity 1. Symmetry of snowflakes.

I tell the boys that the snowflake is so beautiful because it has many symmetries and ask them to show me which symmetries they see. Besides the obvious axes, like AA' in Figure 67, they find less obvious ones, such as BB'.

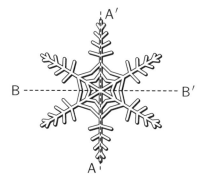

Figure 67. Symmetry axes of a snowflake.

Then I ask whether snowflakes have a center of symmetry. They say it does. I show them a paper snowflake that Alla made for the holiday, noting that it is also very beautiful and symmetric but in one respect it's not like a real snowflake: all snowflakes in nature are 6-pointed, while this one is 8-pointed. I explain that it is easier to create an 8-pointed figure, for when you fold a piece of paper three times, you divide it eightfold. For some time we debate how to fold a sheet of paper to get 6 points. Dima's hands tremble with impatience, so eager is he to start cutting something out! But first I want to fashion the sheet into a circle. Dima can't wait, and starts folding another sheet of paper. I use this delay to finish my snowflake. Unfortunately, the resulting shape has only three axes of symmetry instead of six and thus isn't centrally symmetric (Figure 68). I hadn't thought this through beforehand, since the whole activity of folding and cutting is more or less improvised. I abandon the subject and quickly switch to the pegboard.

Figure 68. My failed "snowflake," with just three axes of symmetry and no center of symmetry. It's symmetric with respect to 120° rotation, but we haven't "covered" this yet.

Activity 2. Making snowflakes on a round pegboard.

The pegboard we use today isn't our usual rectangular box but instead is round with hexagonal pegs. Our task is clear from the title: I put a peg on the board and the boy whose turn it is to play must place all the corresponding pegs symmetrically to "make a snowflake" (if the initial peg is on the ray forming one of the snowflake's points, he must add 5 more pegs, but otherwise, he must add 11 more, see Figure 69). It goes without saying that color is also taken into consideration.

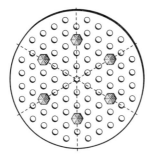 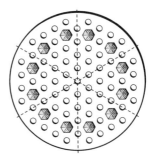

Figure 69. If the peg is on a ray of the snowflake's point, there are five more corresponding pegs; the same is true for the pegs on the ray bisector. In all other cases a peg has 11 corresponding pegs.

Dima and Pete worked without mistakes, while Gene for some reason kept making the same mistake each time. They finished with a rather pretty multicolored snowflake.

Note that "make a snowflake" is a rather vague assignment. For me this is a matter of principle. A precise and accurate problem formulation would demand a discussion of rotations, existence of several axes of symmetry and eventually the automorphism group. There is no way that the kids would have understood or retained any of that. Indeed, the sensible way to work — for adult mathematicians as well — is to gradually acquire an understanding of the necessary details in the process of solving the problem. More than once I had an occasion to see that in research: the final problem formulation became clear only after the problem had been solved.

Activity 3. Associativity (and commutativity) of addition.

I tell the kids that later, in school, they will learn how to count but even now... They instantly interrupt and shout, simultaneously,

Pete: "I can count, but only to one hundred!"

Gene: "I can count the numbers on a clock!"

Dima: "I can count up to very big numbers, but I never tried!"

Obviously, by "counting" they mean the sequential enumeration of numbers: one, two, three, etc. I remark that they also know (a little) about how to add and multiply. But neither Pete nor Gene know the meaning of the word "multiply." I explain that it means adding the same number many times and give an example.

I continue, "The most interesting thing, however, is not to add or to multiply but to know certain secrets about adding and multiplying. And today I am going to divulge one of these secrets."

We discuss two examples: $5 + 6 + 7$ and $6 + 8 + 2$. In each case we do addition in three different ways: first choose two numbers and sum them and then add the third number to the sum.

[I should have started with commutativity.]

Each time we get the same result. I ask the boys why and whether we would always get the same result. Without any surprise, they answer that it happens because each time we add up the same numbers, and thus will always get the same result. I then give them three very big numbers (one of them in the millions) and ask whether they are sure it will be the case for such big numbers. The boys agree that for big numbers, the sums might be different.

Then how they will explain the similar results in our case? Pete repeats the previous argument: we add up the same numbers, so we get the same thing.

I protest vehemently, "What do you mean, the same thing?! Look, here we first got 11, and then added 7, and here we got 13, and then added 5!"

"So what?," retorts Pete.

And I was so eager to surprise them ...

I try another approach.

"So is it true that when we do the same things in a different order we always get the same result?"

"It is", says Pete.

"Look, Pete, imagine that you have to put on socks, boots and galoshes. If you first put on your socks, then boots and then galoshes, it will be OK. (He nods). But if you first put on galoshes, then boots, and then socks?"

The boys burst out laughing and start coming up with other things you can put on in the wrong order.

"Now you see," I say, "that sometimes it's important not only to do the right things but also to do them in the right order."

[I must confess, however, I was not completely honest. The example actually demonstrates violation of commutativity rather than associativity. But we also use the commutativity of addition when we add the first and the last terms and then add the middle one.]

"So why, in the end, did we get the sums to be equal?"

Pete says that he understands why, but cannot explain it.

"OK, if you are so sure we can add up numbers in any order, then add up all these numbers," and I placed cards on the table with the numbers from 1 to 9, which in fact were intended to make a 3×3 magic square. I say the problem is very difficult but if they are shrewd enough and can think of the convenient way to sum up the numbers, the problem will become easy.

But the kids merely start to add the numbers one by one. Dima is the only one who actually calculates. Gene helps when Natasha encourages him. As for Pete, he exclaims at the very beginning, "We'll get a hundred!," at which point his participation ends.

We get 45. I say, "Bravo! You're good calculators, but not very tricky ones, because you could do it in a much easier way." Dima suggests that they start to count from the other end (from 9).

"Well, give it a try, add 9 to 8. Is it easier?"

"No, it isn't", says Dima but Gene interrupts him saying, that if we start from the other end we'll get a bigger number.

"One hundred! We'll get one hundred!" rejoices Pete.

(Just a minute ago he was certain that the result would always be the same!) We start from the other end (again Dima is the only one who really works) and we predictably get 45.

Since the boys are at a loss concerning the reasonable way to add, I ask them a leading question:

"To whom is it easy to add one?" (Rigorous linguists, excuse me: I like my numbers to be alive.)

Dima gives the logical answer that it is easy to add one to any number.

"OK, then, and nine?"

It turns out the easiest thing is to add 1 to 9, and then we get a good number, 10, we can just put it aside and remember. Then the boys guess, that in a similar way, we can add $2 + 8$, $3 + 7$ and $4 + 6$. We get four 10s and a 5.

"And what does that make?"

"One hundred!" shouts Pete.

To my surprise, it is not obvious, not just for Pete, but for Dima and Gene as well, that four times ten plus five equals 45. I have to explain a bit and to ask leading questions. They are probably too tired by that time or else the problem is too difficult. I really have no idea. I just wonder how it was before people had invented the positional number system. Back then, they did not operate with *digits* that represented tens and units separately. Perhaps the operations were less formal and did not obscure the central ideas. But this is just idle speculation.

In conclusion I promise that next time we will try to make a magic square of these numbers. But I doubt that it will be accessible to them. Several attempts that the kids make on the spot (without my participation) convince me of this.

That evening, Dima asked me whether we will always get the same sum, even if we add the numbers up in different ways. I said yes, always. Do I know the explanation? I do. Why haven't I told them? Because I wanted them to think for themselves. And when they find the explanation by themselves, will I tell them? I will.

Session 44. Magic squares

> Saturday, January 16, 1982, 11:20–12:20.
> Dima, Pete, Gene.

It's hard to describe this session. Our first activity was to make a magic square, and it was a good choice to place it first, because it took up an entire hour and proved to be very hard. The whole time we tried out different solutions and hunted for different strategies of exhaustive search (with hints and guidance from me). Roughly speaking, this is what happened.

(1) We decide first to choose a number that will be the sum of each row and each column. They suggest 5. We try to get the sum 5 and come to the conclusion that it is impossible but I demand an explanation. Finally we manage to find one: even the sum of the smallest numbers 1, 2 and 3 exceeds 5.

(2) We try then the sums 6, 8, 10, 12, 13 but fail each time. We're unable to make the second or third row.

(3) I suggest they try to think it over and understand which sum should be chosen. I remind them that the last time we calculated the sum (they remember it was 45). Then we painstakingly divide 45 by 3.

(4) The sum found, we start to put the numbers in rows so that they make the sum of 15. Trial-and-error method eventually works. The boys are especially happy to see that the sum of the last row is 15 without any effort on our part.

(5) Then, permuting the numbers within each row, we try to get 15 in each column. Another success!

(6) Finally, we focus on the diagonals. In one of them the sum is already 15, while in the other it is only 6. We start to move the entire lines or entire columns to get 15 on both diagonals but nothing doing! We have to settle for this incomplete solution:

5	9	1
7	2	6
3	4	8

It's my fault. Had I thought it over beforehand, I would have understood that the central cell must contain 5, and then shuffling a single row and a single column would have yielded a solution:

2	7	6
9	5	1
4	3	8

The next day, I tell Dima why we must have 5 in the central cell (see Figure 70) and together we make a true magic square.

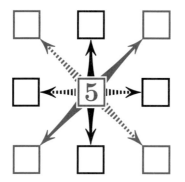

Figure 70. If we are clever enough to put 5 in the center, the whole problem becomes much easier: the sums of the numbers on either side of the 5 must be 10.

I forgot to mention that at the beginning of the session I showed the kids punch cards,[1] explained what it was all about and answered their questions.

Thinking over this problem after the session I invented a good one for adults: Make a *multiplicative* magic square, i.e., a square containing natural numbers and having the same product in the rows, columns, and diagonals. Instead of the additive condition that the numbers be distinct and chosen from the interval $1, 2, 3, \ldots n^2$ (which won't work with multiplicative squares), the condition is that the product be minimal. Squares of size 4×4 and 3×3 are shown in Figure 71.

---

[1]The progress of computer technologies is so rapid that sometimes I feel like a fossil, for I used *paper tape* when I was young. For those who were born later, this is how it worked: you type your program on a perforator machine that punches holes in a long strip of paper. If after two hours of work you make a single mistake, the whole tape must be discarded. For this reason, punch cards were perceived as a technological miracle: instead of discarding the whole pack, it was possible to replace a single spoiled card. However, they had one inconvenience that paper tape did not have. If you dropped them on the floor, it was virtually impossible to restore the right order. I could have written a whole paper about these technologies!

1	42	105	10
30	35	14	3
70	15	6	7
21	2	5	210

3	4	18
36	6	1
2	9	12

Figure 71. Multiplicative magic squares. If we multiply the numbers in each line, each column and each diagonal, the product will be the same: 44,100 for the big square and 216 for the small one.

Here is another solution for the (additive) 3×3 square: Subtract 5 from each number; instead of $1, 2, 3, \ldots, 9$ we have $0, \pm 1, \pm 2, \pm 3, \pm 4$ and the common sum will be equal to 0. If we put 0 in the center, we can fill in the symmetric cells with numbers of opposite sign. Thus we can get the following result:

1	2	-3
-4	0	4
3	-2	-1

$+$

5	5	5
5	5	5
5	5	5

$=$

6	7	2
1	5	9
8	3	4

An interesting observation: Dima thinks that if each number increases by one, then so too will the common sum.

Session 45. Generalized chains

Saturday, January 23, 1982, 11:10–12:00.
Dima, Pete, Gene.

Activity 1.

I show the kids the magic square I have made with Dima, and Dima says that we must put 5 in the center. Pete starts checking the sums, sliding a finger along the rows and columns, repeating under his breath, "Fifteen, fifteen, fifteen." But no further discussion follows and so I decide not to torture them any more.

Activity 2.

One of the activities already described in the previous chapter, so I won't repeat it here.

When the work is over I tell the boys that one day I will give them a puzzle which will be exactly like this one but will look different so they won't realize it is the same. Dima is very excited and asks whether I'll tell them *later*. I reassure him, promising to do so.

Activity 3. "Generalized chains."

I show them a sheet of paper with circles connected by lines. They have to put a Dienes block into each circle so that circles connected by lines contain blocks different by only one attribute (if circles are not connected by lines, it does not matter). The boys get two puzzles (Figure 72).

In the first one, the blocks on the spokes differ from the central one, three by color, two by shape, one by size and one by absence or presence of a hole (seven all in all).

The second puzzle is more difficult. It only has two types of solutions: When the vertices of the triangle contain three figures either of three different colors or of three different shapes. Since the kids start with a big figure and a small one, they cannot find the correct solution for a long time. I have to explain that the third figure can neither be big nor small. They replace one of the figures but the new one differs from the previous one only by a hole. Again I have to explain that the third figure can neither have a hole not be without one.

Finally, Dima discovers one solution and I show them the second possible solution.

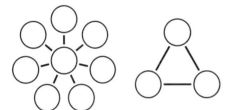

Figure 72. Put Dienes blocks into circles so that those connected by lines contain blocks differing by exactly one attribute.

The session is over but the boys don't want to part with the nice Dienes blocks and ask permission to put them away into the box. Permission is granted.

Pete exclaims, "I'll put away squares!"

Dima, "And me, circles!"

Gene, "And me, small figures!"

I jump at the occasion to ask a mathematically provocative question, "Do you realize, Gene, if Dima puts away circles and you put away small shapes, who will put away small circles?"

I leave them alone but later ask which shapes are the easiest to put away and which are the most difficult. After a short discussion I remark that to put a triangle in its triangular hole, it can be rotated in three ways, a square, in four ways, and for a circle there are infinitely many possibilities. At which point Dima declares that the most difficult will be "uniangles."

The session has an unexpected sequel. I have not yet put the blocks away when our little daughter Jane comes in from a walk and immediately asks to play with them. I give her an age-appropriate assignment (she is 25 months old): I toss out all the shapes from the box and suggest that she put them back. She sets to work with immense enthusiasm. This improvised "math for toddlers" takes up more than an hour (it will be described in more detail below, see pp. 244–246). It always strikes me how long a child can work when a task is self-imposed.

Session 46. Isomorphic problems

> Saturday, January 30, 1982, 11:00–11:45.
> Dima, Pete, Gene.

Activity 1. Isomorphic problems.

We revisit puzzles about $\binom{5}{2}$ (described in the previous chapter). Earlier, we solved them one after the other, but this time we examine them as a whole, and try to see in which way they "resemble" one another.

Activity 2. Continuation of Activity 3 from the previous session.

I say, "You have seen that there are puzzles which seem different but are actually the same. There are also puzzles that help you solve new ones. So let's recall one of the puzzles you had last time, because it will help you to solve today's puzzles." Then I place the triangle from last week (Figure 72, right) on the table. Dima immediately solves it (using shapes of three different colors) while Pete and Gene, pushing each other aside, make two more solutions of this type. I remind them of the non-isomorphic solution with three distinct shapes. Then they get the new puzzle: a diamond plus a diagonal, as shown here on the left:

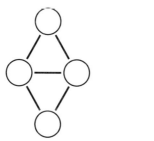 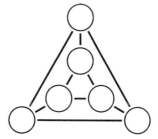

Figures 73 (left) and 74 (right). Two more graphs for the same problem: the figures in adjacent vertices must differ by exactly one attribute.

The boys immediately find a solution; I don't even have time to ask them the question I have prepared, "Is it clear why the previous puzzle helps to solve this one?"

I give them another figure, shown above on the right: two concentric triangles. This time I do ask the question but get no answer since everybody is busy finding the solution. I have to answer it myself, "Because this figure is composed of triangles."

As I say this, Pete has already filled in the internal triangle. Then I point to the old triangle problem of Figure 72 (which is still on the table) and Dima exclaims, "Ah!," and transfers these shapes to the external triangle of the current puzzle.

But it's still not solved! Each triangle independently satisfies the condition but between the exterior and interior triangles, more than one attribute differs. After a short discussion the puzzle is solved. The entire activity has taken five minutes.

Activity 3. Magic squares.

So far, 35 minutes have elapsed. I tell them that they have worked so well, solving all the puzzles, and thus the session is over. But they ask for more. I think a little and say there will be no more puzzles; instead I will tell them about a very simple method I came up with for constructing magic squares (described at the end of Session 44, p. 117). The boys have no trouble with the negative numbers.

Session 47. The end of the story about $\binom{5}{2}$.

Saturday, February 6, 1982, 11:00–11:50.
Dima, Pete, Gene.

Activity 1. Letter squares.

Just for fun, I show the kids two "magic squares" composed of letters that can be read in the same way vertically and horizontally (Figure 75).[1]

D	O	G	S
O	V	A	L
G	A	Z	E
S	L	E	D

Figure 75. A sort of a magic square made of letters, not of numbers.

Activity 2. Continuation of activities from sessions 45 and 46.

I say, "A week ago you solved my puzzles in no time at all, so today I have prepared something more difficult. If you solve it too, I really don't know what to do. I'll give up."

And accompanied by cries of astonishment I unwrap a puzzle made out of five sheets glued together. It doesn't fit on the table (Figure 76).

---

[1]*P. Z.'s Note:* We use an example in English, instead of the original Russian.

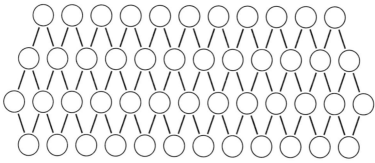

Figure 76. This graph has 48 vertices, as many as Dienes blocks in the kit.

At first the boys seem somewhat frightened but soon they start to work and solve the puzzle. Several times, when they abandon a *systematic* approach, they are stymied. This happens when they stop filling in pairs of shapes according to the scheme shown in Figure 77. Sometimes there arise situations when one of the boys places one of the shapes of a pair, but the other shape has already been used. In such cases I ask which figure they need and after their answer point out that it has been used. This seems to be enough for them to find a solution.

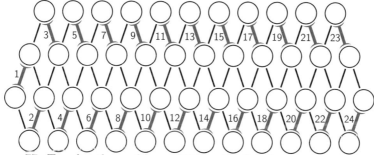

Figure 77. To solve the problem of Figure 76, it is best to lay out certain pairs of shapes, shown by red lines, numbered in order. It is easy to see that each pair (except the very first) must agree with only two previously placed figures.

Strangely, the boys have never implemented the simple strategy of setting aside the shapes that don't fit. They always put them back in the common pile and inevitably repeat already-tested, incorrect attempts. Also, when an attribute has to be changed, it is always either color or hole/no hole. Size is rarely changed, shape even less.

Activity 3. The last variant of the $\binom{5}{2}$ problem: balls in boxes.
See Chapter 3.

Activity 4. The proof that $\binom{5}{2} = 10$.
Again, see Chapter 3.

Session 48. True and false statements.

Saturday, February 20, 1982, 11:20–12:20.
Dima, Pete, Gene.

Activity 1. True and false statements.

This puzzle resembles the one with "boys and girls wearing or not wearing glasses" (see p. 37). There are, however, three essential differences: (1) the statements concern not kids but Dienes blocks; (2) previously, I prepared the cards beforehand, but today I want the kids themselves to choose the Dienes blocks; (3) last time I formulated statements, and the boys had to say whether they were true or false; this time I count on them to generate statements.

So, here is the assignment: One of the boys lays out several Dienes blocks and formulates a statement concerning them. The next one must change the set so that the previous statement becomes false, and then formulate his own true statement, and so on. It seemed like a simple and natural game. I was proven wrong.

I start by laying out two Dienes blocks and ask Pete to formulate a statement concerning them. He immediately baffles me saying, "They differ by one attribute."

Alas, this is true. Then appears the third Dienes block and I ask what the meaning of the statement is now: which blocks differ by an attribute? Pete, not in the least nonplussed, indicates with his finger, "These two differ by one attribute, and these two as well, and these two, by two attributes." And it goes from bad to worse. Each time I ask them to make a true statement they say something like,

"I have a big red square with a hole and two small circles without a hole, one yellow and one green, and a big triangle" (by the time they get to the triangle, they've run out of steam).

The statements are true but this is not what I wanted. I try to persuade the boys to make simpler statements, but I fail.

[Actually, these statements *are* simpler for them as they demand less intellectual efforts. While the statements like "no blocks have holes" are shorter, but they require observation, generalization, checking, etc.]

And changing the set of blocks to make the previous statement false also proves difficult. As a rule, the boys tend to replace the entire set. Again, this is both psychologically easier and logically correct. And I can't do anything about it.

[Next time, I'll introduce logical symbols and attribute symbols and evaluate the complexity of the statements.]

To make matters worse, I cannot restrain myself from muddying the waters with statements involving the empty set. For example, when the set does not have a single red block, I proclaim, "None of the red blocks has a hole," which provokes a heated discussion.

Earlier, back during "boys and girls wearing and not wearing glasses," I thought that the kids understood the meaning of conditional statements. I think I was simply overreaching. Anyway, at that moment they all nodded at me, while now they firmly oppose going on. Good for them! As for me, I've managed to mess up the whole activity.

Activity 2. Prime numbers.

We take, in order, sets of $1, 2, 3, \ldots, 15$ cubical blocks and try several ways of constructing flat rectangles. Thus we obtain factorization of all these numbers. But the prime numbers only allow "stripes."

A bit of programming, just with Dima

March 1–8, 1982.

When I'm alone with Dima, I try to avoid the puzzles from our sessions, so at not to give him an unfair advantage, since even with this precaution, he is a little ahead of the others. This time, however, he is such a pain in the neck and insists on "playing robot" that I give up. He makes his own puzzle, by indicating the starting and the finishing positions of the robot (Figure 78).

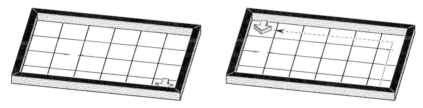

Figure 78. Another assignment for the robot: moving from the position on the left to the one on the right.

On his first attempt, he repeats the program discussed on pp. 108–109 (without the last turn). But after testing it, he (on his own) takes away the semi-circle END and adds the second part of the solution. The resulting program can be seen in Figure 79.

It took quite a few trials. Most of his mistakes are of the following kinds: If he has to take, say, a "step," with square STEP operator already in flowchart, Dima will draw the arrow directly to it. He doesn't realize that once he reaches this operator, he not only has to take the step, but also follow the entire chain of arrows stemming from it. I try to explain this clearly, but then he draws the arrow to a condition-checking diamond or a turn operator. A difficult situation; after all, it was I who advised them that instead of repeating five step operations, it is best to make a loop and return five times to the same block. But it turns out that sometimes this procedure is advisable and sometimes it isn't. How to distinguish between these cases?

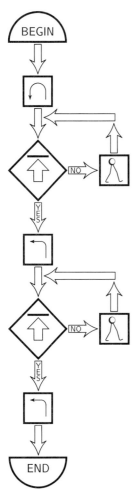

No idea. The second type of error is that Dima draws two arrows from an executable operator (rather than from condition-check diamond). I try to explain that this type of program does not have much sense since it is unclear what arrow one must follow but Dima, apparently at a loss and hopeless to find the solution, only whimpers,

"Da-ad, let's make it this way! Le-et's!"

"But which arrow must the robot follow?"

"This one."

"And when he comes into the corner?"

"Then the other one."

"But how he will know?"

"I'll tell him."

"And you, how will you know?"

"I will see there is a wall in front."

"So why don't you check whether there is a wall?"

"But you've seen that I drew an arrow there (to the first diamond) — no way!"

I lose my patience and say,

"Why don't you make another diamond?"

Whereupon he solves the puzzle.

I didn't dare ask for another card. I thought the fact that their number was limited was an intrinsic part of the language. Not surprisingly since Dad always told us to draw an arrow to the step operator card which was already there, instead of placing another card. — Dima.

Figure 79. Program for the task of Figure 78.

I also help him by cutting out additional cards; I help with program checking (i.e., to see that the program is correctly executed); I refuse to run syntactically incorrect programs (e.g., those that don't have the operator END).

Postscript. While I was writing the text above, Dima ran by, saw his program and wanted to show it to Alla. First, he refused to show her the paper version and insisted on laying it out with cards. Apparently a program drawn on a sheet of paper is "not genuine." I tried to dissuade him but to no avail. Second, he discovered a mistake in the first version of my text that led to adding a turn operator at the very beginning of the program. I had to make corrections in the initial text (the version given here is the corrected one.)

Then Dima attempted the same program but starting with the robot turned around. He found out that depending on the four initial orientations the robot would arrive in each of the four corners, the final orientation always being the same as the initial one (Figure 80).

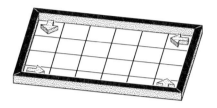

Figure 80. At the start, the robot occupies the same position (the right lower cell). Its final positions for the four possible initial orientations will be as shown here. The final orientation always coincides with the initial one.

Finally, he ran the same program in a way that I could not fathom: He placed the robot at an angle of 45° and with its nose in the corner (and later, perpendicular to this). He interpreted the condition "wall in front" in quite a reasonable and practical way: "impossible to advance." One of the trajectories can be seen in Figure 81.

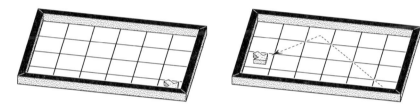

Figure 81. Running the same program in an unusual context.

I explained to him why the initial orientation would always be preserved: because no matter what the condition we started with, the robot would *always* make three turns (one of 180° and two at 90°), regardless of which steps could or could not be taken. He understood everything and immediately retold it to Alla.

Session 49. Thinking about symbols

Saturday, March 6, 1982, 11:10–12:10.
Dima, Pete, Gene.

Activity 1. True and false statements (continuation).

I expand on the earlier activity, by introducing the quantifiers[1] $\exists$ and $\forall$ as well as symbols for attributes:
   (1) Colors: four shapeless colored spots;
   (2) Shapes: $\square, \triangle, \bigcirc$;
   (3) Size: B, S (for big and small);

---

[1] The sign $\exists$ means "there exist(s)" and $\forall$ means "for all" or simply "all."

(4) Presence or absence of a hole: ⟡ and −, respectively.

I must admit that they don't really grasp the idea of symbols. That is, when they have to apply them, they do it easily, but while we are inventing them get into lengthy disputes as the kids propose their own symbols (especially Dima, who is the most avid defender of his inventions). That would have been positive, but they tend to propose "all-inclusive" symbols, i.e., symbols that include several attributes simultaneously (sometimes all four, i.e., exhaustively describing a single Dienes block). In Figure 82 you can see one of the symbols proposed by Dima. It means "a big red square with a hole." I ask them, why not just draw a picture of the block itself, but this idea does not seem silly to them.

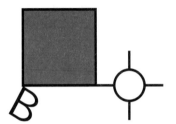

Figure 82. An "all-inclusive" symbol incorporating all four attributes. The fact that the kids use them demonstrates that they have not yet mastered the idea of a symbol standing for an attribute; for them it stands for an object.

I try to convince Dima that such a symbol really counts as four, since it replaces four words at a go. I ask, "And if you need to just say "red" without specifying that it's a square with a hole?"

But the answer would just be another new symbol. To explain the meaning of the red spot, I put all the red objects on the table and say we need a common symbol for all of them. The kids are completely taken aback: how can we draw this pile?

[It seems that kids still cannot distinguish between attributes and objects: many psychologists have observed this. Looking at a specific object, a child can say it's red, but the notion of "red" separate from red objects has no meaning and therefore doesn't need its own symbol. For children, a symbol has to stand for something tangible, not abstract. This subject is more thoroughly discussed in Ch. 5.]

Each boy makes a statement about a set of objects and we write it using these symbols and quantifiers. We score them one point per symbol; the smaller score wins. (Jumping ahead, each boy got 13 points for 6 statements; I was the only one to get 12.) We also scored actions that change a statement from true to false: one point for each block added or removed.

The game becomes more meaningful but it's really not satisfactory. The main problem is that everybody (except me) uses the the ∃ quantifier, and no other. It's easy to use: "there exists such-and-such an object...," and it's also easy to falsify this statement, by removing the object.

I promise the boys that next time we shall change the rules again and only use the ∀ quantifier, and we will only be allowed to add blocks. But when I had time to think about it, I realized that we will have to introduce four other logical symbols[1]$\wedge, \vee, \neg, \Rightarrow$. My acquaintance N. B., who also works with kids, says this works well. We'll see! Or am I going too far again?

Activity 2. Prime numbers (continuation).

I have prepared a big, beautiful table containing the numbers from 1 to 28. Each number has a space for its factors and a special column for "discoveries." At this session we only have time to investigate $16, 17, 18$, and 19. I have a strange feeling that the boys do not really understand what's going on. Pete puts 19 cubes into two rows, as shown in Figure 83, and says, "It's no good."

When I rectify his layout by making one row longer and the other one shorter, he calmly says, "I said it was no good."

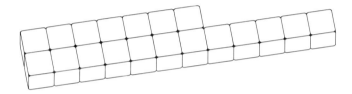

Figure 83.   An attempt to make a rectangle from 19 cubes.

I know that it is wrong to have this pet peeve, but I just cannot control myself when they refuse to work systematically. They have to find factors of the number 19, i.e., make a rectangle out of 19 cubes. What is more obvious than first trying to make two rows of cubes, then, if you fail, try three rows, then four, etc.? Instead, Pete first tries three rows, then two but gives up in the process; tries to make a tower, someone destroys it, he starts another 3-row rectangle and so on.

"Pete, haven't you already tried three rows?"

"I have."

"So why doing it again?"

"I want to check it again."

I try to control myself but cannot help asking, a little sarcastically, "After all, if we can place the cubes in a new way, we'll get a new solution, right?"

To which Dima retorts, "Dad! We've already done that!"

I'm astonished, as we did that at the very first session, exactly two years ago.

At this point, I show them my favorite trick, that 5 and 5 equals 10 counted on two hands, but makes 9 on one hand, which I demonstrate by counting fingers on one hand from the thumb to the little finger and back. I've made my point. But what to do about the number 19? We have not tried all possibilities, and have forgotten which ones we already tried.

---

[1]Logical connectors meaning "and," "or," "not," and "implies."

In any event, Pete's attempts to make three rows of 19 bricks is quite reasonable. Earlier, when we looked at 17, Dima said we couldn't do it, since it's odd, but Pete argued, "So what? We've did it with 9," and showed the factorization $9 = 3 \cdot 3$.

When it was Dima's turn to work with 19, he said again, "It won't work."

And Pete argued again, "Yes, it will! We did it with 9, and we'll do it with 19!"

That's why he started with three rows. Somehow, I overlooked this logic. And when we were at last through with 19, he exclaimed heatedly, "How come it worked for 9 but not for 19?"

I should have helped him with another example, but I just didn't notice at the time, and only realized this later, when I recalled the incident.

[I still have to figure out how to teach them to work systematically. It's vital, both as a skill and as a way to start thinking about proofs. I really don't know how to proceed. Alla, however, thinks this problem is easy to solve: just wait about five years.]

On the whole the session was quite tense. The boys fought constantly and argued who would go first. I had to spend a third of the session dealing with their conflicts. At one point I was so angry at them that I wanted to stop the session.

Session 50. A double anniversary

Sunday, March 21, 1982, 17:00–18:00.
Dima, Pete, Gene.

This session is a double anniversary: First, it's our 50th session and second, on March 23, our circle will be two years old. I tell this to the boys, making no impression at all. The main reason is that I am unable to create a festive atmosphere by speaking in a special voice or making grand gestures. Also, to feel festive you have to know about the holiday beforehand to anticipate it, but for some reason I hid this from them hoping that would be a "surprise."

(In theory, we meet every week. In fact, we have averaged only a session each fortnight due to holidays, illnesses, etc. However, this rhythm is quite reasonable. The French academic year consists of two semesters, each of 12 weeks, i.e., approximately our tempo. It's true that French students also have two exam sessions while we don't.)

The session consists in my reading to them a tale by a Polish author Jerzy Cwirko-Godycki, "How to Beat a Witch". We also solve all the puzzles of the tale as well as get acquainted with the symbols $\wedge, \vee, \sim$ (the last symbol meaning negation, which is more commonly denoted by $\neg$). We'll need them next time when we look at true and false statements.

At the end I give each boy a chocolate bar and a small notebook (Dima and Pete want the same pad so we toss a die; Dima wins).

Session 51. Which path is longer?

Sunday, March 28, 1982, 17:00–18:00.
Dima, Pete, Gene.

Activity 1. A path made of sticks

(This problem is from Alina Szeminska, a student of Piaget.) There are two groups of sticks, long and short (the length proportion is 7 : 5). The long sticks are red, and the short ones are white. (I made them out of counting sticks from the first-graders' kit).

I make a zigzag path out of long sticks (Figure 84), and ask the boys to make a path of the same length of short sticks.

Figure 84. Make a path of the same length but of shorter sticks.

To my surprise, no one constructs their path below mine, so as to compare them. They work at different places on the table trying to imitate the shape of my path. But since their artistic skill can't match their thinking skill, they all make quite horrible squiggles in no way resembling mine. No one tries to show that their path matches mine in length. They occasionally hesitate about whether they should put one more stick.

Apparently we need a discussion but I don't know where to begin. When you get not just a wrong answer, but an absurd one, you are at an impasse, and that is what is happening now. To resolve the situation, I introduce a new condition: all white paths must be straight. They start to make straight paths but again none is doing it below my path. I can't wait any longer and say, "Will this be correct?," and make a white path of 4 sticks right below my red one, so that the ends match (Figure 85).

Figure 85. Is it true that these paths are of the same length? (The lengths of the sticks are such that five long sticks equal seven short ones.)

Dima says that it will be correct. Gene says, "No, we need 5 sticks", and with these words he straightens my zigzag path and compares the white-stick path to it. While we are still working, Pete exclaims, "They're short!"

Indeed, five sticks aren't enough. Gene hesitates and adds two more, so that now we have 7 sticks and both paths become equally long.

Then Dima says sarcastically, "Yes! Sure, they're equal! Look, they're equal!" And he returns the red path to its initial zigzag form. Everybody sees the stubborn reality: there are extra sticks on both sides.

"So what?," says Gene but he makes a compromise and takes away one of the extra sticks.

I ask Dima's opinion and he goes back to the original 4 sticks. I ask then to make a white path of the same length on the other table. The boys have a short discussion. I overhear a promising approach, and support it with a slight hint. When one of the boys says, "There are five of them," I ask, "How many?"

Now they all make a 5-stick path. Pete objects, "But they're short!"

Everybody agrees that the new path is shorter than the initial one. At last comes the moment I was waiting for! I say, "Now look what happens. This path is the same length and it has 4 sticks, and this one is shorter, with 5 sticks. Which means that 5 sticks are shorter than 4."

"Whoa!" says Dima, dumbfounded.

I ask the boys to resolve this contradiction, but nobody has any ideas. Then I ask them for their final opinions. Dima favors 4 sticks. Pete says that both 4 and 5 sticks work.

(That's very typical of him. He is always very sharp at the start but eventually he gets tired or bored and then says whatever comes into his mind. I ask, "Does it mean that the paths of 4 and 5 sticks are of equal length?"

No response.

"But you said yourself that this path is shorter and now you say that this is a correct solution."

Still no response.)

At last Gene says that he thinks his solution (7 sticks) is correct.

I make no comments.

[We should have tried another exercise, to remake the initial paths of 5 sticks so that the distance between the two ends would become shorter and shorter: 3, 2, 1, and 0 short sticks. It would be as if, when we compared buttons and coins long ago (p. 16) I gradually reduced the situation to an absurdity by moving the buttons apart.]

Activity 2. True and false statements again (continued from session #49).

This time all statements have to begin with the quantifier $\forall$ and we can only add Dienes blocks one at a time. We also allow the symbols $\wedge, \vee, \sim$, which the boys have learned from the tale "How to Beat a Witch." Pretty soon the boys encounter a tautology; the statement is true but they can't make it false at the next step. (I don't remember what the statement was, something like "all blocks are big or small.") We discuss this, and agree to avoid tautological statements.

As I have expected, the boys confuse the connectors "and" and "or." For a pair of one red and one green block, they say, "All are green and red."

I try to explain that the statement has to be correct for each separate block (in particular, there is no such thing as a "red and green" block).

It goes without saying that this has not been a great success. For instance, Pete would repeat the same mistake every time it was his turn, even though each time, I would try to explain.

It gets harder and harder for them. I switch gears, and instead I say the true statements and the boys only have to make them false. We do this for a long time. Sometimes the boys volunteer their own true statements, but most often than not they are tautologies.

Session 52. Breaking a code

Saturday, April 3, 1982, 11:00–12:00.
Dima, Pete, Gene.

Activity 1. The code.

Translator's Note: We have omitted the narrative of this activity, because it is completely language-dependent. But since it was quite successful, here is a short summary. The activity involved a simple "letter-to-digit" encoding of just 10 alphabet letters. (Russian, like English, has too many letters for a one-to-one code.) The author explained what a code was, and gave the boys a puzzle consisting of four encoded words, each four letters long, telling them they meant the boy's nicknames, plus the word "PAPA", in some order. (An English equivalent would be the numbers 1212, 3245, 6778, 1908, encoding the words BOOK, SAND, MILK, and MAMA.)

The boys were able to deduce the code rather quickly, and explain their logic. They then deciphered a cute message in the same code: "Mama spreads honey and jam on Dima, Pete, and Gene."

Activity 2. Patronymics.[1]

My idea for the next activity was to give the boys a rather complicated genealogical tree (with 12 entries) as well as 12 cards with a man's first

---

[1]*P. Z.'s Note:* Another language-dependent activity. The Russian patronymic (for males) is a middle name derived from the father's name, usually by adding some form of "vich." For example, if your father's name was "Stepan," your middle name will be "Stepanovich," meaning "son of Stepan." Obviously this has no analogy in English, but considering how poorly Zvonkin's students understood it, it could easily be invented and played with as a sort of code for English-speaking kids. The female form is "ovna" or "evna" (thus "Stepanovna" means "daughter of Stepan").

name and a patronymic. These cards are to be placed on the tree, using the patronymics as a clue. But I start with a training problem, with a simple tree with just two positions (father and son) (Figure 86). The cards are "Nikolai Stepanovich," the other one is "Stepan Petrovich." They have to say who is who.

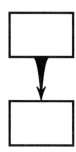

Figure 86. A genealogical tree: father above, son below. One is Nikolai Stepanovich, the other is Stepan Petrovich. Who is the father, who is the son?

As usual, the boys place the cards at random: Nikolai Stepanovich is the father, Stepan Petrovich is the son. I try to make them face their error: How can the father of *Petrovich* be *Nikolai?* But to my horror, nobody sees a contradiction!

It turns out that none of them has the least idea of how patronymics are formed. Neither Dima nor Gene know their patronymics; as to Pete, he knows he is Piotr Vitalievich but does not know why.

I spend the rest of the time explaining how patronymics work, etc. We don't have time to tackle the puzzle.

Session 53. A genealogical tree

> Saturday, April 10, 1982, 11:00–12:00.
> Dima, Pete, Gene.

Activity 1. An oral question.

A chicken weighs 2 kilos (4 pounds). ("Gee!" "What a chicken!"). Here are two questions about it:

(a) How much will it weigh if it stands on one foot?

(b) If it stands with one foot on one scale and with the other foot on the other scale, what will be the readings of each scale?

We discuss the questions one by one: everybody answers the first question; we discuss it and then pass to the second one. These are their opinions:

Gene: (a) 1 kg; (b) 1 kg and 1 kg.

Dima: (a) 2 kg; (b) 2 kg and 2 kg.

Pete: Changes his mind constantly, so I am not sure I remember his final decision.

I ask Gene about his first answer, "So one kilogram is suspended in the air?"

Then I challenge Dima's second answer: "So before it used to weigh 2 kilos, and now it weighs 4 kilos?"

Both say this is how it is. (However, two days later, Dima came into the kitchen and gave me another solution for the problem, namely, Gene's.)

I end with the following lecture: "Two weeks ago we were solving the problems of paths and sticks, one of you gave the right solution and the other two the wrong one..."

Dima interrupts, "I think that the correct solution was mine."

I go on, "Of course, each of you thinks it was him. Because if you, Dima, thought it was wrong why should you give it at all? You would have tried to think of another, correct solution. So each thinks he is right. But you gave me three different solutions; therefore they can't all be right. There was only one who gave the right solution but I won't tell you who it was. What is important to me is not that you know the correct solution but that you learn to think for yourselves. Today it was the same thing: one of you gave the correct answer to the first question, and one correctly answered the second question. But I won't tell you who did what."

The kids whine and beg a little that I tell them but don't put their hearts into it.

Activity 2. Patronymics (continuation).

I have borrowed the following puzzle from a linguistic olympiad. We have a sheet of paper with an empty genealogical tree on it (Figure 87).

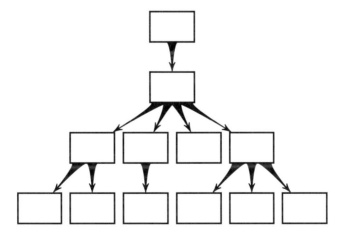

Figure 87.   A genealogical tree.

First I ask them some questions. Where is the father of this man? And the grandfather of that guy? What is the relationship of this man to this one? (Great-grandfather.) How many sons does this guy have? How many grandchildren does this one have? Show me who does not have children (sons, to be more precise)? Then I define "uncle" and "nephew," and ask a few final questions.

Next, I distribute 12 cards with these first names and patronymics:

Aleksandr Petrovich   Evgenii Aleksandrovich
Boris Petrovich   Ivan Sergeyevich
Vasili Borisovich   Nikolai Stepanovich
Victor Petrovich   Oleg Borisovich
Pyotr Ivanovich   Gennady Borisovich
Dmitry Aleksandrovich   Stepan Petrovich

After much trial and error the names are eventually placed correctly. I need to encourage them, because they lose interest and give up when there is an impasse. Dima still struggles with patronymics. When perusing the pair "Stepan Petrovich→Nikolai Stepanovich" it's hard for him to compare the first and the fourth words, as the two middle ones distract him. Pete is really the only one who gets this stuff.

I ask some more oral questions, but this time they include the name and patronymic: How many nephews does Alexander Petrovich have? Who is Gennady Borisovich's grandfather? Pete again shines. He can read well, and therefore finds the names more quickly than Dima or Gene.

Activity 3. Prime numbers (continuation from Session #49).

This time we look at $21, 22, 23, 24, 25$.

Session 54. The end of the school year

Saturday, May 1, 1982, 11:00–12:00.
Dima, Pete, Gene.

The session took place on May 1 but I am writing these notes on October 18. I didn't have time before. It goes without saying that I have forgotten many details, so it's a summary more than anything else.

I start by saying this is the last session in this school year and Dima shouts, "We'll get diplomas again!"

Activity 1. A magic trick with numbers.

This is a neat trick which even impresses adults, if they are not mathematically sophisticated. The general form is: think of a number; add two; subtract the number; you'll always get two! The algorithm can, of course, be varied endlessly: think of a number; add two; add the number; divide by two; subtract the number; you get one, etc. However, this trick requires good calculation skill, which is not exactly our case, so sometimes the trick fails. Dima computes them all well. Gene gets stymied and complains, "I don't know".

Then I give him the initial simplest version quoted before and he does it. Dima understands the gist of the trick, says, "Aha, I see why we get two" and explains it.

Activity 2. Make the word stronger.

This linguistic game employs the *Magnum* transformation, invented by the school of Mel'chuk, Gladky, and Apresyan to make a formalized description of semantics. The boys are given a word and must supply another word with the same sense, only "stronger." For example, *rain* transforms to *pour*. Here are my examples:

wind → hurricane	cold → frost
warm → hot	room → hall
street → avenue	fear → horror
smile → laugh	athlete → champion
smart → wise	big → immense

Linguistic games like this, which point out *significata*, i.e., relations between words, in contrast to *denotata*, i.e., relations between words and objects (if I'm using these terms correctly), are very useful and important for developing the culture of reasoning. Unfortunately, until now I have failed to come up with good ideas, except for the opposite game: "Make the word weaker:"

wet → moist   street → alley   laugh → chuckle

Activity 3. Prime numbers (conclusion).

We investigate the last three numbers 26, 27, 28 and finish the table of prime and composite numbers. Then we wrap things up by putting the letter P opposite prime numbers, draw a square opposite perfect squares (in our case this is not an abstraction; it has the full meaning of a square, since we made real squares with our cubes) and a cube opposite every "cubic" number.

Activity 4. Fives.

Now each boy gets a sheet of paper dissected by straight lines into cells of different size and shape. Each cell contains a number. They have to color with a marker the cells containing prime numbers. "I know," says Dima, "we'll get fives."

Indeed, when the cells are colored in, big beautiful "fives" are revealed.

Diplomas.

I announce that each participant gets a "5" for the school year, a diploma for the second year and a gift (the game of fifteen). The diploma reads:

DIPLOMA OF THE MATHEMATICAL CIRCLE

This diploma is awarded to Dima Zvonkin
for having done mathematics for two years
and becoming even more intelligent than last year.

(Whatever will we write next year?) It is decorated by a drawing of a checkerboard room, a robot, an algorithm written in *Kid*, as well as a die and a ladybird.

The session is over. Boris takes pictures.

Chapter 5

Notation, abstraction, mathematics, and language

Symbols for words

The problems I had trying to introduce "symbols for attributes" (pp. 125–127) led to much reflection, resulting in three papers, published in 1990 and 1991.[1]

The funny thing is that the idea of these papers was inspired by Dima. Only I didn't notice it at the time; I reconstructed events from memory and from my notes.

Recall that the task was to formulate the "simplest possible" statement about a set of Dienes blocks. Even at the beginning of our discussion, Dima suggested that we measure the complexity of a statement by the numbers of words it contained. This was not yet the key moment. But after arguments and mutual incomprehension, he withdrew into himself for a moment to think it over and then said, "I think I've got it, Dad. You want us to invent symbols for words."

I did not pay attention. I think that at the moment I wasn't yet ready to perceive the idea of the message.

Symbols for words! Truly, a quantum leap!

Indeed, take the word "red" — not the attribute behind the word, not the value of the attribute "color," not a class of red objects — but the word itself. The word "red" is very much a concrete thing. It's not as concrete as a cup or a bicycle, for you cannot touch or taste it, but it is not just "one 'value' of the attribute 'color.'" From the point of view of logic, a word is an abstraction, but this is not so from the psychological point of view. Making symbols for words is not surprising, and using letters is commonplace. But if a word is used frequently, why not invent a simpler symbol (like a hieroglyph)? Moreover, I know from experience that the concrete image of a symbol soon becomes unimportant: the kids start to look through it.

---

[1] The first paper was published in the collection of papers *Yazyk i struktura znaniya* (*Language and structure of knowledge*), 1990, the second in the journal *Voprosy yazykoznaniya* (*Problems of linguistics*), 1990, Vol. 6 (both with the blessing of R. M. Frumkina), and the third in the popular science journal *Znanie — Sila* (*Knowledge is Power*), 1991, Vol. 8.

It seems we have witnessed nothing of great importance: the kids have merely learned to put symbols and words into correspondence. But when we return to the real world, and try to establish correspondences between symbols and objects, the objects will no longer be "big red squares with holes" (our initial point of departure) but the entire class of red objects. Instead of a chain like this:

$$attribute \rightarrow one\ of\ its\ values \rightarrow symbol \rightarrow class,$$

which the kids cannot understand, we've made a clearer chain:

$$object \rightarrow word \rightarrow symbol \rightarrow class.$$

The linguistic object "word" appearing in this chain helps to break the vicious circle when symbols are introduced to enhance the understanding of the concept of a class, and the meaning of symbols won't be clear until the concept of a class is.

What makes such a leap possible? Why are words such magic wands?

Thinking it over we arrive at amazing conclusions. We come to realize that words were the very symbols we were so hopelessly trying to construct, symbols corresponding to attribute values yet detached from the object. (The word "color," in fact, is an even higher abstraction: a symbol for a class of objects which are themselves abstractions.) The process of abstraction which seems so difficult for a kid of six or seven was already in place at the age of 18–24 months, when he was learning to speak. When we introduce a word as an intermediary step, we benefit from this unconscious early work. This is what I call "abstractions supported by language" (a title of one of my papers). When trying to invent symbols directly from a set of objects, we strive to do the same work once more, but this time on the conscious level. Most likely, kids cannot yet do this. But basing symbols on words allows language to help us.

Half of Maria Fiedler's book *Mathematics as Early as Kindergarten*[1] is devoted to symbols for attribute values. First of all, most of them fail: they are complex and difficult to reproduce, and kids either cannot imitate them or, if they can, it takes them so long that at the end they forget what they were working on. Second, the meaning of a symbol is not obvious without comparing it to other symbols. For example, a house with two windows seems big only if compared with a one-window house; taken separately, they are not unambiguously big or small. None of this would matter if the book contained the most important advice; namely, that symbols must stand for words, not for classes of objects. The latter can be mastered later, proceeding from the symbols. If, however, the reader follows the advice of the book, which is what I was doing — not because I learned it from the book (I had not read it at the time) — but because I followed a "natural" course of reasoning, he falls into a psychological vicious circle.

---

[1] Translation from Polish: *Matematyka już w przedszkolu*, Warszawa, Wydawnictwa Szkolne i Pedagogiczne, 1978.

"Simplified" notation?

Some tasks involving abstraction lack language support, and prove to be insurmountable for kids. Yet adults may find them rather easy. This is a trap for teachers.

Here's a well-known example. In order to learn to read, children must understand the correspondence between letters and sounds. There are many letters, many sounds; their correspondence is not always unambiguous. Two letters can make one sound, like "ea" or one letter can give two sounds, like "i." To say nothing of different letter combinations, exceptions, etc. Not an easy problem. How can we help?

Well, it seems obvious. First "simplify notation," and then divide the global task into several steps, simple at first, and then progressively more complex. Leaf through a primer[1] to see what these steps are. First are introduced, briefly, symbols denoting sentences and words. Next, symbols for syllables (distinguishing stressed from unstressed).[2] Then come symbols for sounds, though not for specific sounds, but for sounds "in general." Gradually the symbols become more and more varied: a square for sounds "in general;" a rectangle divided by a diagonal for "blended sounds;" a red circle for a vowel, and a black or blue circle for different types of consonants. Furthermore, the phonetic scheme of the word includes some other elements: a stress, a special symbol for the letter we are studying, etc. At some point, the variety of symbols grows so much that they are replaced by actual letters.

What's wrong with this approach? It's always possible to invent a separate symbol for the word "cat," another one for the word "plane," still another for "teapot." Children have no trouble understanding such symbols. If this method becomes coherent, we'll arrive at a hieroglyphic system of writing. It may tax the memory, but psychologically it will look absolutely natural: each symbol will be language-supported. However, as soon as we try to introduce a symbol for "a word in general," a word unknown, that is a sort of algebraic variable taking values in the set of words, we'll fail immediately. The level of abstraction needed is very high while the language support is absent. The difference is exactly analogous to that of using the digit 7 to denote the number "seven" in arithmetic, and using the letter x to denote "a certain number" in algebra.

The same thing happens at the syllable level. It's easy to understand the meaning of symbols for, say, the syllables "no" or "mat," and with their help we can develop syllabic writing (there are historical examples). But a first-grader is incapable of understanding the meaning of an abstract, general syllable. At the letter-sound level, it is undoubtedly easier to understand that a letter corresponds to a certain sound than to understand that a blue

---

[1]I have no idea what primers look like today. I am speaking about primers I used to know some 20 years ago.

[2]*P. Z.'s Note:* The location of the stressed syllable in a Russian word is crucial for its correct prononciation and spelling.

circle corresponds to an element of the set of vowels. The sound "a" is a concrete psychological reality while the set of vowels is an abstraction. At best, the corresponding sound can be guessed: "What do you think this letter is?" (This is how my circle kids treated them: they took pleasure in guessing what was behind the patterns of phonetic analysis, for them they were amusing riddles. Perhaps other intellectually advanced kids do this as well. But they have to already know how to read.)

One more example to explain my point. When we invent symbols for words we can as well invent them for such words as "word," "syllable," and "sound." But in this case, in the phrase, "In the beginning was the word," the symbol for "word" will appear only once instead of six times, while in the phrase, "A tale full of sound and fury," the symbol for "sound" will also appear only once, though the phrase is composed of many more sounds!

I remember our first parent-teacher meeting at school. Teachers know from experience that children, even those who can read, cannot understand all these "phonetic-analysis patterns" without parents' help. Their primary task, then, is to teach the parents. This is the principal goal of our meeting. It happens, however, that not all of the parents are advanced enough to understand it. When the teacher gets to "blended sounds," they start to panic. At this moment the teacher makes a stunning remark; in fact, a statement of the entire "theory." She says,

"Don't panic, when we are over the primer, it will be much easier." Then she ponders a little and adds,

"Only, please, try to read as much as possible at home together. We have a very difficult curriculum and don't have enough time to teach them to read."

The fact that the method was invented precisely to teach children to read has long been forgotten!

All this is quite obvious from the point of view of common sense. But it is hard to "scientifically" refute this learning theory. Formally, the suggested symbols are easier than the current writing system. It proposes only four or five symbols instead of thirty-three letters (twenty-six in English). Besides, there is a simpler, one-to-one correspondence between symbols and what they denote. The problem is not symbols themselves but rather what objects they denote, abstractions without language support. They simply don't exist in the kid's internal world.

Allow me to digress, briefly, about a dispute I once had with a mathematician who was interested in education. He was going to teach middle school (12–14 years old), and was enthralled by his revolutionary idea: teach linear algebra instead of geometry. Yes, because it is much simpler! He invented a system that contains only four axioms! And all the proofs are much shorter and much simpler! Indeed, they are; moreover, they are even more rigorous than the geometrical ones we are accustomed to. But how to *discover* them? Our geometrical intuition, nurtured by experience in the real, three-dimensional, physical world cannot help. His students must have felt like tone-deaf people struggling through solfeggio lessons.

Each person has more than one type of intelligence

Now let's leave school behind, and move on to this miraculous, enigmatic phenomenon, the fact that the task of establishing correspondence between symbols and classes of objects, impossible for a seven-year-old, is easily resolved by toddlers. The more you think about it, the less you understand how it happens. On the contrary, the miracle becomes more and more amazing when you imagine the chasm separating the possibilities for the same person to solve similar problems but using different "subsystems" of his intelligence.

We do many things without being capable of explaining how we do them: walking, eating, or rolling up a paper cone (try to write instruction for doing this!). One such thing is the capacity of speech. This, however, is different from the rest by the constant need to solve intellectual-logical problems. I was once greatly impressed by a 10-page article by the well-known linguist Gregory Kreidlin, devoted to explaining the linguistic rules for the adverb "even." It turns out that its usage can be described by a system of four interrelated, rather complicated logical rules. The paper also demonstrates that violating any of these rules brings about a "wrong" usage grating on the ears (e.g., "a spoon is even on the table"). This means that every time we use this word we solve a very complicated "four-step" problem in a fraction of a second. And this is only one word![1] But we use so many words when we speak (another paper by the same author investigates "but"), to say nothing of grammar, or context, or the many other things of which we may know nothing at this moment. All these problems are solved simultaneously, in a flash.

What is even more amazing is the fact that some mentally retarded children do this equally well. Try to give such children trivial exercises in geometry, and they will fail. But they will use the word "even," naturally, and without mistakes. There is even a term, "verbalism," for mentally retarded children who speak easily and fluently.[2] At first sight they may seem completely normal; their intellectual handicaps do not leap to the eye, so their condition is not readily diagnosed. It becomes obvious only when psychologists observe difficulties displayed by the child while solving logical-mathematical tasks.

---

[1] On the day I was reading the proofs of this chapter I called Professor Kreidlin. Among other things, I learned from him that other linguists took over since then and during the recent 20 years understanding of the word "even" became even broader and more profound. That is, we are solving a more complicated problem than I thought then.

[2] *P. Z.'s Note:* This term, used in Russian psychological literature, apparently includes disorders such as William's Syndrome.

Even more striking is the fact that there are cases of children with congenital retardation who are born into bilingual families, and who master both family languages.

We are obliged to conclude that our brain harbors two (at least two) separate and independently acting intelligences. One is conscious, or, better to say, of which we are conscious. It is used to solve mathematical puzzles, write computer programs, classify, or write user's manuals for vacuum cleaners. The second one is unconscious. It is used to solve similar problems (usually much more difficult ones) in another domain, namely, language. They are certainly not completely separate. On the contrary, the concept of "language support" in order to develop abstract thinking is an appeal to use the connections between them as much as possible, by creating pathways between the two types of intelligence. Nevertheless, these two systems exist and function separately and we must be aware of this fact to make use of their connection.

It is inconceivable that language mastery is based on the same neurobiological structures that govern our conscious intelligence. Our brains constantly develop important neural connections as we grow and develop, including the process of learning speech. That's why no Mowgli could ever be taught to speak. A computer programmer would say that language mastery is built into the hardware. An analogy for "language support" would be hardware-assisted software. Built-in hardware functions exist within a computer not as a text but as a circuit or crystalline structure. On the other hand, software consists of text, which is translated into the consecutive execution of primitive hardware-implemented functions.

The essential difference is that the primitive hardware-implemented functions are incomparably more rapid. In ancient computers the hardware functions were limited to the simplest Boolean operations over bits. In modern computers, particularly specialized ones, these may be represented by fairly complicated operations. If a simpler operation to be performed on the same computer requires a special program, it may happen that its performance will be significantly slowed down.

That gives rise to a paradoxical situation: sometimes, to write an efficient program, the problem has to be reduced to several more complicated problems, but hardware-implemented. Problems that can be easily reducible to hardware-implemented functions are called "hardware-supported." This is why we have chosen the term "language-supported:" a simple puzzle proposed to a child is reduced to a more complicated one, but already solved in the course of our natural verbal development.

There is a very curious mental handicap called early children's autism (more properly, we should just call it autism, since there are also autistic adults). Its origins are largely unknown and its treatment is more of an art than that for more common disorders. The chief problem that autistic children have is that of communication with other people. This also provokes other behavioral problems. In our context, autism is noteworthy, because for many children, autism is the opposite of verbalism: profound verbal handicaps coexisting with highly developed intelligence, with supreme capacities for solving logical-mathematical puzzles, and often, increased interest towards intellectual activities. It is not at all clear if these children can be called mentally retarded. Clara Park, the mother of an autistic daughter, in her book *The Siege*[1] recalls bringing her daughter in a special school for mentally retarded children. The girl was between three and five years ahead of her peers in solving mathematical puzzles, but was as far behind them in her capacity to make a simple sentence of the type, "What's for breakfast?" The impression was that she treated her native tongue as a foreign language. She had to construct each sentence consciously, following explicit grammar rules. It was also curious to see what words were difficult for her to assimilate: she had no problem whatsoever with "sum" or "heptagon" but it took her years to master "myself" or "yes."

In fact, the range of deviations from the norm is much larger than these two types of examples. That is why I have said earlier that there are at least two sorts of intelligence. Numerous examples can be found in the books by the neuropsychologist Oliver Sacks, such as *An Anthropologist on Mars* and *The Man Who Mistook His Wife for a Hat*.[2] Dr. Sacks tells stories of people that psychologists called "idiot savants" in the pre-PC-era. For example, Stephen Wiltshire did not speak until the age of five, and then only rarely, a clear case of mental retardedness. For instance, he does not understand why cars have difficulties going down a steep mountain. At the same time he is a profoundly gifted artist. Albums of his drawings sell brilliantly and both professionals and amateurs are extremely enthusiastic about his talent.

Or Nadya, an autistic girl; another author wrote an entire book about her. At the age of three she started to draw horses but somehow leaped over all the common stages of a child's drawing skills. Kids always start with senseless scribbles, then pass on schematic stick-figures, etc. But Nadya had everything at a professional level in her sketches from the start: space, movement, shading, perspective. These skills can be achieved by other talented kids (for example, Picasso), but no earlier than ten years of age. Also, she constantly experimented with different angles, foreshortenings, and perspectives. As if instead of an "organ of speech" developed by normal children, she developed an organ of drawing. Sacks also tells about Martin, a mentally retarded musician whose favorite composer was Bach. Sacks just couldn't understand how this was possible. Bach, the most intellectual of composers! Apparently, Martin had a special sort of musical intelligence which enabled him to understand—without being able to formulate—the most complicated structure of variations, inversions, combinations of voices in a canon or fugue and many other things. Just imagine that we don't learn grammar

---

[1]Clara Claiborne Park. *The Siege: The first Eight Years of an Autistic Child*, Little, Brown, and Company, 1967.

[2] Oliver Sacks, *An Anthropologist on Mars*, Vintage Books, 1996, and *The Man Who Mistook His Wife for a Hat*, HarperCollins, 1985.

at school and don't have an idea it exits. Our linguistic intelligence will function no less efficiently; we will still be able to conjugate verbs and make sentences according to grammar rules. (Incidentally, the languages of the peoples who never had either writing or science can be just as complicated as ours.) This is the case of Martin: his unconscious musical intelligence is amazingly advanced. But, being mentally retarded, he cannot explain his "musical grammar" to us or to understand the explanations of other people.

Among these "idiot savants" there are also "mathematicians." For example, two autistic twins whose favorite entertainment was to exchange big prime numbers. The only way to gain their confidence was to tell them a big prime. Unfortunately, it would be impossible to make them real mathematicians. Mathematics is a human activity and as in any such activity, the comparative value of problems and their correct choice are much more important than a capacity to make complicated mental calculations.

Oliver Sacks makes reference to a book that develops a theory of several intellectual subsystems within one brain: *Frames of Mind: The Theory of Multiple Intelligences*, by Howard Gardner. (New York, Basic Books, 1983). I have not read it but plan to read it one day.

Many researchers think that a decisive role in mastering language is played by non-verbal communication, i.e., the mimicry, gestures, glances, and intonations that we use instinctively, as animals, like cats or monkeys. These researchers contend that this non-verbal language is the key to the evolution of our subconscious intelligence and verbal language mastery. This idea seems all the more plausible because the communication difficulties of autistic children seem to stem precisely from deficits in this "animal" language. Oliver Sacks thinks so, as does Nikolaas Tinbergen (who studied autism for many years).

However, we are getting far afield, and onto shaky ground. It's time we returned to our everyday world.

Teaching mathematics as a native tongue

Imagine an anti-utopia, where we teach our kids to speak the way we teach them math.

We start by teaching them to pronounce vowels, for these seem to be easier to pronounce than consonants. Then we move on to consonants. Next, syllables. And no rushing ahead: we don't do words until syllables are mastered! After a year or two of assiduous training words appear little by little. But at what moment should we inform the child that words mean something? Not before they have mastered... what? I don't know. I'll stop here. But let me add one more thing. We wise, intelligent adults, know that the ability to speak is incredibly useful in life. With time, kids would come to understand this as well, but not without several years of diligent learning with unclear goals.

Thank God, nothing like this happens in real life. Parental instinct tells us that we should just speak to the baby from the very beginning, that's all. He doesn't understand, but it's OK. His understanding will grow together with him. It's equally unimportant that he can't speak. We know he will learn! But the most important thing is that we don't speak to him in order "to teach him words, expressions and grammatical structures." Instead, we communicate by speech. Furthermore, we communicate by *shared, everyday activities*. We don't tell him, "See Dick run.[1] Say it again! No, not like that, once again!" We ask "You want a carrot?" and we give him a carrot. We say, "Go ahead, join Grandma!" and we point to his grandma who is waiting for him with open arms. The kid does not yet understand every word but he knows very well what he must do.

Luckily, all children (with very few exceptions) have the "language instinct," (the title of the book by Stephen Pinker, mentioned above on p. 33), allowing them to master language, apparently effortlessly. Mathematical mastery seems much harder. And yet, if we lacked any "mathematical instinct," we could not master mathematics at all. Our mathematical intelligence is certainly weaker than our linguistic one. But it makes sense to ask whether we can teach kids math in the same way that we teach them our native tongues. What would it mean in practice?

The Canadian computer scientist Michael Fellows and his colleagues, principally Nancy Casey, have developed an approach called "the whole-language method."[2] This point of view has its roots in a large body of recent research in linguistics and cognitive psychology on language acquisition. The central idea is that children acquire language by actually using it in a community of language users, not through practicing its separate parts until these parts are assembled and the totality is finally used. Language competency develops in a child in a way that does not depend upon instruction and drill. This fact is critical in modern linguistics.

Here is a summary of the main ideas of the whole-language method, quoted from Fellows's work quoted above.

(1) The model of acquisition through real use (not practice exercises) is the best model for thinking about and assisting with all forms of language learning and learning in general.
(2) Language competency is a complex interactive system with many parts (purpose and pragmatics, syntax and semantics of cuing systems, social context, etc.) and is not reducible to those parts.

---

[1] *P. Z.'s Note:* The canonical Russian, that Zvonkin used here, is мама мыла раму (*Mama myla ramu*, "Mom washes a window frame"), from the primers of his time.

[2] Michael Fellows, "Computer SCIENCE and mathematics in elementary schools," preprint, August 1992, 22pp.; and Nancy Casey and Michael Fellows, "What about content? A critical review of the NCTM Standards and a job for discrete mathematics," preprint, April 1995, 14 pp.

(3) The development of language competencies in a child is seen as unfolding naturally and incidentally when that language is a part of the functioning of a community.

(4) Whole language classrooms seek to provide a richly varied and engaging environment of real language usage. The class is a community of language users, and the task of the teacher is to monitor and assist individual students in their projects, to diagnose "stuck points," and to encourage the competencies presently under construction by the individual....

   It can be seen that the easiest way to summarize the project ... is that it attempts to convey to elementary school classrooms the experience of participating in the mathematical science research community. ... What aspects of the mathematical science research community experience are portable to elementary school classrooms? Some vital parts of that experience most definitely can be brought to the elementary grades. ...

(5) Children benefit from exposure to a rich variety of content without regard for hierarchical sequencing of material. Statements of "developmental appropriateness" must be taken in a large context.

(6) Students are drawn forward by exposure to material that they can understand but which is beyond their capacities to produce.

(7) Although skills matter, experience in the discipline cannot be secondary to mastery of them; teachers must find ways to monitor and nurture skill development within the context of meaningful and stimulating (self-selected) projects.

(8) Students must be steered towards mature and independent self-selection of content materials and individual/small group projects which they undertake.

(9) Peer communication about their ideas is not only critical, but inevitable. Teachers must learn to exploit, not suppress the classroom culture.

(10) Students must be given large blocks of time to read, think, talk to one another, share, argue, and write down their ideas. The classroom should be a microcosm of the community into which the students are being initiated.

(11) The teacher is neither spectator nor ambassador from the community into which the students are being initiated, but a participant and a practitioner.

Fellows worked with five- to nine-year-old children, doing interesting problems in graph theory, map coloring, knot theory, and cryptography.

The principal idea is clear: *It's not what you do, but how you do it.* No definitions, theorems and proofs, no standard sequences of exercises, but instead, experiments with actual graphs, maps, and knots, making and testing and reformulating conjectures, competing, looking for the best solutions, etc.

In one of his papers, Fellows proudly lists four research problems born from discussions with children, which later led to publications.

Of course, theorems and proofs are not forbidden, but they are grasped much better if they come as answers to questions *asked by the children*. Somewhat later (p. 222) I mention the series of puzzles concerning "tilted squares" which quite naturally leads to the Pythagorean theorem. But we started to prove it only after the kids asked, "Will it always be like this?"

When asked, "Do you really believe that kids need to know about the theory of knots?" Fellows and his colleagues respond, "And you, do you really think that the kids have to know all the details of Huckleberry Finn's adventures?"

Clearly, the answer is no, to both questions. But kids do need to read, and what they read must be fascinating. Otherwise, what exactly they read is secondary.

Fellows, a computer scientist, is nevertheless skeptical, not to say hostile, toward using computers in schools. My point of view is that they can be useful as one of many educational tools. But by now computers have become omnipresent, so there is great potential for misuse. As for computer games, I don't know of a more stupid pastime. In the Moscow Children's Computer Club (where I was one of the teachers), computer games were outlawed and we even pinned up at the entrance an extract of the criminal code forbidding "brothels and gambling dens."

. . .

(*Added by the author to the American edition:*) Unfortunately, the beautiful ideas expressed above, including my own, are hardly applicable to ordinary schools. To implement them would require all school teachers to become researchers, a utopian project. There is, however, another, more realistic approach that Paul Zeitz writes about in his preface. True researchers become more and more aware of how rewarding it is to work not only with graduate students, but also with schoolchildren. So I would like to ask them not to forget about these youngest of potential participants in mathematical circles.

Chapter 6

The Boys' Math Circle, Year Three

This year Pete and Gene started school, so our sessions moved to the late afternoon.

Session 55. Logical problems

Monday, September 18, 1982, 16:30–17:30.
Dima, Pete, Gene.

Beginning of the school year.
We (Dima and I) give Pete and Gene a box of magic markers and a greeting card congratulating them on the start of the school year.

Activity 1. A story.
I tell the boys a story about a beautiful princess who fell in love with a very intelligent young man. To prevent the marriage, the king decided to cut off his head. To placate his daughter, he announced that the young man could draw lots. He said, "There are two slips of paper, with the words LIFE and DEATH written on them. Your destiny will depend on which one you will draw." But the perfidious king asked his minister to write the word DEATH on both slips of paper. The princess overheard this and managed to warn the young man.

"Now, what do you think he must do?" I ask the boys. They only shrug their shoulders. Then Dima suggests, "He can say the papers are wrong."

I explain that in this case, he'd still have a one-in-two chance of dying. [I should have also said that the princess would have been punished, and he did not want that, since he loved her.]

I continue triumphantly, "I told you he was a very intelligent boy! He said, "I choose this one," and he picked up a slip of paper and immediately ate it up!"

The boys look at me with eyes wide open. How can he eat paper? Obviously they don't understand where the story is going. I continue,

"Then everybody was shouting, "How can we know what was on this slip of paper? You've eaten it up!" But the young man smiled and said, "Look at

the remaining slip." They looked and saw the word DEATH. "That means
the other one had LIFE on it." The king was ashamed to confess his perfidy,
and the young man was saved."

I didn't find this solution any better than ours. — Dima.

This twist made a big impression. They looked at me with eyes full
of wonder for a long time. (That evening, Pete told this problem to his
parents.)

Activity 2. Scrambled tags.

We have three boxes with matches, pins and paper clips. The boxes have
tags saying MATCHES, PINS, or CLIPS, but no tag corresponds to the
contents of its box. We can open one box and then must say which box
contains what.

At first, as in the previous assignment, the boys only shrug their shoulders listlessly. Obviously, after summer vacation they completely lost the
habit of using their brains. Somehow I manage to wake them up, and Gene
solves the puzzle, but can't really explain it. Then I change the content and
position of the boxes, and let each boy try the same puzzle twice.

That evening, Dima spends an hour scribbling something on the boxes.
He is inventing a puzzle for me. What he came up with is rather amusing.
He puts pins and clips, pins and matches, and clips and matches into the
respective boxes. Two of the tags say PINS AND CLIPS, while the third
says PINS AND MATCHES. As with my puzzle, all tags are false and to
know the contents you can only open one box. A notable feature of this
puzzle is that the box with pins and clips can only be under the tag PINS
AND MATCHES; it can't be in the other two boxes. So we only need to
open one of the two boxes tagged with PINS AND CLIPS. In my puzzle, all
the boxes were "equal," since we knew nothing about their content but we
could also open any box. I might propose Dima's puzzle at our next session.

Activity 3. Similarity.

Each boy gets a sheet of graph paper and a pencil. I draw various shapes
and they have to draw similar ones but twice as big (see Figure 88).

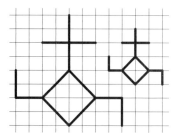

Figure 88. Similarity, on graph
paper.

Dima works flawlessly, but his shapes sometime overlap with mine, as he is unable to foresee how much space he will need. Gene, too, works well, though with a few mistakes, but when I point them out he corrects them. For some reason Pete can't manage at all. He makes mistakes and fails to correct them independently. I explain and even Natasha gets involved, but to no avail.

We decide to continue next time.

Activity 4. The 15-puzzle.

I meticulously explain the rules of the game and then give them three puzzles with the same initial positions, and launch a sort of competition (though I tell them not to be in a hurry). I help all of them at difficult moments.

This classical mathematical puzzle was invented by Noyes Chapman and popularized by Sam Lloyd in the second half of the nineteenth century. A 4 × 4 grid contains 15 square tiles with the numbers from 1 to 15. One square remains empty. The tiles can be slid at will using the empty space; the goal is to place the tiles in order (see Figure 89). It should be kept in mind that the solution is possible for half of the initial positions and is impossible for the other half.

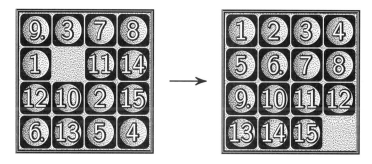

Figure 89.   Rearrange the initial position into the final one by sliding the tiles.

Pete is the first to solve it, and then comes Gene. Dima does a good job, but doesn't pay attention to the configuration that he needs to end with. He is the first to get the first few tiles in order, but he places them on the bottom row instead of the top.

I explain once again and a few moments later discover the following "snake".

He has to start again. He refuses my help and finishes after Pete and Gene leave.

Session 56. Construction foreman

Monday, November 1, 1982, 17:00–18:00.
Dima, Pete, Gene.

Activity 1. Oral questions.

(1) Dima, Pete, and Gene are given two balls and a spade. What object does each boy get, if we know that Dima and Gene have the same thing?

(2) This time they are given two pencils and a pen, and Dima and Pete have got different things. (This question has two different answers.)

(3) All four of us are given three toy cars and a drum; Dima and Pete have the same things, while Pete and Gene have different things.

Activity 2. Dima's puzzle.

I give them the puzzle that Dima invented after last session. No one can remember all three combinations with two things, so it is not really a success.

Activity 3. Making a twice as big figure (similarity).

Pete has at last mastered similarity, and by the end of the session he draws figures twice as big as the initial ones without any mistakes. Dima, in contrast, starts off well, but his drawing deteriorates and eventually it is impossible to tell if his work is correct. Gene does rather well, like last time, but makes a few mistakes.

The boys like this activity a lot and beg for more, so we do two more exercises than I planned.

Activity 4. PERT graphs.

I borrowed this term from operations research theory (PERT means "Program Evaluation and Review Technique"), but in our manual *Algorithmica* published later we called the corresponding chapter "Parallel Computing" (for a reference, see p. 10), because this activity deals with tasks that can sometimes be carried out in parallel (simultaneously). Another title we can use is the "construction foreman puzzle." This proves to be a very fertile source of ideas; here we only touch on some of them.

I borrow a few bricks from Dima's wooden construction kit and write a number on each brick. Each boy in turn is designated as the foreman. Our first object is very simple (Figure 90).

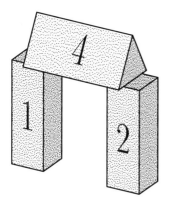

Figure 90. In what order must these elements be assembled?

We carefully determine in what order we can assemble the bricks and draw it as a sort of flowchart, as shown in Figure 91. (More formally, this is called a *partial order* and its possible linear extensions.) While the boys understood the question of the order of construction, my operations-research answer (a directed graph) confused them. I need to think this over.

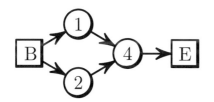

Figure 91. A PERT graph for constructing the object of Figure 90. The letters B and E denote Begin and End.

We discuss in detail the meaning of parallel work streams (#1 and #2 can be carried out independently of one another, in any order or even simultaneously if there are two teams; but #4 can only be done after 1 and 2 are both finished). Each boy gets a sheet of paper and a marker. Then I build a structure, and the boys draw graphs and we discuss them together, whereupon the final graph is made. All the structures of this session and the corresponding graphs can be seen in Figure 92.

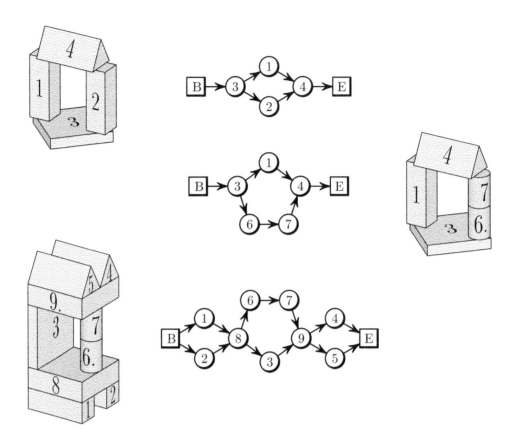

Figure 92.   Three structures with their corresponding graphs.

Session 57. Who is booter, Gobr or Stoon?

Monday, November 15, 1982, 17:30–18:30.
Dima, Pete, Gene.

Activity 1. Oral questions on transitivity.

(1) Nick is booter than Basil and Basil is booter than Tania. Who is the bootest one? It is Dima who gives the right answer but he, as well as the others, pesters me as to what "booter" means.

(2) Gobr is sooger than Wurm and Wurm is sooger than Stoon. Who is the soogest one?

Again it is Dima answers.

> *I had to ask several times to remember the names and the word "sooger." — Dima.*

(3) Anatoly is stronger than Misha. Misha is younger than Vladimir. Vladimir is smaller than Anatoly. Anatoly is older than Vladimir. Vladimir is weaker than Misha. Misha is bigger than Anatoly. Who is the strongest one, the eldest one and the biggest one?

We write the initials A, M, and V on scraps of paper, and for each attribute, place them in decreasing order. I reread the problem each time, and the boys choose what is relevant.

Dima is flummoxed, because he can't remember which attribute we are dealing with. Pete gets it; the others are just bystanders.

Activity 2. Figures on graph paper.

First, I ask them to "double" a shape. No problem. Then I ask them to make it three times as big. Dima does it as easily as before. Gene makes a couple of easily corrected mistakes. To my surprise, Pete fails completely. This is especially odd, since he was a better "doubler" than the others.

I find it difficult to formulate, but apparently the kids learn to solve problems in different ways. Dima seems to have grasped the logical structure of this puzzle, whereas Pete has learned a mechanical sequence of actions leading to the correct result but never understood the underlying structure. I cannot formulate this more clearly, but I remember well that in high school, I understood physics poorly (and still do), but I had straight-A instincts, so I always knew how to get an A on an exam.

Then I ask the boys to draw the same figure lying on the right side, on the left side, and upside-down. Later, I draw a non-symmetric figure and ask them to reflect it first in a horizontal mirror, then draw it upside-down and compare the results. Predictably the puzzle is not an easy one; the boys don't understand the difference between these two operations. After a hint from me, Dima solves the puzzle, and the others copy his drawing, but they now understand it.

I'm not comfortable praising Dima more than the others, but he is, indeed outperforming Gene and Pete. (This is not true for art or English, however.)

Activity 3. PERT graphs.

The tower to be constructed is given in Figure 93.

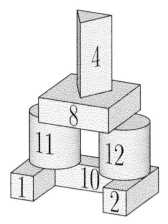

Figure 93.   Make a PERT graph for constructing this tower.

All the boys make admissible graphs, i.e., their graphs don't contradict the logic of the numbered bricks, but only Dima's graph is optimal. Their graphs are shown in Figure 94. Actually, the original drawings were somewhat different. They were less accurate, with poorly placed figures, because the kids had difficulty drawing logical interrelations. Figure 94 is the result of my discussions with them. Note that Gene's solution requires arrows to cross; he hadn't dared to do it, but in the process of our discussion he explains it in words and then agrees with my drawing proposal.

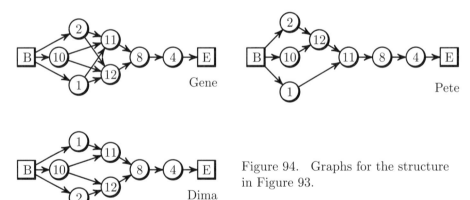

Figure 94.   Graphs for the structure in Figure 93.

Arrow-crossing doesn't bother Dima, so he draws a clean, logically flawless graph. I merely hint at a better arrangement of vertices that would avoid crossing. Pete, once again, is aware that his solution isn't optimal, but doesn't care to improve it. He understands the "modal" logic of the situation better than the others; he tells us that he knows that his instructions are "admissible," and since he is the foreman, he can order construction to suit his whim.

Dima's success is partially due to the fact that earlier this week he constructed a tower and drew its graph, all on his own.

The Spirograph.

After the session, we have fun with a spirograph that Natasha brought. We can't stop drawing curves: dozens of epicycloids and hypocycloids. We've been rolling the small wheel around the big one; Dima suggests doing the opposite.

A spirograph is a set of cog wheels and rings of different diameters. They can be rolled one around the other and small ones can also be rolled inside big ones. They have holes at different distances from the center to insert a pencil; one wheel fixed, you can roll the other around it and draw various interesting curves (Figure 95).

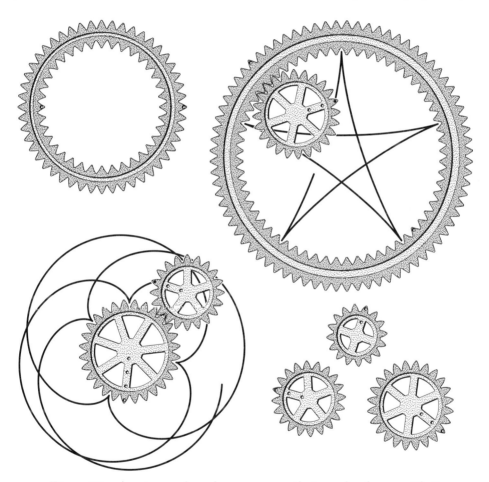

Figure 95. A spirograph and some curves that can be drawn with it.

Session 58. Floor plans

Monday, November 22, 1982, 17:15–18:00.
Dima, Pete, Gene.

Activity 1. Oral questions.

Strengthen the vague expression "I want a..." to a more specific instruction
for creating something. E.g., *I want a house → build me a house.*

Other examples:

a tree	→ plant	a book	→ write
a meal	→ cook	a picture	→ paint
a dress	→ sew	a cake	→ bake
a puzzle	→ invent	a hole	→ dig

I ask the boys to think of their own examples. Dima blurts out, "An
egg!" Seeing my puzzled expression, he explains, "Lay an egg."

Further examples risk trespassing into more dangerous territory. Pete
says, "A baby!"

I hasten to answer myself, "That would be 'give birth to a baby'", and
we move on.

Activity 2. Pentominos.

The assignment is to assemble a figure using two pentominos. We've made
six, and I have made two more.

Figure 96 displays the 12 shapes of the pentomino kit. A standard problem
is to assemble a given figure using these sahpes (not knowing which shapes are to
be used.) The level of difficulty varies greatly. For instance, after removing the
pentominos from a rectangular box (the boxes can be 5×12 and 6×10), it isn't
at all easy to put them back.

Not all elements are axially symmetric, but we can flip them over and thus
obtain another, symmetrical shape (Figure 97).

Figure 96.   A pentomino kit.

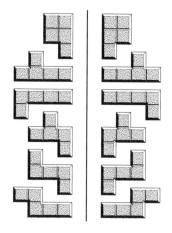

Figure 97.   Flipping over a pentomino we obtain a symmetrical one. So when we assemble figures we can use any of them (but only once).

Activity 3. Floor plans.

Each boy gets a "room:" a rectangle drawn on a sheet of paper, with the door indicated on it. Additionally, everyone gets little cardboard figures for a sofa, a writing desk, a piano, a table, bookshelves, etc. They must place these in the big rectangle in the same way that they are actually placed in our living room. The boys do it so quickly and easily, that I have to invent another activity on the spot.

I bring each of them a sheet of paper and a magic marker and ask them to draw the plan. It's hard to say whether they have succeeded or not: the furniture is in the right place, but the scale is monstrous, especially in Dima's drawing; his piano is smaller then the bookshelves. He works carelessly, his objects are crooked, and my comments make him giggle.

To conclude I show Pete and Gene a Japanese top which, when whirled, turns over and jumps up on its "foot." (Figure 98.)

Figure 98.   A "Japanese top." When whirled, it turns over and jumps up on its "foot."

After the session, I show Dima *Polyominoes*, by S. W. Golomb. Among other things, we look at three figures for which it is unknown whether they can be tiled with distinct pentominos. Without the slightest hesitation Dima says, "I'll try it," and starts working.

Then he invents puzzles for me. He assembles various figures (absolutely non-symmetrical) and, asking me not to look, draws them accurately on graph paper.

A long hiatus

At this point, sessions stopped for more than two months. First Dima had an operation; then he had chicken-pox, and then our little Jane caught it. Then it was the New Year's holidays and the boys were off to the Puppet Theater and New Year parties, using up two more Mondays.

When at last we started again, I was horrified to discover that I'd lost all my momentum. I forgot what we were doing and where we were. As a result I failed to get ready for the session and had to postpone it for another week. And the moral of the story is that I should never have taken such a long break. The sessions should be held regularly, whether there are two boys or even one. This moral was immediately validated, because Pete's sister Sandy got chicken-pox, putting Pete into quarantine for at least a month.

Meanwhile, Dima rapidly advances. When he was ill, he often played with pentominos and tangrams (Figure 99).

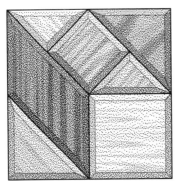

Figure 99. A tangram puzzle (it was called a "Pythagoras" puzzle in Russia at that time). A square is cut into 7 parts to be used for assembling various figures.

As usual, he prefers inventing puzzles to solving them. I shift gears (realizing this only as I write about it). I start to hint what kind of a puzzle he could invent. For instance,

"Try to come up with a puzzle for tiling a 5×5 square with pentominos."

"What do you mean?"

I would explain, and he would willingly "come up with" a puzzle without realizing that he was solving it.

I thought I was inventing, with Dad's help, puzzles for someone else. — Dima.

Thus he constructed, among others, a series of rectangles of dimensions 3×5, 4×5, 5×5, 6×5, and 7×5 before losing interest. Some of his constructions are shown in Figures 100–103.

Figure 100. Three ways of tiling a 3×5 rectangle with pentominos.

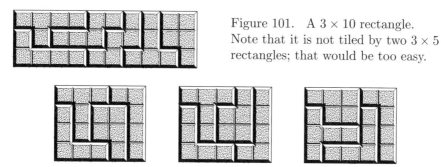

Figure 101. A 3×10 rectangle.
Note that it is not tiled by two 3×5
rectangles; that would be too easy.

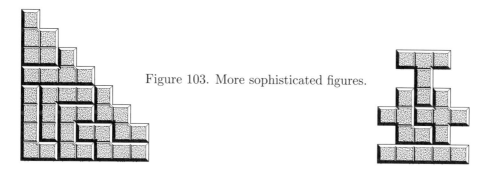

Figure 102. Three tilings of the 4×5 rectangle. Add a 1×5 strip to get
a 5×5 square.

Figure 103. More sophisticated figures.

This leads to an awkward moment. Dima has the firm intention of
publishing his puzzles.

Otherwise, who did I invent them for? — Dima.

I try to dissuade him, but my arguments are unconvincing, since I cannot
tell him the truth — that no one will be interested. I'm not sure about his
motivations. Vanity is involved, but I'm not quite sure in what way. I ask
him,

"Do you want praise for publishing your puzzles?"

"But how can they? They don't know me [personally]."

Apparently, he thinks that a job has been done and it's a pity it will be
lost, and later someone will have to do it again. Besides, publishing must
seem to him an ordinary thing. On our bookshelves there are books written
by his grandfather, by Pete's parents, by our close friend Misha Shubin,[1]
translations by his mom and dad, etc. All these people who live in the same
building and whose children are his playmates. From his point of view, a
typical day is getting up, making your bed, brushing your teeth, publishing
a book, playing with kids, and so on.

---

[1]A mathematician, currently a professor in the United States.

*Here Dad obviously overestimated me. At that time, I had
no idea of all those books. Nevertheless, I did not see any
problem in publishing. — Dima.* [This is not quite accurate.
I remember that once Dima asked Alla, pointing to a book,
"Mom, for some reason, your last name's on that book." It
was a book about Aeschylus written by his grandfather, Vik-
tor Yarkho. I think he forgot about this. — A. Z.]

My childhood sharply differed. For me, writers existed in another Universe. My mother worked in a factory in Vitebsk (in what is now Belarus).
Her factory hosted an official visitor, a third-rate writer, who signed copies
of his book after the meeting. She asked him to sign a book for her son,
the honors student. In the evening she brought me the autographed book,
inscribed "To Sasha Zvonkin, honors student," from the author. I couldn't
believe my eyes. An actual writer inscribed his book — to me!

Finally I tell Dima that there are parents who like to boast about their
kids, but I am not like this, so here is the popular science journal *Kvant*,
and if he can find the address he is free to send them his puzzles. A cheap
trick, but effective. Of course, Dima fails to find the address but he leafs
through the journal, reads the titles carefully, asks me about many of them
and later even tells Alla how interesting it is.

Then he sits down and invents a few nice tangram puzzles (Figures 104–
106). He mistakenly thought that the nearly identical figures (Figure 105)
actually were congruent.

The tangram set contains a leaflet with about hundred figures to make.
These are mostly rabbits, roosters and teddy-bears but there are also geometrical figures, like the ones we do. I hunt for figures Dima has made
already but don't find any. Only #87 slightly resembles one of his figures,
which at close scrutiny is impossible to construct. (Two tangram pieces are
small triangles; the rest can be cut either into 2 or 4 triangles of equal size,
thus we'll have in total 16 triangles, whereas figure #87 includes 19 such
triangles.) We discuss this with Dima.

I think I didn't understand. — Dima. [Of course not! My
explanations relied on conservation of area. For a long time I
insisted that this idea was not mastered at this age. Yet here
I "applied" it without a second thought, entirely forgetting
my previous assertions. — A. Z.]

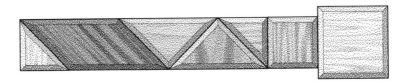

Figure 104. One of Dima's tangram problems.

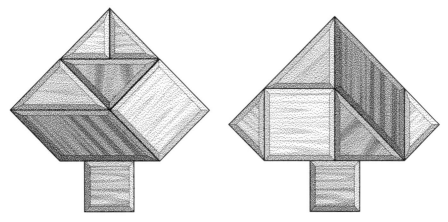

Figure 105. These two figures seem equal but they are not: the one on the right is broader than the one on the left.

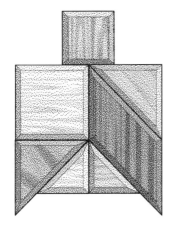

Figure 106. Another of Dima's tangram problems.

Dima continues his progress. At a friend's recently, he managed to divide 31 by 4 (mentally, of course) and got $7\frac{3}{4}$. He himself recognizes that his acquaintance with musical notes also helps him to understand fractions with denominators that are powers of two.

He also makes a funny attempt to evaluate the number of possible "alphabets," or permutations of 33 letters;[1] I notice in his reasoning budding combinatorial ideas. He assumes that there are 33 letters and 33 places where one can put them, so they must be multiplied (which he performs incorrectly). Then he remembers that the second letter has only 32 possibilities and so subtracts 1 from the total. Later I explain to him what $n!$ means, and when he visits me at work, we try to compute 33! with an ISKRA calculator, but we only get to 18! before the calculator overflows.

Also — memories keep coming back to me! — at the New Year party for the kids at work, I take Dima and another boy on a tour of our computer center, where they made two punch cards.

---

[1] *P. Z.'s Note:* There are 33 letters in the Russian alphabet.

Session 59. What does the other person see?

Monday, January 31, 1983, 16:00–17:00.
Dima, Gene.

Activity 1. Oral questions.

"It takes two hours to cook two kilos of meat. How long will it take to cook one kilo of meat?"

Dima replies, "An hour."

"Why?"

"No, two hours."

"What do you think, Gene?"

Dima goes on, "Well, probably less than two hours. Because the heat goes through faster. Was it cut or not?"

"And if it was cut?"

"Then more rapidly."

At this point, Gene wakes up and understands what's going on. He says, "An hour."

"Why?"

Silence.

I tell Gene, "OK, a sausage boils in two minutes; how long will it take to boil five sausages?"

Gene (pondering for a moment), "Five minutes."

"Why five?"

"There are more sausages now!"

"How many times more?"

"Three times."

We go back to the original question; soon Gene comes up with "10 minutes," and explains that they should be boiled one by one.

Dima and Natasha compete to explain the solution. He gets it but shows no enthusiasm, no such thing as "Oh yes! I see!" He seems bored, "OK, if you say so. . ."

The powerful soporific effect of school is obvious.[1] Natasha herself admits that Gene has really deteriorated since he started school; it's certainly evident from the above scene. Recently Alla heard Dima telling Pete,

---

[1]You'll come across many indignant observations and reflections concerning school in this book. They were heartfelt opinions at the time, and I don't want to take them back. Later, however, after my own brief experience teaching in a school, my viewpoint did not change dramatically, but it was enriched by many additional nuances and better understanding of school problems. These latter are so enormous that I feel it to be a true miracle that schools manage to solve at least some of them. And with little moral support from society. And with nothing but criticism from writers like me. Alas.

"My dad told me a funny story about a man who had to walk 100 kilometers, but after he had walked 99, he got tired and said, 'It's too far, I'd better walk back,'" to which Pete answered,

"Of course, he had 1 kilometer to go back."

Dima shouted, "What are you talking about! He has to walk 198 kilometers!"

Alla's relatives told us a similar story: before going to school our nephew easily handled three-digit numbers, and at the beginning of his first school year excelled at a math exam for 10-year-olds. But now, at age 9, he has completely "unlearned" how to think for himself; when confronted with a problem, the only thing he worries about is finding out into which pattern it should be classified. We will soon be in the same boat. I still hope there will be a miracle and Dima will be able to preserve his capacities but there is no ground for this hope except my very strong wish for it to be so.

Our circle now faces a new organizational problem. Before, Dima was already somewhat stronger than the others. Now he keeps advancing, while they move backwards.

Activity 2. A probability game.

Each of us (including me) tosses a die three times to produce a three-digit number. Each toss is placed into one of three cells, indicating the hundreds, tens, and units digit of the number (see Figure 107). The first toss can go into any cell, the second one will go into another cell and the third into the remaining cell. The largest three-digit number wins.

Figure 107. A three-celled board for a probabilistic game. We toss a die and put the number into a cell; then the die is tossed again and the second number is put into another cell; we do this three times. The largest three-digit number wins.

Dima is the first to come up with a reasonable strategy: put a larger number into the hundreds cell. Still, Gene wins 4 games out of 9; I win 3, and Dima only 2. Gene's performance is partly due to the way he tosses the die. He holds it low above the table with the number 5 on top and sees to it that it doesn't tumble over too much (I don't know why he didn't hold it to try this with the 6 on top; perhaps he wasn't smart or bold enough).

[The optimal strategy for this game is not obvious. I wasn't sure even for a 2-player, 2-digit game. Simply maximizing the expected number, at least for the second player, won't work. For example, suppose we're the second player, and we toss a 5. Should we place it in the tens cell or the unit cell? The answer depends on what the first player has placed in the 1st cell. If this was 6, then if we put 5 into our tens cell, we maximize the expected value but the probability of winning is zero. However, if we write 5 in the units cell, we could hope to get 6 on the next toss and then possibly win.

What about the first player? Should he maximize his expectation or he could find another strategy that would respond to the optimal strategy of the second player? More players add considerable complexity.]

Activity 3. What does the other person see?

I seat Dima and Gene opposite each other at a table. Then I place a line drawing of an object in front of each boy. They must draw what the other one sees. The images are shown in Figure 108.

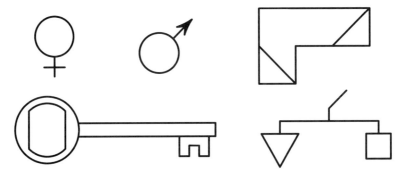

Figure 108.   One of these images is on the table in front of you. Draw what the person sitting across the table sees.

The boys do better than I thought they would, though they make mistakes. This activity is more difficult than an earlier one, where we had to draw a figure upside down. Amusingly, Dima tries to be slick, by drawing the figure as he sees it and then turning his drawing upside down. But even this did not help him guess that the problem is equivalent to turning the figure upside down.

This activity, besides its purely geometric content, also contains the idea of reflection ("what does the other person know?"). I've long dreamed of inventing puzzles involving reflection. This gives me an idea: show two persons sitting opposite one another a card with different numbers written on each side. I need to think about this.

Illustrations from Gleizer's *History of School Mathematics*:[1] images of numerals, invented by different peoples throughout history.

I have two goals. The first, poorly implemented so far, is to emphasize the semiotic function of mathematics; in particular, the fact that notational systems can be invented, that they may be different for the same objects,

---

[1]G. I. Gleizer, *History of School Mathematics, 4th-6th School Years* (Moscow, Prosveshchenie, 1981); similar volumes for 7th-8th years (1982), and 9th-10th years (1983). Unbelievable: I just took the book down from the shelf to check the reference and the bookmarks were still in their places!

that they exist and are important. The second is not really well-formulated, but I just think it's good for the kids to look at illustrations from various books. It's important for general culture, and it also helps me deal with them at the end of the session, when they are tired. I can make it a tradition.

Session 60. Reflection

> Monday, February 7, 1983, 17:00–18:15.
> Dima, Gene.

Activity 1. Placing chairs.

A sheet of paper is a "room" and chips are "chairs." Four chairs are to be placed so that there be two chairs at each wall. Dima says, "Borya has already given us this problem" and places the chairs into the corners.

I add a 5th chair, and ask the same question. They do it correctly (replace one corner chair by two chairs on walls meeting at that corner). I add the 6th chair. Again, no problem. But the 7th chair stymies them. Their solutions for 5 and 6 chairs are *ad hoc*, not modifications of the preceding puzzles. They are still swayed by the idea that chairs must first go into the corners. For 7 chairs, this is true only for one chair, but the boys, however, start by putting several chairs into corners and get stuck. After several failures they start to panic, and I am on the verge of leaving this as their homework when Dima tries once more, and gets it.

I add the 8th chair, Dima again solves it. I propose that we add a 9th chair. No one objects that it is impossible, but all think it will be hard.

Activity 2. Rebus puzzles.

We did only simple, one-word rebus puzzles, for example, the letter "P" next to a picture of a can yields "pecan."[1] The boys solved three puzzles, after I explained the first one.

Activity 3. A probability game.

The same dice game done in the previous session, but now the boys get 3, 2, or 1 points, depending on whether the number is biggest, next biggest, or smallest.

While it's all the same to the boys, the puzzle now becomes easier. Each player needs only to take care of his own number without worrying about the other participants. Of course, the strategy still depends on the number of points. If we replace $1, 2, 3$ by $0, 0, 1000$, the puzzle reduces to the preceding one. So the "grown-up problem" remains open.

---

[1] *P. Z.'s Note:* Zvonkin's examples, of course, were in Russian.

After 9 games, I have 21 points, Dima has 18, and Gene 17, which means we made a calculation mistake, since the sum must equal 54. Somehow I missed it. Besides, the boys are getting too antsy, so I hurry on to another activity.

Pictures of polyhedra.

We look at the pictures in the book by Wenninger[1] and read the names of various polyhedra. The stellated polyhedra really impress them, especially compared with regular polyhedra.

Activity 4. A reflection game.

We have 12 opaque cards. Four of them have "1" written on one side and "2" on the other side. Another four have "2" on one side and "3" on the other, and the last four have "3" and "4" on each side. I show them to the boys, explaining that each card has consecutive numbers, and the biggest number is 4.

I shuffle the cards (including the sides) and place them in a pile in a box. The boys sit down one opposite the other. I take out the cards one by one and show one side to Dima and the other one to Gene. They must name the number that the other one sees. (The used card is turned over and put at the back of the pack so that it returns into the game 12 steps further, but this time turned over, restoring the "fairness" of the game.) I observe six clearly distinct stages:

(1) The boys don't understand the question, and name their own number.

(2) They get it. He who sees on his side "1" or "4," names the other number correctly; he who sees "2" or "3" makes a wild guess. I'll tell them to say "I don't know."

(3) He who sees "2" (or "3") begins to realize that if the opponent names his number without hesitation, that means he has "1" (or "4"). But errors are still frequent. I introduce the new rule: if someone has made a mistake, the card is not counted. The number of mistakes goes down.

(4) He who sees "2" (or "3") starts to understand that if his opponent says, "I don't know," it means he has "3" (or "2"). Dima is the first to get this.

(5) Something funny happens. Gene sees "2" and Dima sees "3." Each should have said "I don't know." However, they already know from experience that if you say this too soon, your opponent will immediately guess your number, but if you wait until he says "I don't know" you will be the one who will guess the number. Therefore, both are waiting, each wanting to be the second person to speak. At this moment it

---

[1]M. Wenninger, *Polyhedron Models*, Cambridge University Press, 1974. The figures in the book have very funny names: great cubicuboctahedron, small ditrigonal dodecicosidodecahedron, quasirhombicuboctahedron, great retrosnub icosidodecahedron, etc.

dawns upon Dima that if Gene saw "4" he would have already known what to say. But he's been silent for some time already; hence he too is waiting. So Dima confidently announces, "2!"

Gene misinterprets his confidence and says, "1!" They burst out laughing and start to explain. Dima's take on it is that, "I see that he [Gene] is unsure and keeps glancing at Dad..."

(6) Gene sees "1" and Dima sees "2." Gene unexpectedly bluffs. Instead of asserting that Dima has "2," he pretends, rather theatrically, to hesitate and even darts glances at me (as Dima noticed he was doing). And Dima takes the bait! He says, "Gene sees 3." Endless fun.

> *I did think that Gene was hesitating somewhat unnaturally. But had I said "1," it would have meant that the previous time I acted correctly and this time made a mistake, which would have been annoying. Instead, I had acted as before, and though this time it didn't work, my strategy was coherent. — Dima.*

I see that the boys completely understand the game and try to stop playing. But they insist on more.

After the activity, they play with Rubik's snake and then sit down to play the reflection game once more. I'm very pleased, and consider this to be one of my best creations. I'm also happy to have implemented the idea of reflection (though it is so rich it could give birth to many more puzzles). But this game does have the drawback that only two can play.

Rubik's snake.

I show it to Gene and Natasha and use it to make several shapes, including #86 from Wenninger's book ("the small rhombihexahedron"). As I mentioned above, after playing with the snake, the boys go play the reflection game by themselves.

Session 61. How do you add invisible numbers?

> Monday, February 14, 1983, 17:10–18:00.
> Dima, Gene.

Activity 1. Oral questions.

(1) Two fathers and two sons shared three oranges, and each got one orange. How can this happen? The boys are unable to solve this puzzle and suggest all kinds of silly answers.

(2) A father has six sons, and each son has a sister. How many children
has the father? They answer: 12. I really don't know what to do. I
ask how many sons and daughters there are, it turns out there are six
of each.

"So, how many sisters has each son?"

"Six."

"OK, then solve the following problem: A father has six sons and
each son has six sisters. How many children all in all?"

"Oh, we have to count a lot here!"

I try another approach. I show how we can get $4 + 4 = 5$ (I count
four fingers on a hand and then count another four of fingers of the same
hand). Then I say that 2 multiplied by 2 is 4 while 2 tens multiplied by
2 tens won't give 4 tens. Dima immediately starts to count and comes
out with 40 tens.

"That is, 400?"

But he doesn't take my words for granted and counts himself. His
result is 280! We are stuck again. When at last we arrive at 400,
everybody has forgotten what it was all about.

To make a long story short, by the time I finally give them a hint
for the first two puzzles, they've lost interest, and the whole activity
ends with complete mutual dissatisfaction.

Activity 2. Adding invisible numbers (a magic trick).

A 12×12 table contains different numbers. I turn my back to the table, and
the boys cover 4 neighboring cells, either vertical or horizontal, with a strip
of paper. Then I look at the table and in no time tell the sum of the hidden
numbers. The secret is that the sum of every five contiguous numbers (either
vertical or horizontal) is 20. So, to get the sum of the hidden numbers you
just subtract from 20 the number closest to the strip (to the right or left if
the strip is horizontal, above or below if it is vertical; see Figure 109).

To say that the boys are impressed by the trick would be an understate-
ment. They are ready to believe that I know the whole table by heart or
that I can see through the strip!

All day long, Dima pesters me to tell him the secret, but I hold firm. In
the evening, he sits down to study the table. Earlier he noticed that lines
and columns are periodic: if you move 5 cells horizontally or vertically, the
numbers repeat. He uses this to find a strip parallel to the covered one that
contains exactly the same numbers, and then to sum them up (Figure 110).
He can now do the trick, but painfully slowly.

Earlier, when he advanced silly hypotheses for the secret of the trick
I would say, "So can you now do it yourself? If you think I have just
memorized all the numbers, go ahead and memorize them yourself!"

0	3	9	1	7	0	3	9	1	7	0	3
4	5	2	8	1	4	5	2	8	1	4	5
7	6	0	4	3	7	6	0	4	3	7	6
8	4	6	2	0	8	4	6	2	0	8	4
1	2	3	▧	▧	▧	▧	3	5	9	1	2
0	3	9	1	7	0	3	9	1	7	0	3
4	5	2	8	1	4	5	2	8	1	4	5
7	6	0	4	3	7	6	0	4	3	7	6
8	4	6	2	0	8	4	6	2	0	8	4
1	2	3	5	9	1	2	3	5	9	1	2
0	3	9	1	7	0	3	9	1	7	0	3
4	5	2	8	1	4	5	2	8	1	4	5

Figure 109 (left) and Figure 110 (right). Four numbers are hidden. To find their sum there is a trick: subtract from 20 the contents of the next cell to the right or to the left (here, $20 - 3 = 17$). Right: another way to solve the problem: using the table's periodicity, we can find a row containing the same numbers, and add them up.

But now, when he can actually perform the trick, and is pretty sure that I just calculate faster than him, I'm forced to disclose the secret.

Activity 3.

The same reflection game as before, with a slight modification of the rules: The first person to give the correct answer gets 2 points, and the second person with a correct answer gets 1 point. Wrong answers (or "I don't know") get 0. The game ends in a 28-28 draw.

Gene uses a mixed strategy. When he sees "2," he does not hesitate, but immediately says "3" or "1," sometimes guessing right and winning 2 points. His confidence knocks Dima off-balance. For example, Dima sees "3" and Gene instantly announces "3." Then Dima says "4," and gets 0 points.

I wonder which strategy would be optimal.

Pictures.

I show them several illustrations, mostly about polyhedrons, from books and *Kvant*. In particular, we look at Kepler's famous design (from *The Harmony of the World*) showing the five regular polyhedra nested, via inscribed and circumscribed spheres (spheres represent planetary orbits).

These pictures make no impression on the boys; nor does a striking model of the celestial sphere by Regiomontanus, from the book *Entdecker des Himmels* ("Discoverers of the Sky") by D. Herrmann. I am puzzled and disappointed by their unresponsiveness.

Session 62. Which room is larger?

Monday, February 21, 1983, 17:00–18:10.
Dima, Pete, Gene.

Activity 1. An oral question.

I show the boys the first two volumes of the encyclopedia standing on the bookshelf, and say that each volume has 600 pages. How many pages are there between the first page of the first volume and the last page of the second volume? (The correct answer is zero.) As often with oral questions, we drift away in an unpredictable direction: Dima adds $600 + 600$ and gets 1200; Pete adds $600 + 600$ and gets 1002; they start arguing, Gene remains silent. I ask him to be the judge.

Gene says, "Wrong."

"What's wrong?"

It turns out that he forgot the question and added $60 + 60$; in fact, he hadn't actually added them, but just sat waiting. When I remind him of the question, he adds correctly and takes Dima's side. Then Dima thinks that if the question concerns the number of pages *between* the first and the last one, they should not be counted, and therefore 2 must be subtracted from 1200 (but he makes a mistake and gets 1180). Gene thinks that 4 must be subtracted (apparently he means two sheets, not two pages). We talk a bit about how the books have 600 pages each and that $1200 - 2$ is approximately 1200. Finally, I pull the books from the shelf and demonstrate the correct solution: zero pages! Pete is the first to grasp it. Then I explain the answer is independent of the number of pages in the books.

Activity 2. Which room is larger?

On two sheets of graph paper I have drawn two "rooms." The boys must determine which room is larger. I don't explain what "larger" means but Dima starts to count the numbers of cells saying that such a room will have "more place to put things into."

The "rooms" are rectangular: first 3×5 and 3×6, then 3×6 and 5×3 (that is, the second rectangle is vertical). I start by changing first just one dimension and then change dimension and orientation. On the third sheet the rectangles are 3×6 and 5×4 (it is at this moment that Dima starts counting the cells). The shapes to follow are more complicated and soon become quite whimsical, as in Figure 111.

Then Dima starts drawing mazes of "rooms",
and I can hardly stop him.

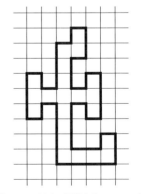

Figure 111. Which room is larger, this one or a 5×4 rectangle?

Nevertheless, the boys give correct answers. More precisely, Dima counts cells, Gene estimates visually (not a single mistake!) and Pete keeps silent.

Activity 3. A trick with dice.

The secret of this trick is very simple, and I was sure Dima would easily guess it, because recently I told him that the sum of the numbers on the opposite faces of a die is always seven. I even told him not to disclose it if he guessed the secret. But he didn't guess it.

I give two dice to the boys and tell them to toss them and count the sum, then turn the dice over and count the sum again, and then add both sums. I leave the room. Natasha stays to make sure that they follow instructions. When they are finished (I cannot see or hear them), I come back and announce the result: 14.

Then the trick is repeated with 3 and 4 dice (the results being 21 and 28, respectively). This amazed them, just like the last magic trick.

Dima brightens up, asks me to bring the table from the previous "invisible numbers" trick (p. 170), and performs for Pete and Gene, giving them hints about how it works. I stop him, but not without difficulty. (This reminds me of the stories by Saltykov-Shchedrin about a merchant, all of which ended with the phrase, "They had to drag him away." I should be happy to have a son so captivated by math. But sometimes I worry that I'm overdoing it. He hasn't even turned seven yet.)

Incidentally, I seem to have underestimated the difficulty of the invisible numbers trick. Tuesday evening Dima performed it for Grisha Galperin,[1] who couldn't guess the secret, even after thinking for half an hour. When I told him later about Dima's solution he was thrilled, and told me he liked it better than my method, since it was a product of research and reasoning, not just a guess.

Certainly, I must continue with magic tricks.

Pictures.

This time, the book is *Die Welt im Spiegel* ("The World in a Mirror"), by W. Gilde. But we go even further. The book has photos of experiments with two mirrors. I take down the mirror in the kitchen, and we have a great time placing it at different angles to the hall mirror.

Session 63. Reason versus chance

Monday, February 28, 1983, 17:15–18:15.
Dima, Pete, Gene.

---

[1]Gregory Galperin is not only a brilliant mathematician (he is now a professor in Illinois) but also an accomplished puzzlemeister. *Translator's Note:* Grisha Galperin is one of the most creative problem composers in the world today, frequently contributing to the USA Mathematical Olympiad.

On the notion of a set.

We try to see what words are used to denote collections of cows (herd), birds (flock), flowers (bunch), athletes (team), etc. Then I explain mathematicians don't want to invent so many different words, so they just use the word "set." You can't say "a bunch of cows" or "a flock of flowers," but you can always say "a set of cows" and "a set of flowers."

Activity 1. An oral question.

A brother is twice as old as his sister. A year ago he was three times as old. How is it possible?

The boys give totally weird explanations: that these are different children; that the sister is a daughter of a step-mother; that the brother ate too little and grew more slowly. (Dima asks me, "Is he older by age or by size?") When I firmly discard all these explanations they equally firmly conclude that it is impossible.

Later it turns out that they have no idea what "twice as old" means. Pete comes home and presents the puzzle to his parents in the following way: "A brother is two years older than his sister and a year ago he was three years older."

Activity 2. Capital punishment, or how to influence chance.

One of the boys ("the executioner") leaves the room, while the other one (the "condemned") gets four white and four black balls. He then distributes them into two boxes any way he wants. The executioner comes back, randomly selects a box, and draws a ball from it (also at random). A black ball means death and a white means freedom. Each boy goes through six trials, recording his results with black and white chips. All in all, Dima is "executed" 3 times, Pete 3 times, and Gene 2 times. From the start, Pete found the optimal strategy: he puts one white ball in a box and the rest of the balls (3 white and 4 black ones) into the other box. In this case the probability of freedom equals

$$\frac{1}{2} \cdot 1 + \frac{1}{2} \cdot \frac{3}{7} = \frac{5}{7},$$

and thus the probability of death is 2/7. However, his "score" in the first two trials is 1–1, worse than Gene's, who plays without any special strategy but wins both times. Dima chooses the worst possible strategy, with a single black ball in one box (so the probability of death and freedom are 5/7 and 2/7, respectively). Seeing this, Pete exclaims,

"Oh no, Dimka, what have you done?"

Nevertheless he also gets a 1–1 score, like Pete. This is partially explained by the fact that when Gene was the executioner, he peeked into the boxes before drawing the ball.

Dima's reasoning: you may be lucky, and the box with the black ball isn't chosen, then the second box will have fewer black than white balls. But if you are not lucky, and the first box is chosen, you're done for, but you can't always be lucky. Pursuing this logic, he somewhat improves his strategy. He starts to segregate the black balls, first putting two in one box, then all four; thus he passes from the worst strategy to an intermediate one which gives him equal chances of winning and losing. Interestingly, Dima sways Pete, who now worsens his strategy. Gene has a completely different strategy. He explains that he noticed that the boxes are blue and lilac, and that everybody always chooses the lilac one. So he starts to put two white balls into it.

This puzzle (or rather the way I present it) has two drawbacks. First, the box is chosen subjectively. (Gene says the lilac one is chosen most often; I think it is the left one.) We need a more objective method, perhaps a coin toss. Also, the kids can't see the balls in the box and are therefore unable to observe what is happening. I need to think it over some more.

Activity 3. Calculation magic tricks.

I attempt to demonstrate calculation tricks again (see p. 134), but am hindered by an unforeseen problem: both Pete and Gene have lost their computational skills. When I say "multiply by 2," they don't understand. When I say "divide by 2," Pete mentally imagines two halves, both at the same time, and when I say "Now add 1" he doesn't understand where it should be added (to one of the halves or to both?).

Dima does fairly well; he invents quite sophisticated sequences of operations and does not make mistakes. But he is impatient to give away the secrets of the tricks, and when I don't let him, he reverts to tricks like: "Think of a number; add 1; subtract your starting number; you have 1." But no one else gets it.

I also learn that in the middle of the past week Dima gave away the secret of the invisible numbers trick (p. 170) to Pete. Now Pete asks me to bring the table of numbers and starts performing the trick. Dima is equally eager to do so, but Gene cuts him down, "You already showed it to me."

When the session is over, Pete asks to borrow the table to perform the trick in front of his parents. I think, for the sake of justice, that now I must disclose the secret to Gene.

Pictures (of tilings).

To conclude, I show the boys symmetric tilings (repeating patterns that fill the plane without gaps or overlaps) from *A Mathematical Kaleidoscope*, by H. Steinhaus. We also look at Escher's "lizard tiling." When Pete and Gene are putting on their coats to leave I propose a puzzle that Dima knows already:

> *I watch piglets and roosters march, and see 11 tails and 30 feet. How many of each animal were there?* [1]

The puzzle provokes a lot of giggles and a lively discussion but no serious attempt to think it over. Gene persists in wanting to divide 11 by 2, and when we remark that will mean 5 and a half piglets, he is genuinely surprised and asks what more we can do. Later he calls me from home to get the details of the puzzle (how many feet and how many tails), most likely pressed by his parents.

I'm happy that Dima keeps thinking about puzzles that he hasn't solved. For instance, on Tuesday he solved the puzzle from Activity 1 (p. 174) all by himself (he wanted to explain to Alla that it was impossible, started to make up examples and quite by chance came across the relation $(3, 9) \to (6, 12)$).

> *I had already realized that the proportion would be different. I saw that in a year, the brother and sister would be 10 and 4, respectively, and that 10 is not divisible by 4. But I wasn't sure. When I saw that the proportion changed, I lost interest. Though the puzzle says that the brother became twice as old as the sister a year later and not three years later, I was quite satisfied with my solution. — Dima.*

He also made Alla play the executioner game with him but only arrived at the strategy (1 white, 1 black), (3 white, 3 black).

A funny thing happened when I told about the calculation trick at work on Tuesday. Only one colleague understood what the trick was about. The rest were genuinely amazed by my ability to guess the number.

Alla pointed out how characteristically the boys reacted, when I announced that I wouldn't tell them the correct answer for the execution game, but I would say who played the game the best possible way.

Pete said, "I think it was me."

And Dima said, "I think it was Gene." (Gene had the smallest number of black chips.)

But then I remarked that there was also someone who had chosen the worst possible strategy.

Pete said, "I think it was me."

While Gene said, "I think it was Dima."

All their personalities are plainly visible.

Session 64. We battle against the odds, again

> Monday, March 14, 1983, 17:00–18:00.
> Dima, Pete, Gene.

---

[1] *P. Z.'s Note:* The original is in verse, from *Count, Ponder, Guess!*, by V. P. Trudnev (Moscow: Prosveshchenie, 1964).

Activity 1.

I remind the boys of the puzzle about the brother who is twice as old as his sister (p. 174) and ask Dima explain his solution. He gives both of his solutions: $(3, 1) + 1 = (4, 2)$ and $(9, 3) + 3 = (12, 6)$. It turns out that Dima already told Pete about this. Gene is very surprised by the solution and keeps asking how it is possible.

Activity 2. Capital punishment with "transparency."

We play the same "escape execution" game as before (p. 174), but its physical presentation has been radically changed. I now use the board from the Mastermind game (with little holes) and use 10 pegs from the same game: 5 black ones and 5 white ones (thus the number of balls has been changed too). Instead of putting balls into boxes, we put pegs into two rows of the board: this way the boys see them all the time. And the random choice takes place right in front of them (Figure 112).

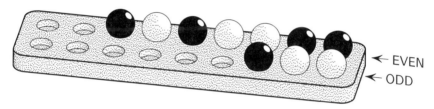

Figure 112. If the random number is even, we choose the first row; if it is odd, we choose the second row. If we are in the first row, we choose a random number between 1 and 7; in the second row, the number will be between 1 and 3. The number thus chosen indicates which chip is to be taken. At last, if the chosen chip is black, we are "beheaded," if white, we are freed.

The random choice ("fate" or "the executioner") is made by means of a table of random numbers. The first number (odd or even) indicates the "box," that is, the first or the second row. If the chosen row contains, for example, 7 chips, we scan the numbers of the table and choose the first one within the limits $1 \leq i \leq 7$, which indicates the number of the ball to take in the chosen row.

Each of the boys sets the chips as he thinks reasonable, and then he plays 10 games. Dima is the first player. His rows are [3, 2] and [2, 3]; his score is 5-5. Then Gene shifts the pegs around several times and finally arrives at [2, 3] and [3, 2]. I mention that we just did this. He goes ahead, however, and gets a score of 3-7, that is, he dies 7 times. Then Pete puts down, once again, the rows [3, 2] and [2, 3]! I am flabbergasted. I explain again that this is the same as before and that we have just seen for ourselves, with two examples, that it is either neutral or even disadvantageous.

> *Dad repeated several times that statistically speaking, this*
> *combination was somewhat disadvantageous, so I was really*
> *thrown off. I even started to think of reasons why it would be*
> *unprofitable, even though it was symmetrical. — Dima.*

Nevertheless, we play again with a score of 5-5. Dima's turn is next, and he sets up his favorite worst solution: [0, 1] and [5, 4] (i.e., an isolated black peg with the remaining nine in the other row). Spectacularly, he loses all 10 trials! Everyone, including Dima, enjoys this immensely. At the end of the 10 trials, there is a twinkle in his eyes and he says, "Aha, I know how to play next time!" Clearly, he now sees the correct strategy.

But it's Gene's turn next and he does [3, 2] and [2, 3] again. Even Dima is surprised and remarks, "It's the same as before!"

I am genuinely upset. The score is 5-5. I decide to discuss the situation in detail. We sum up all the results over the four games that used this setup, getting 18-22. I advise them to try other configurations of pegs, to think, not just count on their luck.

"Look, Gene didn't want to think..."

"Dima's score was even worse," Gene counters.

I agree, and say that at the same time, Dima has tried something new, and that perhaps "at the cost of his own life" he has found a good strategy and he will eventually demonstrate it ...I go on like this at least for five minutes until it's Pete's turn. To my complete dismay, he sets up [2, 3] and [3, 2] once again!

> *And to my relief. I was terribly afraid that someone else*
> *would think of the best strategy and I wouldn't win. To prevent*
> *others from thinking I tried to pretend that nothing special*
> *was going on (though I was so excited that my teeth were*
> *clattering). When I said "It's the same as before" I was just*
> *pretending: everything is as it should be, I'm just surprised*
> *it's the same combination once more. But as if to spite me,*
> *Dad told them that I had found a good strategy! But when*
> *Pete set up [2,3] and [3,2] I was reassured. — Dima.*

I can't restrain myself from commenting, "Pete still doesn't want to use his brains. OK, Pete, it's your head which is at stake, it's you who will be beheaded, not us."

Pete just giggles coquettishly as if to say, "Look how charming I am! I even don't want to use my brains!"

And Gene says, "Dima's score was even worse!"

As usual, the score is 5-5.

Dima's up next. As I expected, he chooses the best possible configuration of [1, 0] and [4, 5] and gets a score of 9-1. Then Gene says he'll keep this setup, and he too gets 9-1. Pete follows suit and also wins, although with a less impressive 6-4. We add up all three games, getting an overall score of 24-6.

> *I was surprised by this adding of scores. Just a minute ago*
> *we were competing and now for some reason we add up all*
> *the results! — Dima.*

Note that the probability of winning with this strategy equals

$$\frac{1}{2} \cdot 1 + \frac{1}{2} \cdot \frac{4}{9} = \frac{1}{2} + \frac{2}{9} = \frac{13}{18} < \frac{24}{30} = \frac{4}{5},$$

so the results we have obtained were even better than the theoretical prediction, thus more vividly validating the strategy.

As has happened before, I only understood some things after the session was over. The boys spent a long time debating how to place the pegs *within* one row! So I wasn't completely justified or, better to say, was completely unjustified fuming about all these repeating combinations of $[2, 3]$ and $[3, 2]$. It may well be they didn't seem the same to them. It may even be that, like roulette players, they watched attentively which numbers were drawn more often than other ones and tried to put white pegs into these positions. If this were the case, I missed it all during the session. I was completely blinded by my superior knowledge: the "self-evidence" of probabilities being independent of the pegs' positions. With regard to Piaget's phenomena, my reading had taught me what to expect from normal children. But I'd never read anything about the perception of chance. So I immediately reverted to a standard omniscient teacher who knew how to proceed and therefore demanded that the children followed his ideas.

A geometry magic trick.

The previous activity has taken up almost all our time. With just a few minutes left, there's no time for another activity, so I show them a simple geometric trick. In front of them, I draw a few vertical lines on a sheet of paper, and then cut the sheet diagonally. Then I slide one of the halves with respect to the other one, and there a line disappears! (See Figure 113.)

 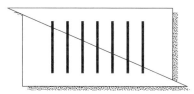

Figure 113.   There were eight vertical lines (left), and now there are seven. Where did the eighth one go?

But the boys easily figure it out.

The session ends, but Pete asks, "Will there be pictures?"

I had prepared pictures for the activity that we didn't get to. I say as much and promise to show them next time.

Session 65. Homeomorphism

Monday, March 21, 1983, 16:10–17:10.
Dima, Pete, Gene.

Activity 1. Cutting computes chance.

We return to the capital punishment problem and attempt to estimate the chance of winning. Adding fractions is out of the question, to say nothing of applying abstract rules for computing probabilities. But I see that the boys understand it intuitively, and try the following:

I cut a large number of paper strips, each 1.5 cm wide and 40 cm long. Each strip is divided by a line into two 20 cm strips. That means that we have equal chances to pick either of the two boxes. Then each half is further divided into equal parts, though the number of parts is different, e.g., the left one can be divided into 2 parts and the right one into 8 parts; or perhaps, the left one into 3, and the right one into 7; and of course we have strips with the left part undivided while the right one is divided into 9 parts.

Then the boys place the pegs in different ways and we calculate the chances of death and freedom. First we cut the strip into two halves and then cut each half proportionally, according to the number of white and black balls in each box; the white (winning) parts of the strip go to the right, the black ones, to the left. By comparing lengths, it becomes obvious which strategy is better.

However, two things are still a little murky. First, Pete has not mastered the distinction between the conservation of number and conservation of length. Recall that in Session 51, we compared lengths of paths with the number of path elements (p. 129); at that time, only Gene understood what it was all about. Pete argues that "there are five chances here and five there," counting the same number of strips, but of different lengths. I try to explain, but I'm afraid it goes in one ear and out the other.

Second, the boys are still trying to permute the balls within one row. I think about taking a nine-part half and cutting out not the first four parts but those four corresponding to the places taken up by the pegs. I hope this way they will see for themselves that the position of the pegs within a row is irrelevant. But I am afraid of making the activity too long and dull.

I forgot to mention that before this activity, I had shown them a picture from Kuhn's *Myths and Legends of Ancient Greece*: Hermes weighing the destinies of Achilles and Memnon on a balance. "But since we don't have a balance we would compare them by length," I say.

Activity 2. Homeomorphism of letters.

Supposedly, the mathematician Vladimir I. Arnold loved to give this problem to math students: *Classify all the letters of the alphabet according to topological equivalence.*[1] I start by describing the task in terms as accessible and intuitive as possible; I explain that the shapes I am going to draw are made of bendable wire which can be compressed, squished, and extended at will, but can't be torn or glued. Then each of us draws a homeomorphic[2] image of a circle. I draw letters one by one and we put them in columns, sorting out which ones are homeomorphic:

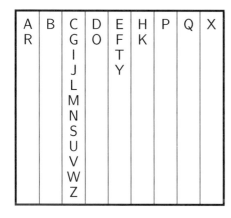

Table 4. Topological classification of uppercase letters. Letters in the same column are homeomorphic, but letters in different columns are not.

I write certain letters in two versions. For example, here are two variants of the same letter:

$$Q \qquad Q$$

The form on the right, with the stick not crossing the circle but only extending in one direction, belongs in the same column as the letter P!

During our discussion, I sometimes deliberately call a circle a triangle, etc.

The boys do well, much better than expected. We get through the first 21 letters.[3] We'll continue next time.

Pictures.

This time, the book is *Differential Geometry and Topology*, by A. Fomenko and A. Mishchenko. I specify that the book is for university students, not schoolchildren.

Among others, we look at a homeomorphic transformation of a giraffe into a hippopotamus. When we get to the Möbius band, I am struck that Gene's remembered it from a previous session. That was two years ago, February 1981! Pete and Dima, helped by Gene, now remember it too.

---

[1]*P. Z.'s Note:* Vladimir Igorevich Arnold (1937–2010) is universally considered to have been one of the most creative and influential mathematicians of the twentieth century. He also had a very strong interest in teaching kids mathematics.

[2]*P. Z.'s Note:* See the footnote on p. 46 for the definition of this term.

[3]*P. Z.'s Note:* The author was actually using the Russian alphabet, which contains 33 letters.

The obvious conclusion is that whatever we do in our circle, no matter how strange, is never lost, and may resurface, when needed.

I can't help showing them Fomenko's inscription in the book to me.

Activity 3. A magic trick.

I hadn't planned any magic tricks today, but since Dima already showed Pete how the invisible number trick worked, and Pete took the table home to perform it for his parents, it's only fair that we show the secret to Gene so that he will be able to show off in front of his parents.

Since Pete's younger sister Sandy tore the table, I decide to make another one, this time with Dima. On Friday, we cut out 25 paper squares, and write a number on each square (their sum must be $5 \cdot 20 = 100$), and Dima starts placing them so as to compose a "magic square" with, as far as possible, distinct numbers in each row and column. At the end I help him a bit. Here's our square:

4	0	2	8	6
5	7	1	4	3
1	3	9	5	2
7	4	8	1	0
3	6	0	2	9

On Sunday, Alla used our 5×5 square to make a 15×15 table, so that Dima is able to perform the trick for Grandma and Grandpa.

> *The table for that trick is composed of nine copies of the 5×5 square. The sum of five neighbor cells is 20 even if some of them belong to another square. I couldn't figure out why, but didn't ask. — Dima.*

This gave us an idea of a new trick: hide six figures instead of four. The sum will obviously be 20 plus the "end number;" the latter can be found using the periodicity of the table.

I perform this last version a few times at the end of the session, casually, just for fun. Mostly, I try to explain it to Gene. He reacts in typical "school" fashion. These days, when I address him directly, he withdraws into himself, stiffens and loses his tongue. He hastens to nod at my every word, though it's obvious that he's not there. When I finish my explanation and ask, "You got it?" he keeps nodding. I hide four numbers and ask him what their sum is. His eyes widen in horror, for his nodding hasn't helped him to drive away the persecutors; he has to answer now and he has missed everything! One can observe him virtually rewinding what has just been said. But half a minute later he gets the idea and says, "Subtract 4." The subtraction of 4 from 20 takes up another minute; he is still very stiff. But eventually he learns to do the trick as easily and quickly as Dima.

Session 66. Topology

Monday, March 28, 1983, 17:15–18:00.
Dima, Pete.

This session is shorter as tonight we have company, and I'm in a bit of a hurry.

Activity 1. Homeomorphism (continuation).

We finished the Russian alphabet, then examined the Roman alphabet, numerals, and musical notes and notation (flat, sharp, natural), classifying all by topological equivalence. The boys work amazingly well and almost independently. They fail to see homeomorphism just in a few tricky cases: the Russian letter Щ is equivalent to H, and ♮ is equivalent to A. But even then, they understand my explanations easily and sometime a mere hint suffices.

I'll have to think up more homeomorphism puzzles.

Activity 2. Houses and wells.

I vividly remember this classical puzzle, which asks how to connect three houses and three wells by paths so that no two paths cross (Figure 114).

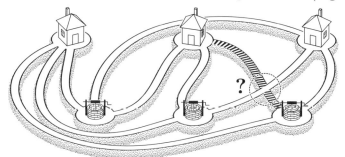

Figure 114. Three houses, three wells and nine paths. It is impossible to draw all nine paths on the plane without intersection.

When I was just a boy, a woman who lived in our communal apartment[1] (who later died from alcoholism) showed it to me, saying that whoever solved it would get rich. I remember spending quite a lot of time trying to solve it. Several years later I rediscovered it, an old acquaintance, in a popular book of mathematical puzzles.

This puzzle is known to have no solution, for the corresponding graph, $K_{3,3}$[2] is not planar. The boys work on it for a while, and then I ask them

---

[1]*P. Z.'s Note:* In the Soviet era, it was common for unrelated people to share one apartment.

[2]*P. Z.'s Note:* $K_{3,3}$ denotes the graph (network of vertices and edges) with two sets of three vertices each, such that each vertex of the one set is connected to each vertex of the other set, but within each set, no vertices are connected. An equivalent graph would

to continue for homework. Dima is amazed by the fact that each time we manage to draw all the paths but the last one.

Session 67. Four colors

> Thursday, April 28, 1983, 17:00–18.20.
> Dima, Pete, Gene.

Activity 1. A *Nim*-like game.[2]

The first player writes a number from 1 to 10, the second one adds another number from 1 to 10, etc. The first player to reach 100 is the winner. This game is really for two players. If there are three, no one can assure his own victory, but at some point he can "hand over" his victory, at will, to either of the other players. For example, if the sum is 88, the player cannot win (assuming that the others don't play stupidly), but he can assure the victory of one of his rivals by adding either 1 or 2. Sooner or later each player finds himself in such a situation. Dima hands over a win to Gene, and then Pete. Gene does the same once for Dima and then for me (I played the last game).

Activity 2. Four colors.

I show the boys a map and explain why different countries have different colors. We discuss why we don't need to have as many colors as countries; we need neighboring countries to be colored differently, so we can see they are not the same country.

I draw various "maps," more and more complicated, and the boys "color" them in four colors. I put the word "color" in quotation marks because they do not really paint the regions of the map: we have chips of four colors and the boys just put them on the corresponding "countries." This method helps us to change the colors easily, to test different versions, to correct mistakes, etc.

We color three maps in this way. Then I tell the boys about the four color map theorem that went unsolved for a century, until it was finally solved by computers working for 1200 hours, performing a million operations per second.

---

depict a dance between three boys and three girls, where each boy must dance with each girl, but no same-sex dancing happens.

[2]*P. Z.'s Note:* This is a much simplified version of the game most people call *Nim*. In *Nim*, two players take turns moving. The game starts with several piles of chips. A legal turn consists of picking one and only pile, and removing at least one chip from that pile. The player who takes the last chip(s) wins.

Pictures.

We look at illustrations from *The World of Numbers*, by I. Depman. Our discussion proves to be very enriching. After just a few pages we come across a small drawing of Stonehenge. The boys ask about it; I start explaining, and show them three more books about Stonehenge: *Beyond Stonehenge* and *Stonehenge Decoded*, by G. S. Hawkins, and *Sun, Moon, and Standing Stones*, by J. E. Wood. We look at some photos, return to Depman's book, and this time we encounter Egyptian pyramids. As it turns out, none of them has ever heard about pyramids. I take out *The Art of Ancient Egypt* and we spend some time looking at pictures in it. Then the session is over.

. . .

In fact, the school year ends here. I no longer remember why (holidays? illness?), but we did not continue the sessions into May. At the end of the summer, I wrote in my notes, "I plan to continue the sessions with the boys in October, and if I am not too busy, I'll start with the girls after the New Year."

Miscellaneous jokes, conversations, and puzzles

In his seminal *Mindstorms: Children, Computers, and Powerful Ideas*, the outstanding American educator Seymour Papert wrote, "Does this allow us to conjecture that mathematics shares more with jokes, dreams, and hysteria than is commonly recognized?"

We'd better leave dreams and hysteria to more serious people. But I'm certain that humor is intimately related to logic. It's no coincidence that Lewis Carroll is also one of the founders of contemporary mathematical logic!

Earlier, I described a conversation we had after visiting the zoo, about monkeys (p. 81). I realized then that such casual conversations were an integral part of our mathematical sessions. So I started to keep notes from time to time. Sometimes they were "brainy" (like the debate with Dima about which bodies fall more quickly), and sometimes they were just funny. Of course, these are not verbatim "notes." These conversations start and develop spontaneously and quickly fade into the background. When I make a special effort to recall some of them, I realize that I remember the situation, the kids' reaction and many other details but not always the topic of conversation! But even if I remember the topic, parts of the conversation are almost fully reinvented. After all, an actual conversation may be interrupted at any moment, before the subject is actually exhausted. In this genre of reporting conversations, it's no sin to embellish a bit. I am sure this is what Carroll was doing: he talked with the true Alice Liddell and then added to their conversation.

However, this book is a journal, not fiction, so I will strive stick with what I noted during these conversations.

The conversations below evolve from common chat to more serious topics and further afield to discussions of mathematical subjects that took place with Dima outside our sessions.

Conversations

1. Lunch.

Late March, 1983. We are having fried fish for lunch.

Me: Jane, what part of the fish do you like best, legs or wings?

Jane: Legs.

Dima: Jane, really, do fish have legs or wings?

Jane: Yes, they do.

Dima: No, they don't. Fish swim in water and they don't need legs for that.

Jane: But Dima, this is not a real fish! It's not swimming now! Because we're going to eat it.

Dima: But it swam before!

Me: I don't get it. I swam before, but I have legs.

Jane: Dad swam in the lake!

Dima: All the same! Fish almost always move in water and Dad moves on earth!

Alla: Like a locomotive. (Giggles.)

Dima: Not that fast! I know, now you will say "like a snail." (He pauses to think). All the same, locomotives move, snails crawl and Dad walks.

Alla: So does the rain. (Everyone laughs.)[1]

Dima: No!! The rain falls from above and Dad doesn't!

Me: I think if they put me on a cloud I will pretty well fall down from above.

Dima: No, but the rain falls in separate drops. The rain drips, and Dad doesn't.

Alla: Well you know, sometimes Dad also drips. (Alla and I exchange glances at this double entendre.)

Dima: No, he doesn't! Go ahead, tell me when he drips.

Alla: For instance, after a shower.

Dima: It's not *he* who drips, it's *from* him.

Me (after a pause): All right, I am ready to admit that Dad does not drip. But how does it imply that fish don't have legs? It's beyond me.

(Everyone laughs again.)

But then we notice that Dima, carried away by the discussion, has gotten his food all over him. We send him to wash and the chat is over.

---

[1]*P. Z.'s Note:* The Russian for "it's raining" says, literally, "rain is walking".

2. Distracting maneuvers.

Early March, 1983. The kids (Dima and Jane) come inside. Jane is in a capricious mood, and demands that Dima help her to unbutton her coat. Dima responds sternly, "Ask in a nice voice." (Being an elder brother he never misses a chance to educate her.)

Jane screams, "I am asking in a nice voice!"

Time for me to intervene.

Me: Listen, honey, what is your nicest possible voice?

Jane: I don't have any voice, I only have a head! (???... A weird answer, but that's par for the course for a three-and-a-half-year-old.)

Me: But what is a head?

Jane: It's what is up. (???)

Me (pointing at the cupboard): This one is up. Does that mean this is a head?

Jane: No, it's a cupboard.

Me: So where is the head?

Jane (somewhat calmed down, points): Here it is.

Me: No, that's a hat.

Jane (taking off hat): Here, here it is!

Me: No, that's your hair.

Dima, who adores this type of talk, is impatiently jumping around and eventually interrupts.

Dima: A head, this is what it is (gestures around his head).

Me: What exactly?

Dima: A head—it's a nose, a mouth, hair, a chin, whiskers, eyes—everything!

Jane (repeating Dima's gestures, as if washing her face). A head, that's it! (now rather merry).

Me: OK, so you say that a head is eyes, a mouth, whiskers; for example, your eyes, my whiskers, Jane's nose...

Dima: No, not that! Only my eyes, my nose!

Me: There is one thing I don't understand: what does "your" mean?

Dima: Come on! "My" means mine, what I have!

Me: And what is "you?"

Dima: Me, that's me. Here I am (pokes his finger into his chest).

Me: So you are this button.

Dima: No, this is me!

Me: I see, this shirt!

Dima: The shirt, the button, all of it; that's me.

Me: So "me" means "everything which is mine."

Dima: Right.

Me: For example, Jane is mine. She is my little daughter.

Dima: No, Jane is not part of you! You are all your parts.

Me: Which parts?

Dima: Well, legs, arms, a head ...

Me: A head! I still don't know what a head is. You were just trying to explain it!

Dima: I've told you already! (Apparently he does not see that we've come full circle.)

Actually I did, but I did not want to acknowledge it. — Dima.

Me: When you were trying to explain what a head was, you used the word "my" which I didn't understand. So I asked you to explain what "my" meant and now you are explaining "my" using the word "head" which I don't know yet.

Jane: I'm thirsty! Daddy, please, may I have a glass of lemonade? Daddy, I am a good girl, so I say "please."

Me (concluding): You see, Dima, how it is sometimes difficult to explain the most simple things.

[I don't claim to be always good at solving difficult educational problems, but it's more fun to write about successes.]

3. On Karl Popper's "falsifiability principle."

Summer holidays, Ukraine. We walked along a river bank, meeting dozens of frogs on our way. Alla asked how many frogs we thought we had seen. She herself was of the opinion that there were about a hundred. Dima said he thought there were about thirty. I said three hundred. When we asked Jane, she said, "A lot."

I asked Dima, "What do you think, which of us gave the right answer?"

"I think it was you."

"No, it's Jane who is certainly right. Each of us could be wrong but Jane really gave the correct answer: there are a lot of frogs."

Besides being touched by Jane's spontaneity, I could not let the moment pass without using it for philosophical edification, "And the moral is," said I, "that if a person is always right, that does not mean he or she is the most intelligent of all."

"Why so?"

"Because an intelligent person says things which are not only right but also non-trivial, not immediately obvious. And even if this person is not always right, he or she is still intelligent. But those who always say self-evident things; these things are not really worth being repeated time and again. You don't have to be intelligent to always be right."

To which Dima asked, "Dad, why do you always say a moral?"

4. Zeno's Paradox.

May 5, 1983. A while ago, using *Physics for Kids*, we made a stroboscope, a simple animation device. This inspired the following question from Dima.

"Listen, Dad, I understand how a leg moves in an animated cartoon, they show it in tiny jumps and then it seems to move. But the *real* leg, how does *it* move? There are no jumps whatsoever, even tiny ones. So how can it move?"

And then he gave me a somewhat confused but quite reasonable version of Zeno's paradox. My part of the dialogue is less interesting. I told him about Zeno, Diogenes, even some quantum mechanics (why it's impossible to see the motion of an electron), recited Pushkin's verse on the same subject. ("'There is no motion,' said the bearded sage / Silently, another walked before him...")[1]

The point I was trying to make was that his question did not concern phenomenon itself, but our reasoning about it; that we could not "know how actually things happen," but only reason about things without contradictions. From his remarks, I thought that he understood what I was talking about, but that evening he asked me, once again, how the real leg moved.

> *If I remember our conversation correctly, it seems that Dad did not answer my question. He only said that Zeno had asked the same one. Actually, I don't think that an honest answer (with time and distance tending to zero) would have satisfied me, even if I had been able to understand it. — Dima.*

I also told Dima that when we "just see something," it is not that simple: the rays of light are reflected by the object, are refracted by the lens, imprinted on the retina, the rods and cones send signals into the brain, etc. And we think we "just see."

What's typical is not that Dima asks "clever" questions (most often than not they are silly), but what he chooses to ask about. When Jane asks "clever" questions, they always concern things of a different kind, like "Why did Karabas-Barabas give Buratino[2] five golden coins, but Buratino did not give Karabas-Barabas the golden key?"

5. Semantics.

Beginning of September, 1983.

"Dad, do you know where the word "nonetheless" comes from?"

I answer that it's really three words: "none – the – less, which is to say 'all the same'".

"No, you're wrong," replies Dima suddenly. "It could be the same, but it could also be more."

Back to math

We return to our main topic and have to go back in time.

---

[1]Opening verses of the poem Движение ("Motion").

[2]Characters in A. N. Tolstoy's adaptation of C. Collodi's *The Adventures of Pinocchio*.

1. Gauss's problem.

April 3, 1983. Ten days ago, on March 23, was the 3d anniversary of our circle. Yesterday, on April 2, there happened something that I consider important enough to be noted here: Dima solved Gauss's problem; that is, he added up all the numbers from 1 to 100.

This is how it happened. About a year ago I told him the well-known story how Gauss at age seven computed this sum in only a minute (while the teacher expected his pupils to spend the whole lesson on it). Of course, Dima asked me how Gauss did it. Of course, I did not tell him.

In the course of a year he accosted me a few times, "Da-ad, tell me how he did it."

I always refused. Yesterday he called me to his bed (he's sick, normally a time for him of great intellectual progress, evidently, due to inactivity) and said he had solved the problem.

"How did you do it?"

"This is how: take 0 and 100, then 1 and 50, then 2 and... – no, not like this. Take 0 and 100, then 1 and 99, then 2 and 98, and the last time you get 50 and 50."

"That's right except there is one error; you should take 50 only once."

"OK, I see."

"Well, since you are already there, now count how much it makes."

"Just a moment."

A minute later he calls me again,

"You know, Dad, each time I get as far as 700, I get lost."

"But why do you count like this?"

"Is there any other way?"

"You just count how many hundreds there are."

"I see."

I was sure he would not finish it, there would be a mistake either in the number of hundreds, or in the multiplication, or he would forget about 50. But no, just a minute later he shouted the sum from the other room: 5,050.

It may be that my impression of this event is heavily charged by the historical prominence of the problem, the name of Gauss, etc. Nevertheless it *is* a real achievement, especially when we take into account that he solved it verbally, and is still a few weeks shy of seven. In schools, the formula for the sum of an arithmetic progression is usually done at age 15. (It is deduced in a similar way. And very few students understand it well.) I'm also struck by the fact that Dima was thinking about this problem for more than a year before finally solving it. He does not give the impression of a brilliant, exceptionally gifted child but he possesses the valuable inclination to ponder over things he does not understand, and stubbornly strives to incorporate them into a system. His character is less like Gauss but more like Darwin or Bohr. (It goes without saying that I am not comparing the size of talent, but rather the type of personality; not the magnitude of the vector, but its direction.)

I complimented him, and he answered with a modest smile that he had not solved the problem completely by himself, but was inspired by the table for the invisible numbers trick that we worked on together. I said that I would like to give him something to commemorate the event. I scanned the bookshelves but couldn't find anything better than D. Herrmann's *Entdecker des Himmels* ("Discoverers of the Sky"), a history of astronomy with beautiful pictures. Dima looked at the first picture rather indifferently.

"What's this, the moon?"

"Yes."

"And here? What's this?"

"There's the caption, read it."

But he wouldn't do it and said, pointing to the Rubik's cube, "I want this."

"You want me to give you the cube?"

"No, I want you to teach me how to solve it."

"That's a bargain."

I warned Dima, however, that this was complicated and would therefore take a lot of time.

So far, I have yet to get him interested in reading.

2. How many seconds in a day?

April 27, 1983. Today I got another surprise from Dima who computed (in his head, of course) the number of seconds in a day. I helped him a bit. First, I told him that there were 24 hours in a day (he had no idea just what a "day" meant). Earlier he computed the number of seconds in "a day" which, to his mind, contained 12 hours. Then I hinted that if he had already multiplied 36 by 12, he doesn't have to multiply 36 by 24 – he could just double the previous result. Also, after he computed $60 \cdot 60 = 3600, 36 \cdot 12 = 432$, and $432 \cdot 2 = 864$, he forgot what to do next and asked me. But this time I refused to answer and said this was the most important thing about computing: not just computing, but understanding what you were doing and why. He spent about two minutes reconstructing his reasoning, and then saw that he should multiply the result by 100. But by then, he had forgotten what he had to multiply 100 by. Here I helped him for the third time, mentioning that the number was 864, whereupon he gave me the final number: 86,400.

I think I can say my system has been justified. When I say "system," I mean that I never taught him to compute, never trained him or worked on special skills. At our sessions, too, there were relatively few puzzles demanding computation and even when they had to compute I never said it was the most important thing. And when we did compute, we added points either playing a *Nim*-style game, or tossing dice, never just "did sums."

It's typical though, that Dima is absolutely unreliable in his computing results. Recently he multiplied 60 by 10 and got 320!

He will turn seven in two weeks.

3. How many people live in our apartment building?

Another case of computation that I didn't record immediately; it happened in late 1982 or early 1983. At some point, the boys became aware of the fact that the immense galaxy around which they orbit as small planets is our APPARTMENT BUILDING, an enormous semi-circular building, of which our neighborhood, Yasenevo[1] has plenty. Just walking around it takes twenty minutes.

"How many people live here?" asks Dima. We start to calculate: there are 12 entrances; in every entrance there are 16 floors, 4 apartments on each.

"And four people in each apartment." This is Dima's guess: we are four, so apparently there are four people in every apartment. I don't remember the details of the calculation; I only remember it took a long time. Dima sorted through the debris of errors and forgotten steps and finally tracked down the correct answer like a hunter after his quarry.

4. Never boast about your kids.

I am giving this advice not to the reader, but to myself. As a matter of fact, I know very well that I shouldn't, but it's so hard sometimes to restrain myself.

Soon after the above calculation took place, we went to visit my cousin Irina. She is a terrific primary school teacher, one of the best I know. When I began work later in a primary school I often used her advice. But long before that — I wasn't yet married — whenever I visited her, she told many engaging stories about school. So now, it was only too natural that we spoke about Dima's entering school next year and Irina decided to assess his level. She asked him to add 5 and 3. I just couldn't stand it!

"No, Dima, better multiply 33 by 17," said I (or something of the same level of difficulty).

"What do you mean?" asked Dima as if he had never before heard about multiplication. I began to explain, but he didn't understand. He was stressed out by the visit, as well as Irina saying that I was out of my mind. He started to calculate, managed to multiply 17 by 30 (making mistakes) and then subtracted three 17s instead of adding them. I pointed this out, he didn't understand immediately, and when he did, he forgot which number it should be added to. In short, he became aware that he had failed the "exam" and burst into tears. I was horribly ashamed.

Emotions aside, we should never overlook such an important thing as *motivation.* You may have a burning desire to calculate how many people

---

[1]A residential district in southwestern Moscow.

live in an enormous building. Or you may be told to multiply two numbers, for no reason. What for?

5. Floors.

I ask Dima, "A man climbed up to the fifth floor and than climbed the same number of floors up. What floor is he now on?"

"The 10th floor."

"Wrong."

Dima ponders, and then says, "I remember once Mom said it was the same to go up to the fifth floor and from the fifth floor to the tenth floor and you said it was wrong, but I never saw why." He ponders a bit more and then says he thinks the point is you don't have to go up to arrive at the ground floor, but fails to explain how these things are related.

6. One hundred geese.

Summer 1983. During a walk in a forest I tell Dima a classical puzzle: A flying goose encounters a flock of geese and greets them, "Hello, one hundred geese!" To which they say, "We are not one hundred. If we took our number, added another flock as large, plus another half as large, plus another one-quarter as large, and you, a single goose, then we would be one hundred geese." How many geese are there in the flock?

As a rule it is always difficult to judge by Dima's behavior what is going on inside. He responded to this puzzle in his typical way: listened and went on without displaying any interest. The next morning, however, he called to me from his bed, said he had solved it, and gave the correct answer: 36 geese.

7. Laying eggs.

September 1983. At dinner I give Dima the following puzzle: Two chickens lay two eggs in two days. How many eggs will four chickens lay in four days?

This is a simplified version of Asimov's puzzle from the story "Escape!:" A chicken-and-a-half lays an egg-and-a-half in a day-and-a half. How many eggs will 9 chickens lay in 9 days? (To help the reader, the answer is 54.)

This time the usual pattern is realized only halfway: Dima listened to the puzzle without displaying any interest and never mentioned it again. Or is this the influence of school? That's another story...

8. How to divide up 17 camels.

September 1983. At bedtime, I tell Dima the following mathematical tale (I don't remember its origin, but it is well known): An old man had three sons. When he died he left them 17 camels. In his will he specified that his eldest son is entitled to 1/2 of the herd, the middle son to 1/3, and the youngest son to 1/9. When the brothers started to divide the herd they were at a loss: you can't divide 17 either by 2, by 3, or by 9. What should they do? A wise man passed by at this moment. When asked for advice, he told them, "Let me give you my only camel. Perhaps, it will help you." Now the brothers had 18 camels. The eldest took half. How many? Right! 9 camels. The second one took a third, i.e., 6 camels; the youngest took one-ninth, i.e., 2 camels. Adding $9 + 6 + 2$ makes 17, so one camel (that of the sage!) turned out to be too many! The sage took it back, said goodbye to the brothers and went away, and the brothers were ever so happy they had managed to divide the herd.

In fact, there is no real mystery to this puzzle. At its core is the fact that

$$\frac{1}{2} + \frac{1}{3} + \frac{1}{9} = \frac{17}{18},$$

which is not 1, as was implicitly suggested in the will. But kids, Dima in particular, perceive it as a sheer paradox. Dima was utterly shaken and kept asking, "So it means you can divide 17 by 2?"

But I remained silent and it remained a mystery.

$\cdots$

Meanwhile October came, and with it, a new year. Not a new school year. A new circle year!

Chapter 7

The Boys' Math Circle, Final Six Months

Session 68. Calendar conundrum

Monday, October 3, 1983, 18:00–19:00.
Dima, Pete, Gene.

It's a bit odd, but our new year began without any celebration. According to my journal, we jumped right into the first activity.

Activity 1. Calendar conundrum.

I ask Dima how old he is.

"Seven."

"And how old will you be next year?"

"Eight."

So far so good. Then I ask Pete, "How old are you?"

"Eight."

"And how old will you be next year?"

"Nine."

For Gene it's a bit more complicated.

"How old are you?"

"Seven."

"And how old will you be next year?"

Gene's birthday is in November, so he will turn eight this year, and next year he will turn nine. At first Gene erroneously says he will be eight.

"Wrong!"

He catches up. "Yes, of course, I'll be nine."

Pete and Dima are puzzled, "How can that be?" Then Pete gets it. Dima remarks,

"I think it has something to do with the elevator story."

"Nope," I say.

At this moment Alla asks, "Do you know when Jane's birthday is?"

Dima doesn't know. Alla says, "In a month, in November."

Then Dima gets it, and gives a correct explanation.

Now for the puzzle. A boy says, "The day before yesterday I was 10, and next year I'll turn 13." How is it possible? Dima conjectures that it has to do with leap-years. I refute this. Other ideas arrive, sometimes leading in the right direction, in which case I support them. Little by little, with a bit of help on my part, we find the correct answer:

(a) The statement is made on January 1;

(b) Yesterday, i.e., on December 31, the boy turned 11;

(c) The day before yesterday, i.e., on December 30, he was still 10;

(d) On the December 31 of this year (almost in a year's time) he will turn 12;

(e) And thus, next year he will turn 13.

Pete is the first to get the right answer. Dima still doesn't see the point. I draw intervals of time (years) on a sheet of paper and indicate birthday points.

"Aha," says Dima, "I thought you couldn't have two birthdays in a year." He still hasn't grasped it.

> *Besides, I didn't really see the difference between "being 13" and "turning 13." Thus I found it more logical to say that next year the boy would be 12, not 13 (he would be 12 during almost all of the year). Thus the statement concerning about being 13 years old seemed to me true only with great contortions. If his birthday were on December 30, there would be a whole day in the year when he was 13. But with his birthday on December 31, we must consider that he was already 13 on this very day. This is possible, but stretches credulity. — Dima.*

Pete intervenes, continuing my drawing to the left indicating at which point the boy turned 10. Then Dima gets it as well.

Activity 2. An oral question about phonetics.

I ask them what words are made of. Pete says they are made of letters.

Dima retorts, "We were told words were divided into syllables."

"And syllables?," I ask.

"Syllables are divided into sounds."

I sum up: Pete thinks words are made of letters and Dima thinks they are made of sounds.

Pete explains right away the difference between a written word and a spoken one. We also agree that letters are signs to denote sounds. Is it true that each sound is denoted by one letter and vice versa? No, it isn't; we give examples.

Then I give them an assignment: think of two words with the same spelling, but different pronounciation. Unfortunately, even when I gave them an example, they could not find any on their own.

I tell them it will be homework, but they are so shocked by the word "homework" (apparently charged with unpleasant school associations), that I equivocate, and say they should just think about it at home, and maybe they'll get an idea.

Activity 3. Programming.

We recall the robot game and I explain that like words are made of letters, the robot's movements are also built out of the simplest movements; and just as letters denote sounds, or notes denote musical tones, our square cards with symbols denote simple movements and arrows indicate the sequence of moves. (Unfortunately, I couldn't think of an equally succinct analogy for logical "conditions"). I ask them to come up with a flowchart of their own design, and then figure out what the robot will have to do.

It goes without saying that their flowchart is quite absurd and cumbersome. While they work on it, I point out syntax errors: two arrows going out of a square, three arrows going out of a diamond, etc., and explain why the robot will be unable to understand these commands. We put the robot into different positions in the squares of the "room" and the boys, one by one, make it move. Sometimes it moves erratically and absurdly, collides with the wall and "breaks its nose," which makes them all laugh. Then the boys remark that for some reason the very first condition always sends the robot to the "no" arrow. They work backwards and discover the position resulting in "yes." Then the robot immediately breaks its nose. It turns out (I show them) that the algorithm checks whether there is a wall in front of the robot, and if it's there, it makes a step forward.

The boys begin to correct the flowchart. Then I draw another one, which makes the robot walk from a wall to the opposite one and back without stopping. Another jubilant explosion. We correct it so that the robot walks around the room along the walls. They have lots of fun and can go on for a long time, but I move on.

Reading.

I read two chapters of I. Depman's *The World of Numbers*.

Session 69. Oral puzzles

> Monday, October 17, 1983 , 18:00–19:00.
> Dima, Pete, Gene.

Activity 1. Oral puzzles.

At this session oral puzzles took half an hour since the boys demanded more and more.

We start with wordplay, inspired by words that have the same spelling and different pronunciation and conversely (words with the same pronunciation but different spelling).[1]

Then we move on to a puzzle which Dima already knows, so I ask him to keep silent: A man climbs up to the fifth floor and then climbs up as many floors as before. What floor is he on now?

Without the slightest hesitation Pete and Gene both answer, "The 10th." I start "descending," that is, restating the same puzzle, but with the "fifth floor" replaced by "fourth floor," "third," etc. Gene gets it, but can't explain it coherently and adds instead of subtracting one. Pete understands on the next try, and correctly explains (after the second floor we arrive on the third floor). We also draw all these floors.

The next puzzle: We bought a book and paid one ruble, but still have to pay as much as we would have had to pay if we had paid as much as we still have to pay. What's the price of the book? (Kvant, #5, 1983.)

Of course this one is too difficult for them; I was just giving in to their demands for another puzzle. Dima guessed the correct answer (2 rubles), but he thought the puzzle was: we paid a ruble for the book and we still have to pay the same amount. He says he only understood my explanations after I tried for the third time.

The boys demand more puzzles but I'm tapped out. I tell them that I don't have any more puzzles handy, because nobody thinks up puzzles for such small fry.

Dima is astonished. "What about school?"

"OK, you want a school puzzle. Which is greater, 5 or 3?"

He turns gray and recoils, as if I told him something foul and mumbles, "Please, don't... "

Pete, however, lets his imagination run, and says, "There were 5 cars, 2 went away, how many are left?"

I join in, "There were 5 candles burning, 2 were put out, how many remained?" The answer makes them laugh: it is the 2 candles that were put out that remain; the other 3 burnt away.

Activity 2. Programming.

Here's the task: the robot, starting at an arbitrary square, must end up in a corner (any corner) and stop there. Dima shoots back with the solution: check at every step if there is a wall in front, go as far as the wall and then turn in any direction; e.g., to the left, then do the same; i.e., go as far as the wall, and then stop.

But when he begins to compose a flowchart, he makes a mistake. He places the check-for-wall diamond, then the take-a-step square, and instead

---

[1]*P. Z.'s Note:* Russian, while less well-endowed with spelling peculiarities as English, is a much less phonetic language than many people think.

of looping back to the initial wall-check diamond, he places a new one (Figure 115).

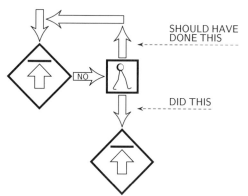

SHOULD HAVE DONE THIS

NO

DID THIS

Figure 115. An error in the flowchart.

Then, having forgotten the "no" branch, he moves on to the "yes" branch and finishes the flowchart. Gene points out a few syntax errors (some arrows don't lead anywhere). But Dima ignores him and starts checking his algorithm. A moment later the errors are forgotten as there is a much more important issue on the agenda: who will be the first to play the robot, who will be next, etc. I manage to adjudicate.

It goes without saying that Dima's algorithm doesn't work: either the robot doesn't get into the corner, or the program simply "crashes" (because of the arrows that don't lead anywhere).

The boys correct it together. But their corrections are *ad hoc*; having discovered an error, they change the corresponding element of the flowchart without giving a thought as to how it will affect the entire algorithm.

After half an hour of work including multiple checks, trials and adjustments they arrive at a huge, poorly structured flowchart (Figure 116).

It's most surprising, but it works! Checking from all sorts of initial positions invariably brings the robot into a corner.

Our session is almost over, but they're so enthusiastic that I find it hard to stop them. We don't read from Depman's book, nor look at the cubes in *Scientific American*. I have a tricky job, checking whether their program is actually correct. I spend almost an hour analyzing it and see for myself that, indeed, the algorithm always brings the robot into a corner, because the room's dimensions are both odd: 5×7. It will also work in a room with only one odd dimension. But in a room with even dimensions, e.g., 4×6, the algorithm will get stuck in a loop.

Next time I'll show this to the boys.

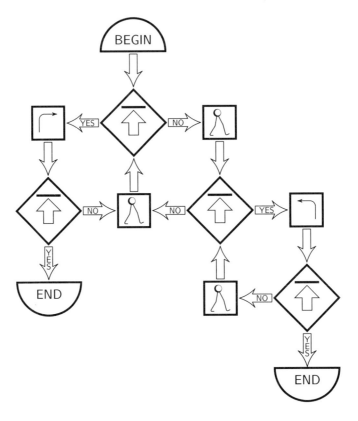

Figure 116. Is it possible to understand this program? Does it work correctly?

Session 70. More programming

Thursday, October 27, 1983, 18:00–19:15.
Dima, Pete, Gene.

Activity 1. Programming.

As intended, I show the boys that their algorithm is caught in a loop when
the room has dimensions 4×6. They are not in the least concerned. When
they discover that the robot turns "in the wrong direction," they just replace
the left turn command by a right turn command. Next time, with a different
initial position, another turn — a right turn — is "wrong" (the one in the left
upper corner in the flowchart, Figure 116), and they change it into a left turn
in the same nonchalant way. Then the unexpected (for me!) happens: the
new algorithm — like the one in Figure 116 but with the right turn changed
into a left turn and vice versa) does work! We try it from various initial
positions, with odd and even room dimensions, and amazingly enough, it
always works! It sends the robot into the corner like nobody's business!

Thus all my appeals for a more structural approach ("you can do it simpler and better") slip away. What does "better" mean, if it works this way?

But I don't give up easily, especially because Dima keeps asking me how it can be simpler. I take out an old notebook with earlier algorithms and show the boys their algorithm for "go up to the wall and stop." (Actually, I gave them hints for this algorithm, but they forgot and I didn't remind them. I think it's psychologically better to give them credit for our joint achievements.) I ask if this old solution can help them. In a calm and in a businesslike manner, like adults, they analyze the assignment, check the algorithm, and then Dima, as before, gives a correct explanation: they must begin with this algorithm, but then make a turn instead of finish (he hesitates whether this must be a turn to the right or to the left) and then do the same again, i.e., go as far as the wall.

"We can even do the same checking," he says suddenly (that is, after the turn proceed to the same wall-check diamond as before).

I am about to object when he pauses, ponders and says that one check won't be enough, we'll need at least two. I rejoice at this first manifestation of "global" (as opposed to "local," *ad hoc*) reasoning, but fail to really see his logic (why he thinks one diamond isn't enough). In his program, local reasoning still has the upper hand (Figure 117).

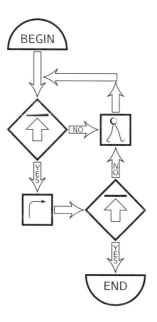

Figure 117. Much better, but there is always an error!

While Dima sees the point of having two diamonds, he overlooks it for the "take a step" squares, and fails to make two sequential loops. His program naturally gets stuck. It's already half past six and I decide to put a stop to programming.

By the way, Pete suggests that we introduce a new symbol for a 45°
turn. I jump at this idea, not so much to improve robot turning, but in
order to introduce new symbols, in particular for subprograms.

Activity 2. An oral puzzle.

Ann, Alice, Bill, and Brian went mushroom picking. Ann picked more than
everybody else and Alice no less than everybody else. Who picked more
mushrooms, boys or girls?

They answer in chorus that girls did.

"Why?"

"Because Ann picked more than everybody else", says Pete.

"Wrong!"

"What do you mean, wrong?"

"The answer is right but the explanation is wrong."

"Also because Alice picked no less than everybody else", adds someone.

But after Pete's faulty explanation I am not sure I got the correct reply
and not just repetition of the puzzle formulation. I insist on having a proper
explanation, but after much badgering I still have no tangible result. The
boys mostly cite examples proving they are right.

I give my own explanation but they don't see why it's any better. They
assert that they made the same argument.

> *I think it would have been better to have asked, "Is it possible
> that the boys picked more mushrooms than the girls?" This
> formulation makes it clear that the girls picked more, and the
> question is only whether there is a catch somewhere. When
> Dad gave his explanation I saw that, unlike ours, it did not
> leave room for doubt. But on the other hand, our explanation
> was also correct... — Dima.*

So, after 20 minutes of being a bore and a nag, I succeeded in annoying
everybody, including myself. On the whole I think that this session has been
a failure, mainly because of this activity.

Activity 3. Ciphers.

Lately, Pete and Dima really enjoy making coded messages. I decide to join
them in their favorite activities and for the first time in all these years give
them homework. They are to invent a cipher, i.e., a table where each letter
is replaced by a symbol (each letter has a different symbol). Then they must
take an arbitrary sentence from an arbitrary book, encode it and bring it
to me (of course, without their table-cipher). My task will be to decode it.
This assignment makes a big splash.

Rubik-style puzzles.

We are still absorbed by cryptology, when I notice that it's already past seven and again I won't have time to show the boys the modified Rubik's cubes cited in D. Hofstadter's mathematics column in *Scientific American.* Next week the magazine is due back at the library, so I prolong our session for 5 minutes and show them all the pictures.

Ciphers.

The boys handed in their ciphers; Pete and Dima on Sunday, October 30, and Gene at the next session, November 3. Pete's cipher is the simplest: he replaced voiced consonants by the corresponding voiceless ones, palatalized vowels by their non-palatalized counterparts and vice versa, etc. Besides, he prefaced his cipher with "from the book ... p. 72." So it's easy for me to decode his message. I have much more trouble with Dima's cipher but finally I succeed. The letter-frequency table from A. Yaglom and I. Yaglom's *Probability and Information* is a great help. I think out loud, while Dima stands by my side watching me work. Dima is awfully excited. For some reason Gene's cipher proves even more difficult, and it takes me an hour-and-a-half and much effort to decode it. Spelling errors in all three messages provided additional challenge.

My principal problem now is to protect myself from a barrage of encoded letters: Dima has already sent me three on the same day, each with a different code. Pete is also preparing one.

> *I saw that Dad was using a letter-frequency table and tried to find a sentence in a book where the most frequent letter wouldn't be E. — Dima.*

Session 71. Classroom puzzles ... almost

Thursday, November 3, 1983, 17:55–19:05.
Dima, Gene.

Activity 1. Oral puzzles.

The failure of the puzzle last week made me think that I probably got too carried away, and it's time to introduce, little by little, more "school-like" material. And I was right!

Trudnev's *Count, Ponder, Guess!* (p. 176) is the only book on my shelves with the subtitle "for students," not "for teachers." It contains quite acceptable simple puzzles, so I decide to use them one by one. I was planning to use ten of them today, but we get stuck on the third one:

"Mom left equal numbers of apples on each of two plates, but when she returned, there were this many apples (a picture shows two plates, one with three apples, the other with eight). From which plate were more apples taken, and how many more?"

The boys get the first question right, but they are stumped by the second one. Neither Dima nor Gene can say how many more apples have been taken from the first plate, compared with the second plate. So! It turns out not to be obvious at all that if there remain five fewer apples, it means that five more apples have been taken away! Apparently, what is not obvious is mainly the fact that it does not depend on the initial quantity of apples. Dima keeps asking how many apples there were at the beginning. He wants to compute how many were taken from each plate and then find the difference. I tell him that we don't know the initial quantity. Gene suggests there were five more. He says that no apples have been taken from the second plate because it looks full. Dima argues that 16 apples have been taken from the first plate but doesn't have any explanation for this statement.

Gene insists on five. He says, "If it is asked "how many more," we have to subtract."

I suggest the following puzzle: "There were a certain number of apples on the plate. Dad added 2 apples and Mom added 4 apples. How many more apples are there on the plate?"

Both agree that though this puzzle also contains the expression "how many more," we have to add, not subtract.

At last we take two "plates" (sheets of paper), put "apples" (chips) on them and carry out four experiments. Each time the answer is 5. But I never get a general conclusion from them. Gene insists this is "what he said," without seeing the difference between the answer and the solution; Dima doesn't see why this will be the case for any amount of apples. He even surmises that for a million apples, this will probably not be so.

Piaget would have said that the boys had not yet formed the understanding that addition and subtraction are inverse to each other. Or something else, even more sophisticated. In any event, some law of preservation has clearly not yet been assimilated.

Activity 2. A probability game.

Since Pete is sick I decide to skip programming. Some time ago, Dima asked me to play the game of three dice again (Figure 118; compare p. 90). So today is the day.

We toss a die to determine who will be sitting in the middle, and I am the lucky one. I take 10 chips and distribute 15 to each of the boys. Then I emphasize that I have fewer chips and fewer winning squares, and we start the game.

The game is fun and boisterous and the boys don't want to stop. But its "instructional value" is pretty low. This is because Dima loses 15 times in a row and goes broke. According to the rules he must drop out of the game, but I have pity of him, so when a new move brings about "his" number, Gene and I each give him a chip, without any comments on my part.

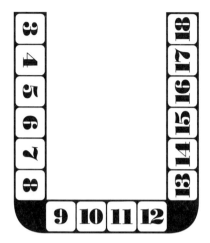

Figure 118. Our old acquaintance, the board for the game of three dice.

And so it goes: both Dima and Gene go broke from time to time, but the chips keep coming. Under such conditions it's hard for me to win, especially since the sum of the probabilities of their winning is greater than mine. When we finish, I have 25 chips, Dima has 8 and Gene has 7.

Reading.

I read the third chapter of Depman. Gene recognized a picture of Stonehenge and says, "You have already read this to us."

But then we remember I haven't. I have only shown them the picture.

Session 72. Subprograms

Monday, November 8, 1983, 15:30–16:30.
Dima, Pete, Gene.

Gene's cipher.

I show Gene the decoding of his letter. He reads the text but it is not enough for him to conclude that all the letters have also been decoded correctly. He produces his table and we check together. Then I explain a bit about my methods.

Activity 1. Oral puzzles.

We move on to do five more of Trudnev's puzzles. No detours this time except that we learn that Gene's father also has this book, and he has shown the kids some puzzles from it.

Activity 2. Programming: introducing subprograms.

At last, a programming session that is a success and intellectually stimulating. I have been hoping that the kids would arrive at the idea of subprograms on their own. Then I realized that I'd probably need to wait ten more years.

It may well be that the idea of a subprogram is too unexpected. Besides, our language doesn't obviously support structured programming. Anyway, I can't wait any longer and introduce a special symbol for a subprogram: a 3×6 cm rectangle with two semi-circles on the upper and the lower sides, representing "Begin" and "End" (Figure 119).

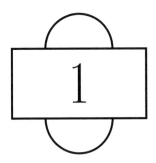

Figure 119. Program #1 is noted in a special notebook, accompanied by a description of what operation it performs (for instance, "go as far as the wall and stop"). When we need to use it as a subprogram in a more complicated program, we'll replace it by this symbol.

We record all the algorithms we've composed in a special notebook (as well as the original puzzle formulations). If we later need this algorithm as part of a new program, we just insert a new symbol with the number of the program. It's better to mark the number with a pencil, so that we could use the same card to denote different subprograms.

I explain all this to the boys. It takes them some time to understand what it is all about, but then we are able to solve the puzzle we had at two previous sessions: "go into the corner and stop," using subprogram #1.

We've solved the problem in two ways. The first is straightforward, and the next is somewhat more sophisticated, handling the case when the robot starts at a corner, and then avoiding the second loop. Both programs can be seen in Figure 120.

(Unfortunately, it's too complicated to design an algorithm that doesn't make any moves if the robot is already at a corner and travels for only a single loop if the robot isn't at a corner, but is already at a wall.)

We decode the simpler, straightforward program, that is, replace both subprogram entries by their "complete text." Thus we obtain a true complete version of the program (Figure 121).

We check the new program several times, but soon decide that we don't have to check it any more; its performance is obvious. I remind the kids that I once promised to show them a simpler program to solve this puzzle. Well, here it is.

I disliked this whole idea of subprograms. Before we had them, it was fairly interesting to compose programs taking the robot into a corner. You have to think, to try, to change, to adapt; all this is well described in the journal. But as soon as you start using subprograms, the entire enterprise becomes routine: first you must say what is to be done (go as far as the wall, turn, once more go as far as the wall, stop). So far, so good. But then you have to open the notebook and read which program does what to find the right

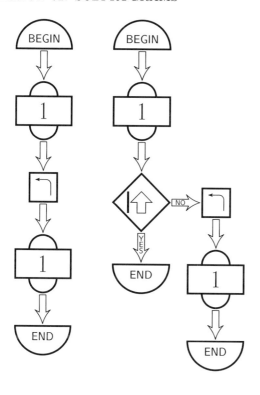

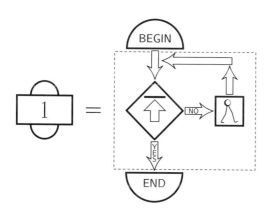

Figure 120. Above left: the simplest version of the program "go to a corner and stop." Above right: a slightly more sophisticated version which handles the case where the robot is already in a corner. Below: subprogram #1.

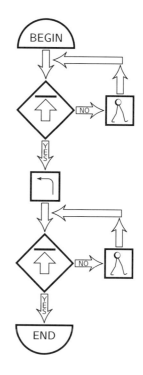

Figure 121. The program "go to a corner and stop" with both subprograms explicitly shown.

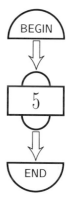

Figure 122. Our most recent program is #5.

one. (Of course, one can always leave the reading to Pete, for him reading is not a problem, but what can I do?) You can't just take a ready-made cardboard square, you have to write a number on it. And when you're done, you can't even show the composed program to anyone, nor perform it without the notebook. — Dima.

To conclude, I ask the "assessment question:" what do you think this program (see Figure 122) does?

The boys rush to check the notebook but so far it only contains four entries. There is no #5.

"Which program I am going to add there as #5?"

Now they have guessed it will be our program that takes the robot into a corner. We are able now to reduce it to such a simple form.

Reading.

Depman, half of Chapter 4.

Session 73. Odd numbers and squares

Thursday, November 17, 1983, 18:00–19:00.
Dima, Pete, Gene.

Activity 1. Roman numerals.

Last time, while reading Depman, we encountered Roman numerals. So now I suggest that we practice them, and, one by one, we say numbers and write them as Roman numerals. For example,

$$2498 = \text{MMCDXCVIII}.$$

Activity 2. Oral puzzles.

A few more of Trudnev's pseudo-classroom puzzles.

Activity 3. Odd numbers and squares.

I wanted to start this topic at the beginning of the fall, but didn't have enough time. Ideally, every session should have four parts: oral puzzles, programming, number sequences, and reading Depman. But I never manage to squeeze all of them into one session. This time, though, I don't have a good programming assignment, so there's time for number sequences. I ask the kids what types of numbers they know. They don't see what I mean. I hint, "Well, even numbers..."

Then they recall odd numbers and primes, but it turns out that not everybody remembers what exactly a prime number is. We discuss it. Then I ask if they remember what a square number is. They do, vaguely. We make squares of small plastic cubes and note the numbers obtained. After we reach 16, I ask what number will come next. Pete says we have to add 4 blocks to each side, only he doesn't know, to two sides or to four sides. I show what we'll get: a square missing a cube (Figure 123).

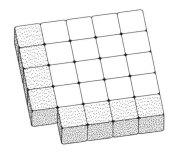

Figure 123. To get a 5 × 5 square from a 4 × 4 square, we add two strips of length 4. But we don't quite get a square: we need one more cube.

Now Dima understands that we should add not 8, but 9 and he says the correct answer of 25. Then he correctly adds 11 to 25 and gets 36. In this way, by adding sequentially 13, 15, 17, 19 we get up to 100.

It's funny: they have quite independently and quite rapidly guessed the pattern to which I was leading them, namely, that the sum of odd numbers equals a square, However, they don't manage to guess what seems self-evident to me; that a square can be calculated as a product of $4 \cdot 4, 5 \cdot 5$, etc. In front of us is a is a 5 × 5 square, but when I ask them how we can calculate the number of cubes, the kids trace all kinds of zigzags and spirals but it never occurs to them they can just take five rows of five. I do my best to hint at the possibility, ask how much is $6 \cdot 6, 7 \cdot 7$ but they don't really count, they tell me the answer checking in their notebook. Their faith in pattterns is unshakable. In conclusion I give them a home assignment: calculate the sum $1 + 3 + 5 + 7 + \cdots + 99$. Pete and Gene giggle and say, "Uh-oh, ninety nine!"

Dima's attitude is more businesslike. He says, "I've already solved a similar puzzle but I don't remember how."

When the others are gone, he recalls that one has to add leftmost and rightmost numbers, which will each sum to 100: $1 + 99 = 100, 3 + 97 = 100$, etc. But his answer is erroneous, he says 5000.

"Wrong!"

For about 5 minutes he pesters me, insisting it's correct. Then it dawns on him:

"Aha! It won't be 50 times 100, only half of it!"

And he gives me the correct answer: 2500.

A few days later Dima himself suggests calculating the sum of odd numbers from 1 to 199 and gets the right answer: 10,000. I propose that he calculate the sum of the odds up to 999. He is a bit scared but gets started. While dividing 500 by two he makes a mistake and gets 270, so that his first attempt at the answer is 270,000. I say it's wrong and he rectifies it.

As usual, his method has nothing to do I was leading the boys to during the sessions, as he's not computing squares. To be more precise, the formula that I had in mind for calculating the sum $1 + 3 + \cdots + (2n + 1)$ was n^2, while Dima is computing $2n \cdot \dfrac{2n}{4}$. At one point, I tried to hint at the idea of counting how many numbers are in the sum and multiply this amount by itself. Dima thought this over and responded with a rather non-trivial remark,

"Your method is better, because mine isn't good for all numbers, only for those that are divisible by 4."

(What he means is that $2n$ must be divisible by 4.)

Session 74. The geometry of numbers

Thursday, November 24, 1983, 18:00–19:00.
Dima, Pete, Gene.

Activity 1. The "square out of nowhere" trick.

I show the boys a well-known trick where a new square appears out of nowhere. An 8×8 square is cut into 4 parts: two triangles and two quadrilaterals, which are reassembled to form a 5×13 rectangle (Figure 124).

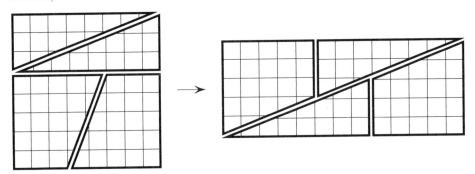

Figure 124.   An $8 \times 8 = 64$ square is cut into parts, which reassemble to form a $5 \times 13 = 65$ rectangle. Where does the new square come from?

We carry out all the steps by hand. We draw shapes on paper, cut, reassemble, etc. At the same time, we discuss many useful things: what is a square centimeter, why the area of an $8\,\text{cm} \times 8\,\text{cm}$ room is not $8\,\text{cm}^2$, but $64\,\text{cm}^2$ (the boys call it "a square eight-centimeter"), and so on. They start forming an idea of area. At first they don't really grasp what it is all about, and certainly do not deduce that the area of a room is the product of its dimensions. Nevertheless, they are truly bewildered by the appearance of the extra square. Of course, I don't disclose the secret.[1]

---

[1]*P. Z.'s Note:* If you are unfamiliar with this classic puzzler, it can be quite bewildering. The secret is that the "rectangle" on the right of Figure 124 is not actually a solid rectangle. The slope of the hypotenuse of the bottom triangle is 3/8, while the slope of

I was sure we had made a mistake in calculation and recalculated it many times, but to no avail. — Dima.

It was funny seeing Dima trying to count the number of squares of a chessboard. For some reason the most natural way of counting — 8-square rows — doesn't occur to him. He first counts along a spiral (Figure 125) and after a few turns gets lost and proceeds with the wrong row. Pete points this out, and they start arguing and forget where they were and where to go next. Then Dima chooses another method, "corners" (Figure 126). He says, "16 squares (two times 8) in the first corner, 14 in the second one, etc."

I attempt to carry out his reasoning to its conclusion and we get $16 + 14 + 12 + \cdots + 4 + 2 = 72$ squares, though it becomes obvious toward the end that 4 must be replaced by 3, and 2 by 1. Dima notices this error himself. Then we move on to adding odd numbers, i.e., the sum $15 + 13 + 11 + \ldots$. We remember that last week, this was how we got square numbers. We consult our notes and find the number 64. But we also obtain this answer by sequential doubling: $8 \cdot 2 = 16$, $16 \cdot 2 = 32$, $32 \cdot 2 = 64$. Dima indicates this on the chessboard: two rows, then half the board, then the entire board.

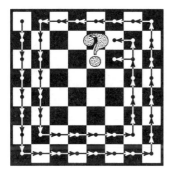 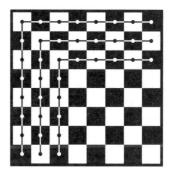

Figure 125 (left) and Figure 126 (right).   It is possible to count the numbers of squares on a chessboard following a spiral but it's easy to get lost! The method on the right is a bit better, but it is still far from being the simplest.

Activity 2. Roman numerals.

We convert a few more numbers into Roman numeral form.

Reading.

We finish the chapter from Depman that we started last week. In particular, we read about Mayan numerals. Perhaps we could do a few puzzles on this topic, or would it be too exotic?

---

the line on the top of the trapezoid to its right is 2/5. These slopes are very close, but not equal, so the two line segments do not actually form a diagonal.

Session 75. The Mayans

Monday, December 5, 1983, 17:00–18:10.
Dima, Pete, Gene.

Activity 1. Adding odd numbers.

I tell the boys that Dima has added all the odd numbers from 1 to 99 and suggest that he explain his solution. To my great regret, he starts out with complete nonsense.

"You add 1, get 100, then divide by 4 and then multiply again by 100, and you will get 2500."

Naturally, nobody understands a thing. I ask why this or that is so, and he says,

"OK, give me a sheet of paper. Here, we take 199..." I decide it's time to interrupt him and explain everything myself: we add $1 + 99$, then $3 + 97$, then $5 + 95$, and each time get 100. The boys look at me blankly; obviously it doesn't ring a bell.

"This way, if we count how many hundreds there are, we get the answer."

"Huh, what do you mean?"

Now it's Dima's turn to interrupt me,

"You explain all wrong! You must divide by 4 and..."

"But why by 4? Can you tell me?"

"Because when we added all the numbers, I divided by 2 and we got 5,000."

"5,000?! Not at all!"

"How come "not at all"?"

"We don't understand a thing," poor Pete and Gene moan in unison. After half an hour of efforts I manage to make Pete understand the solution. Gene seems to remain in the dark: he chortles, chuckles, giggles and says,

"Oops, I am stuck again."

As to Dima, I almost fail to fight with him, as I am unable to stop the flow of words pouring from his mouth. Quite an unexpected ordeal.

It's really shocking how much more difficult it is to present one's ideas in a logical way than to discover these same ideas.

A couple of days before our session, Dad warned me that I would have to present my solution. I was a bit scared. As a matter of fact, I had to solve these summation each time anew. I knew the general rule: add the first number to the last one, the second number to the last but one, etc. But then came a worried thought: $0 + 100 = 100$, $1 + 99 = 100$, $2 + 98 = 100$... How would this series end? How many hundreds will I get? So I decided I'd better prepare myself and, using the sum $1 + 3 + 5 + \cdots + 99$ as a basis, deduced the following rule:

(a) Add 1 and 99. Get 100.

(b) *Divide* 100 *by* 4, *get* 25. *This is the number of hundreds to
be summed up.*

(c) *Multiply* 25 *by* 100. *This is the final answer.* (*I also deduced
a similar rule for the sum* $1 + 2 + \cdots + 100$, *but it was wrong.*)

Now I could wait for the session without fear. — *Dima.*

The Mayans.

The second half of the session is more history than math. We discuss why
the inhabitants of the Northern America are called Indians, trace Magellan's
voyage on the globe, and look at the pictures of palaces and pyramids in
two books: *The Culture of Ancient Maya* by R. Kinzhalov, and *Maya: the
Riddle and Rediscovery of a Lost Civilization* by C. Gallencamp. Then we
examine samples of Mayan writing in the above book as well as *The History
of Writing* by J. Friedrich and *A Study of Writing* by I. Gelb. I tell them
how the palaces were destroyed and manuscripts burnt, and that at present
only four of them remain, which is why it has been so difficult to decipher
them. I also talk about using computers to decode the manuscripts (recalling
our experience of coded letters to explain the role of computers).

At last we're ready to move on to Mayan numerals. I've decided, in
response to last week's doubts, that this will be fun and instructive in many
ways. First, I feel it's good to stimulate a desire to pursue *useless* things
if they are interesting; this is a good way to live. Second, kids, when they
read books, shouldn't be accustomed to just nodding their heads and taking
everything for granted. They should think things over and tackle details.
Third, this specific puzzle is useful because it is an example of base-20
representation of numbers, and can serve as a passage to studying positional
notation in general.

The kids have not yet grasped the general principle of Mayan numerals,
so we'll discuss it later.

Pictures of fractals.

Today we look at illustrations from an exceptionally beautiful book, *The
Fractal Geometry of Nature*, by B. Mandelbrot. I tell the boys that not
far from us, in our neighborhood, lives the great mathematician Vladimir
Igorevich Arnold, who received this book as a gift from its author. Arnold
lent it to Misha Shubin, who lent it to me, and I am now showing it to
them. I also tell them that computers can not only read and decipher
ancient manuscripts, they can also draw. Then we look at picture after
picture of fractals.

Games on the way to school.

We have a tradition of playing mathematical games when I take Pete and
Dima to school. One of them is Dima's invention: he names three numbers and then three more; the other player must find operations using the
numbers in each triple that yield the same number. For example, if the

triples are $2, 3, 5$ and $7, 1, 4$, an answer could be $(3 + 5)/2 = 7 + 1 - 4$. Then the players switch roles. The boys invented the game on their own. I only learned about it on the third day that they played it.

Another game was inspired by my puzzle: "Pete and Dima think of the same number. Pete divides it by 2 and subtracts 3; Dima, on the contrary, divides it by 3 and subtracts 2, and they obtain the same result. What was the number that they started with?"

The boys invent all sorts of modifications of this puzzle. Here is one by Dima: "I think of a number. I divide it by 2, add 15 and get the starting number. What is it?"

Incidentally, while solving these puzzles we discuss what the product should be of $2 \cdot 0$, $(-1) \cdot (-1)$, and $\frac{1}{2} \cdot \frac{1}{2}$. With the first two, I ask leading questions, and they find the answers; Dima gets the answer to the third one independently, explaining, "If we take half of half a loaf of bread, we'll get a quarter of a loaf."

Session 76. All things must end, sometime

Monday, December 12, 1983, 17:00–18:00.
Dima, Pete, Gene.

Activity 1. Puzzles #12 and #13 from Trudnev.

We stop before puzzle #14, as it involves division with remainder. We think about, however, what is the biggest remainder when you divide by 4.

I discover that Dima determines the remainder when dividing 19 by 4 in the following way: 19 can't be divided by 2, so the remainder is 1; divide 18 by 2, get 9; 9 can't be divided by 2 either, that gives another 1, so the total remainder is 2. He is very much surprised that the actual remainder is 3, not 2.

Activity 2. Adding powers of two.

I start with the legend about the inventor of chess who asked to be rewarded by a grain of rice on the first square, and by twice as much with each new square, and what happened. Then we calculate and note the powers of two. We sum them up and note the results under the corresponding number (Figure 127).

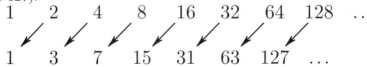

Figure 127. In the upper row we write the powers of two, in the lower row, their sums. It's apparent that the sum of consecutive powers of two equals the next power of two, minus 1.

I ask the boys to find the pattern. Pete is the first to see it, and explains it. We note a few more sums after 511, without calculating them. Dima is ready to calculate 2 to the power 64 right away, but I manage to stop him.

> *But only during the circle. Afterwards, I pursued the calculations to the end. It took me several days, and I noted results on stray sheets. Dad wouldn't think of checking if all the calculations were correct, but he checked that the number of digits and the last digit were correct. When I finished, I forgot what we were talking about at the session and thought it was the number of grains on the last square. Even when Dad reminded me it was a sum I didn't get it. — Dima.*

In conclusion, I link this activity with our earlier summation of odd numbers (in the sense that when a pattern is observed, it helps a lot to simplify the calculations).

Activity 3. Mayan numerals.

This time I don't let the boys name numbers to convert, but do it myself, practically counting the natural numbers in sequence. The kids grasp the notation better than last time, but still haven't mastered it. Incidentally, we discover that numbers seem not to always have unique notation. For instance, according to Mayan system of notation, 105 and 200 are written the same way. It may be that to denote 105 the upper dash must be put at a greater distance from the lower one but this is merely my hypothesis (the boys have the same theory). See Figure 128.

The Mayans wrote numbers in the following way:[1] 1 was denoted by a large dot; 2, by two dots; 3, by three dots; 4, by four dots; 5 was a horizontal dash; 10, two dashes. For example, 13 was denoted by two dashes and three dots (see Figure 128). The number 20 had quite a complicated pictogram: a dot and a human eye below (we drew an oval). The eye played the role of zero but it multiplied the value not by 10, but by 20. An eye below a number meant the number multiplied by 20; two eyes below would mean the number times 400.

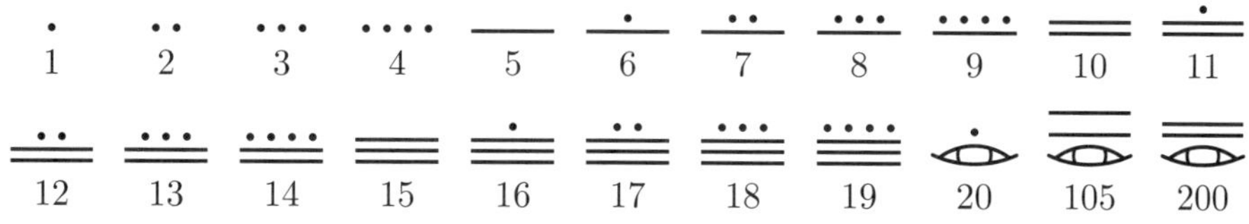

Figure 128. Mayan number system. The last two entries are a guess about how one could distinguish between 105 (5 times 20, plus 5) and 200 (5 plus 5, times 20). We've never found a clarification of this point.

---

[1] I learned about this from the previously mentioned book by Gleizer for the 4th-6th school years (p. 166). Later I learned from a more scholarly source that the system was somewhat more complicated; besides base 20, an important role was played by the number 18. But my story isn't really concerned with all this.

With both Mayan and Roman numerals, Pete is ahead of Dima.

Reading.

We begin the chapter of Depman's book dealing with ancient Egypt. It's a long one, so we don't even get halfway through it. Along the way, I tell them about the pyramids, about The Seven Wonders of the World, etc. The kids don't understand the passage about fractions. I also mention Champollion's deciphering of Egyptian writing, and how much more difficult his task was compared to my decoding work. I knew what language the messages had been written in, and I had to decipher letters, not ideograms. I think it would be useful to do more history next time. I'd like to show them more pictures about Egypt.

Conclusion.

I told the boys that this session would be the final one of the year. On December 14, I'm going on a business trip and will return just before New Year's. Next year I will conduct two circles: one with the girls and one in Dima's class at school. I will hardly have enough energy to continue this journal. Besides, our topics are becoming more and more like standard classroom enrichment math and thus are no longer unique. So I have decided that I won't be writing this journal any longer; this is its last page.

What I should do instead is to concentrate on the journal with the girls, especially the initial stages, which I had not recorded in this journal. That's my rough plan.

December 13, 1983.

Chapter 8

At Home and in School

Our circle did include a few more sessions, but I have virtually no record of them. Below I mention, in passing, several puzzles that I found interesting. Also, Dima and I continued our mathematical activities, without any regularity or system, but there was enough material to fill a small notebook.

The second part of this chapter contains a few scattered observations that I made while teaching first graders at two different schools.

Mathematical discussions, with sad digressions about school

October 3, 1983. After a month at school.

(Recorded after Session 68 (p. 195), during which we encountered the puzzle about the boy who would turn 13 next year.)

For some unexplainable reason I hoped till recently that school wouldn't affect Dima the way it affects other kids (the words "deadening effect" seem too scary; let's just say "negative"). But I start to observe certain "bugs" in his reasoning lately. For instance, once he asked me,

"Dad, four weeks make how many days? Do I add four times 7 to 228 or do I subtract?"

He could never tell me where the number 228 came from.

Another time, on our way home from school we were calculating whether one teacher could teach all the PE lessons for the entire school. He was in a haze as to what he should do and why, failed to calculate the number of lessons per week, hesitated as to whether he should divide or multiply by 2 (two lessons per week per class).

Today he wasn't up to snuff, either. It is not that his reasoning was slower than usual but he produced fewer, and less varied ideas.

Here's a typical story from Galya Z. about her son. Their second-grade textbook has a section of so-called "non-standard puzzles." During the school year, Leo was unable to solve any of them. But after two weeks of holidays he did it quite easily, as if school had relaxed its grip on him.

November 1983. The school monster.

(Recorded on the day that Dima added up the odd numbers, first from 1 to 99 and then from 1 to 999.)

On the day of our session (17 November) Dima came back from school rather late. The weather was fine, and I let him go outside. So he ended up doing his school homework after the circle, which made the contrast between his performance at school and the circle especially striking. In school they start to grade the pupils only in the second term (starting 10 November). This week Dima got four marks in math: 3−, 2, 3, 2.[1] It was on the day of our circle, on Thursday, that Dima brought his grade book home so that we, the parents of a dunce, could sign it to show we are aware of his progress.

So, what's the matter with the pupil Dima Zvonkin? I look through his notebook attentively. He has filled about one third of it. What I notice first of all is that it does not contain a single — I stress — not a single mistake in calculations. I'm surprised, since I know Dima's not that reliable with calculation. His best grade, 3, is for "sums," that is, pure calculation exercises of the kind $9 - 4 - 3 = 2$. His only fault here is bad handwriting. Had he written better, he could have got a 5. The rest of the grades are for "word problems," which goes worse for him. It goes without saying that all the problems are solved correctly (and clearly the teacher realizes that too). But *presentation* is the root of all evil, it seems. His handwriting is poor, and this is not the worst. The points of criticism are as follows (collecting the remarks for several problems): The word "problem" is written without capitalizing the first letter; there's no period after it; the word "answer" also lacks the initial capital; at another point this word abbreviated as "ans." The word "answer" must be followed by a colon. Dima is not aware of this but after my question he specifically asks at school: I was right, the colon should be there. However, next time he puts it in the wrong place: "Answer 6 : r." (Does this colon mean anything at all to him?) Also, one should be very careful with units (at this stage they have them in all word problems). For example, one has to add 3 and 4 cows. The abbreviated form must be 3 c. and 4 c., for example:[2]

$$\left. \begin{array}{lcl} \text{In the pasture} & - & \text{3 c.} \\ \text{In the field} & - & \text{4 c.} \end{array} \right\} \; ?$$

The abbreviation disappears when the arithmetic operation is set up: $3 + 4 = \cdots$. When the sum is written in , the abbreviation reappears, but this time in parentheses: "$\cdots = 7$ (c.)." (In principle, the parentheses are reasonable; otherwise we would have pure numbers on the left and cows on the right. But what do first-graders make of this?) And for the final

---

[1]*P. Z.'s Note:* Recall the Russian 5-point grading system, described on p. xiii. So these grades are very poor; 2 indicates failure.

[2]*P. Z.'s Note:* In written Russian the dash (—) often stands in for forms of the verb *to be* that are absent from the sentence. "In the pasture 3 cows" is a normal sentence in spoken Russian, generally represented in writing as "In the pasture — 3 cows".

answer, this "c." must be without parentheses. Dima doesn't grasp the system immediately. He sometimes uses extra parentheses, and sometimes forgets to put the names in altogether. For an implicit addition (there is one more cow in the field than in the pasture: how many are there in the field?), the setup must be one line, like this:

In the field — ?   (1 c. more).

But for an explicit addition (how many cows are there in all?) there must be two lines bracketed by the question mark (see previous page). This setup at least makes it clear that it's an addition problem. But Dima doesn't get this either. He doesn't ascribe any specific meaning to the square bracket and sees it intuitively rather as a symbol for "something to be found." So sometimes he attaches the bracket to subtraction problems as well (this happened when we drilled him at home).

I think the reader has already guessed what our reaction was: we start training Dima to fulfill the school requirements. Alla gives him the following problem: "Nancy had 8 daisies; she gave 3 to another girl; how many are left?" (All this after we had done arithmetic progressions!) Of course, Dima's task is not to solve the problem but to write it down correctly.

At first, all goes well. He writes the word "Problem" with a capital letter and does not forget to add the period. Then we start to argue: I think he must write "Nancy has 8 d.", while Dima insists it should be "Nancy — 8 d." We can't ignore these questions; his grade has already suffered for smaller infractions. I'm not sure about his version, but the preceding problems have been presented the way he says. I agree to his format, though not without misgivings. Having written the first line, Dima ponders it for a while and then I hear him utter a sentence I hoped to never hear from him,

"We haven't done problems like that yet."

What on earth?!! It turns out he doesn't know how to note the second line. If he writes "Nancy — ?   (3 d. less)," with "?" standing for 5 d., isn't this contradicting the first line?

"Someone *else* has to have less," explains Dima.

Alla and I are shocked and panic-stricken, but conceal our emotions and proceed to change the problem formulation ("... and Betty has 3 fewer daisies than Nancy"). But we still need to resolve the dash. Should we perhaps write both "has" and the dash? I feel completely at a loss. Mind you, all this should be done with perfect handwriting, with letters precisely like those in their model copybook, but on quad-ruled paper. It's amazing that with all this, Dima manages to subtract 3 from 8 correctly.

Incidentally, the way they are taught to calculate is not left to chance, either. Dima tells us, "For example, suppose you have to add 7 and 3. But if you just do that, it will be wrong. You have to go: $7 + 2 + 1$."

(I didn't believe him initially, and started to argue, but soon I was forced to acknowledge that he was speaking the truth.)

"And if you have to add 6 and 4, you add like this: $6 + 2 + 2$. Our teacher asks,

"How much is 6 and 4?"

"Ten."

"How did you add it?"

"$6 + 4$."

"Wrong! Sit down! And how did you add it?"

"$6 + 1 + 1 + 1 + 1$."

"Wrong! And you?"

"$6 + 2 + 2$."

"Correct!"

"And you, how do you do it?" asks Alla.

"Well, I add $6 + 4$, but when I am asked, I say I added $6 + 2 + 2$," and Dima giggles, proud to have been such a crafty little devil.

It seems that the method of teaching is to progress along the set of natural numbers, the maximal step being 1 or 2. It may be helpful for the kids who can't count yet. But this thick-headed monster — that is, school, for the teachers are not to blame — makes everybody obey its primitive principles. And there is no escape!

December 30, 1983. Long multiplication.

I have taught Dima to do long multiplication and addition. We have calculated the number of seconds in a year (to be more accurate, in 365 days). Every day now he invents his own puzzles and solves them. Makes many mistakes.

January 2, 1984. The binary system.

On our way to the movies and back we have mastered the binary number system. It was Dima's idea. He didn't like the Mayan system because the "eye," when written under a number, increased it twentyfold (too much). It would be simpler if the number just doubled. However, he didn't guess from the start that such a system only needed two numerals; I had to ask him a few leading questions.

Then we amused ourselves by converting all kinds of numbers into binary and pointed out patterns (e.g., which numbers are written only with ones).

That evening, he told Alla that there also was a ternary system, as well as base-four and base-five systems (he invents funny words for them), though we never mentioned that before.

[The philosophy of goal-setting has its own logic, which is why it's so difficult to transmit one's system of values to another person. Imagine you live in a society where only people carrying big briefcases are respected; the bigger the briefcase the greater the respect. You want to convince members of this society that their criterion for respect is wrong. But if you want them to listen to you, you must first become yourself a person with a big briefcase, otherwise your opinion won't be of any value to them.

To a certain degree, I am playing the role of this sort of society. I hesitated before teaching the boys something so clearly useless as Mayan numerals. Perhaps the reader found this subject even crazier than I did. So, have I discovered the answer to my doubts? "Yes, you may and you should do useless things... because it's useful! After all, Mayan numerals made Dima think of the binary system. And there is hardly anyone who would deny the utility of the binary system!" But I'm not sure I've advanced my point of view with such arguments. Have I validated the idea that one should do useless things in life, or have I made it look even less convincing?]

February 5, 1984. Tutoring.

Dima spent about an hour watching my private lesson with a high school graduate who is studying for a university entrance examination. He had a look at a problem's answer and saw $x < -2$, $x > 0$. He asked me how it could be that an x be less than -2 and bigger than 0. I explained. He checked with a few examples to see if he had got the point, and asked, among other things, about the boundary values of -2 and 0. Then he said,

"So, among whole numbers, only three won't do?"

"Which ones?"

"-2, -1, and 0."

"Right. What about fractions?"

"For fractions, you can have as many as you wish."

In short, he had understood it better than my high school student.

February 11, 1984. Areas of various shapes.

(A math circle activity.) We discussed various things concerning areas, such as dividing a unit area into smaller portions. We also cut various shapes out of paper and weighed them on a drug-store scale. Then we determined the area of a right triangle. At the end I explained the standard procedure: creating a rectangle out of two triangles. But before that, the boys proposed their own method — correct, if somewhat exotic (Figure 129).

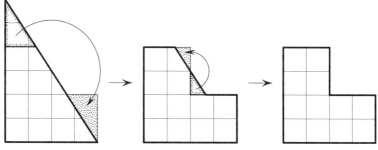

Figure 129. A method for determining an area of a right triangle: a bit exotic, but it works!

February 16, 1984. Strange: is binary easier than fractions?

Yesterday and today, Dima busily multiplied large binary numbers and then checked the results in the decimal system. This was all self-motivated work. He multiplied 10 by 100 and 1000 by 1000 and then checked if the results would be 1000 and 1000000. He understood all by himself how, while adding a large number of units, to organize the positions of the digits ("1 + 1 + 1 + 1, write 0, carry 0 here and carry 1 there"). Still, he did make mistakes forgetting what number was carried in what position. I showed where he could write the carried numbers.

Today we discussed the relations of the binary system to the octal and hexadecimal systems. He understood everything. Curiously, he still is unable to compare $\frac{3}{5}$ and $\frac{4}{7}$. His thinks too formally; he strives to think of an algorithm instead of thinking over the meaning of the problem.

February 20, 1984. A square with an area equal to 2 units.

(At a circle session again.) Pete surprised me today. The assignment was to make a square with area equal to 2 little unit squares on the graph paper. Dima first tried $\left(1 + \frac{1}{2}\right)^2$ (see left figure), then $\left(1 + \frac{1}{4}\right)^2$ (middle figure); he calculated the areas correctly and realized that he didn't get 2. I was looking forward shocking the kids with my solution, when Pete almost immediately produced the right solution (right).[1]

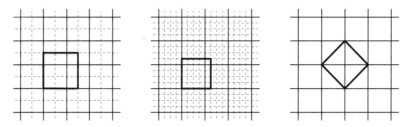

Figure 130. The first attempt (left): the side of the square equals $1\frac{1}{2}$ and the area is composed of a unit cell, two halves of a cell, and one quarter, i.e., $2\frac{1}{4}$. The second attempt (middle): the side is $1\frac{1}{4}$ and the area is $1 + \frac{2}{4} + \frac{1}{16} = 1\frac{9}{16}$. (An assignment for the reader: consider a square with side $1\frac{1}{3}$.) Finally, the area of the square (right) is exactly two unit cells: obviously it is composed of four triangle-shaped halves of a cell.

---

[1]The "tilted squares" problem proved to be extremely rich, but more suitable for older kids. In 1989 in the Pereslavl-Zalessky summer camp we gave it to a group of 10–14-year-olds, and there was enough material to last a couple of weeks. It led to the Pythagorean theorem, then to Euler's question asking which triangular numbers are equal to square ones (how many pebbles can make both a triangle and a square), then to Pell's equation (find the integer solutions to $x^2 - 2y^2 = 1$), and finally to the competition to find the largest Pythagorean triples (integers a, b, c such that $a^2 + b^2 = c^2$). Strange as it may seem, the winner was a 9-year-old boy named Mitya. Later, inspired by our sessions, Mitya asked us if it was possible to make a pyramid and a cube with the same number of balls. This problem belongs to the domain of serious mathematics which does not even

The other day I discussed the irrationality of $\sqrt{2}$ with Dima. He asked fairly intelligent questions, "Does that mean that $\sqrt{2} - 1$ is also irrational? And $2\sqrt{2}$?," etc.

> *Dad told me the proof, but I didn't understand. First, it seemed too long; second, I never before saw a proof ad absurdum. They assumed the fraction was irreducible; then, in a somewhat cloudy way, proved it was reducible; and somehow that meant such a fraction didn't exist. — Dima.*

Multiplying odds and evens.

At the same session, we played the following game: at a signal we displayed a few fingers and calculated the product. I won if it was even, and I lost if it was odd. Naturally, I was winning all the time. Dima was the first to guess why, Pete took some time before guessing; Gene was clueless.

March 8, 1984. Long division.

Taught Dima to perform long division. He has not yet learned it well. By the end of the day I found that I had forgotten to teach him how to subtract (that is, to borrow from the high-order digit to the low-order one; the rest is obvious), but he invented his own method: he increased both terms so that the first had a bigger value in its units digit (e.g., $50 - 47 = 57 - 54$).

March 23–25, 1984. Number systems.

The third term is over, Dima got his grades, a 4 in math (his only 5 is in PE, the rest are 4s). His school-desk neighbor Kostya also got 4 in math (his only 4, the rest are 5s). Dima told me that at the last test Kostya asked him what was $12 - 6$. Being a model student, Dima didn't tell him, so Kostya, after some reflection, wrote $12 - 6 = 8$.

That gave me an idea, and I asked Dima for which base of a number system this result would be correct. He told me right away it had to be no less than base 9, to include the figure 8. Then he repeated, "I have no idea, no idea." To my great regret, this behavior has become habitual lately: he starts by convincing himself he wouldn't be able to solve a puzzle and only then sets up to solve it. After I put him to shame, he did solve it and came up with the base-12 system.

I said, "So you see, it seems Kostya has just solved the puzzle in the base-12 system."

Dima demanded some more puzzles of this sort and solved them. For the next two days, he kept inventing many similar puzzles for me to solve; e.g.,

---

get into the university curriculum, namely, the arithmetic of elliptic curves. After some search in scientific journals one of our teachers finally discovered an article demonstrating that there were no such numbers other than 1.

in which system is the equality $22 - 7 = 1E$ true?[1] The answer: base-19. Dima was very amazed by the rapidity of my answers; he solves them by trial-and-error.

At some point we wondered why certain equalities are valid in any system in which they are meaningful (i.e., where the necessary figures exist, so, for example, $32 + 23 = 55$ is true in base-6 and higher), while others are only valid in one system. Dima's initial idea was completely absurd and had nothing to do with the matter. But then it occurred to him that it depended on whether there was a carry from one position to the next, or whether the operations were performed independently in each position.

When he was over with correct explanations I couldn't help saying encouragingly, "Great work! You'll probably be able to get a 5 in math at the end of the year!"

March, April, May.

During all these months Dima kept begging to use my calculator and begging for things to calculate. Along the way, he learned a lot and keeps learning new things. First he learned what a decimal was. Then raising numbers to integer powers. Then the number π and what it meant. At his request I showed him how to measure angles in degrees and radians. Then I explained what a sine was.

"Where is the inverse sine?," asked Dima as if the idea of an inverse function was the most natural thing in the world.

We haven't yet gotten to the difficult notion of representing a number as a mantissa-exponent pair.

Sometimes, but rarely, he calculated the answers to meaningful questions, like "how many seconds are there in a year." He spent a lot of time on the problem of "hailstone numbers"[2] (*Scientific American*, January 1984). It concerns a sequence u_n defined by the recurrence formula

$$u_{n+1} = \begin{cases} u_n/2, & \text{if } u_n \text{ is even;} \\ 3u_n + 1, & \text{if } u_n \text{ is odd.} \end{cases}$$

If we start with the number $u_0 = 1$, we get the cycle $1 \to 4 \to 2 \to 1$. Therefore it seems natural to introduce the convention that when we get $u = 1$, stop. Let's see what will happen if we start with 7:

$$7 \to 22 \to 11 \to 34 \to 17 \to 52 \to 26 \to 13 \to$$
$$40 \to 20 \to 10 \to 5 \to 16 \to 8 \to 4 \to 2 \to 1.$$

---

[1] In systems with a base bigger than 10 he replaced the missing digits by the letters of the Russian alphabet; using the English alphabet we may denote 10 by A, 11 by B, etc., so here E means 14.

[2] This problem later became very famous under many names (for instance, the Syracuse problem, the Collatz conjecture, the Ulam conjecture). It is still an open problem.

If we start with 27, we'll have to make more than one hundred steps; our numbers will go into the thousands, yet eventually return to 1. The open problem is *whether we shall always return to one, no matter what number we start with.* That is what Dima verified for many initial values.[1]

The rest of his occupations were rather senseless. For instance, time and again he would calculate the powers of two.

When we walked outdoors and he would cajole a puzzle from me to solve, I gave him mostly fractions. At first he had a rough time with them; in fact, he failed all the time. Eventually, he started to grasp the concepts, and finally reached a level at which he almost always gave correct answers to problems like:

$$\frac{1}{2} - \frac{1}{3}, \quad \frac{1}{5} + \frac{1}{6}, \quad \frac{3}{5} + \frac{4}{7}, \text{ etc.}$$

But I don't know what procedures he uses, and don't understand his explanations. It seems that each time he acts differently and has not yet grasped the idea of the common denominator.

> *If memory serves, what I did was actually look for the common denominator. I took 1/2 and 1/3 of any number that easily lent itself to the operation, e.g., I used 6 or 12, then I subtracted one result from the other and divided again by the same number. I had no idea why the answer was always the same but knew it would be correct (Dad told me so). I tried to find the least possible number, so actually it often was the least common denominator. — Dima.*

After one of his requests for a puzzle, I just gave him Trudnev's book, and told him to look for puzzles by himself. For a few days he was solving puzzles one after another, but then got tired of it. Clearly, it's not just math that is important, but "mathematical communication."

Also, when he was sick, he asked me for a second-grade school math textbook. I brought it, as well as those for third and fourth grades, but he leafed through them rather lazily and put them aside.

I have an impression that if I started to teach him a lesson every day, as they do at school, by next year we could probably get up to the 8th grade curriculum. Naturally, I would never do this. I feel such lessons could be conceivable no earlier than the age of 11 or 12.

[What I mean by "such lessons" is "content-driven instruction." I could have explained to him what a common denominator is and how to add and subtract fractions. It would have taken half an hour, and he would long ago be able to do that. Instead, I try to make him do independent research, and it has been going on for almost a year. I know that content-driven instruction is possible and even necessary (one can't really hope to advance without it),

---

[1]Using computers, this has been shown to be true for all starting values up to a very large number, which is currently, according to the *Wikipedia*, $5 \cdot 2^{60} \approx 5.764 \cdot 10^{18}$.

but only beginning with a certain age, when Piaget's "formal-operational structures" have formed.]

June 10, 1984. A grade of 4 for the year.

Today Dima brought home his annual record card. He got a 4 in math. This is the only mark which I find unjust. What a shame that his teacher doesn't have the slightest idea how far ahead he is compared to the school curriculum. But how could she possibly know?

June 17, 1984. A university entrance-exam problem.

Today Dima solved an entrance-exam problem for the physics department of Moscow State University[1] (1983, version #1, problem #4, categorized as "medium difficulty"[2]). Here's the problem:

> If a certain two-digit number is divided by the sum of its digits, the quotient will be 7, with a remainder of 6. If the same number is divided by the product of its digits, the quotient will be 3, with a remainder of 11. Find this two-digit number.

The high-school student whom I was tutoring was unable to solve it. It took about a half an hour of hard work to explain the solution to him. I think it was my irritation that made me give the problem to Dima after my tutoring session was over. To avoid swelling his head, I didn't thrust the exam book on him but presented him with the problem copied on a sheet. The first thing he said after having listened to the problem was, "So they divided by no less than 12, didn't they?"

(In other words, he understood right away what had been the principal stumbling block for my student.) Then he started thinking. I should say that the circumstances weren't conducive to concentration. We were having dinner, then he sat on the sofa to think and Jane was pestering him, then Alla made him do his English homework, then he tried to get rid of Jane once more, and so on.

This is how I solved the problem myself and presented it to my student. From the first condition we obtain that our number has the form $7k + 6$, k being at least 7 (otherwise, the remainder of division by k can't be equal to 6). We sort out all such two-digit numbers: 55, 62, 69, 76, 83, 90, 97. Then we check the second condition, which is valid only for the number 83. Thus our number is 83.

---

[1]*P. Z.'s Note:* Moscow State University, for Soviet citizens at that time, had roughly the status that Harvard and MIT, combined, have for Americans.

[2]A written entrance examination usually contained five problems: three easy ones, one of intermediate difficulty, and a difficult one.

I quoted my own solution because it contained a very subtle mistake. I was shocked by the fact that Dima had avoided it (this is how I learned about my mistake, from his solution!). As a matter of fact, the number we are looking for must not only have the form $7k + 6$ but k must also equal the sum of its digits. I didn't check this last condition. Once this is taken into consideration, only two numbers of the above list satisfy the condition: 62 and 83.

Some time after dinner Dima told me, "I have found the answer to the first sentence but it doesn't suit the second one."

"What is the number?"

"62. But when you divide it by 12, you don't get 3 with remainder 11, but 5 with remainder 2."

"And how did you find it?"

"I multiplied 7 by 8 and added 6" (another thing impossible to explain to my student).

"Why did you multiply right away by 8, not by 7?"

"I did, but I got 55. And its sum of digits is 10, not 7."

"Hum...Indeed...Humph..."

Dima's words that he has "found the answer" to the first condition show that he, as usual, isn't concerned about finding all the solutions (or to prove the uniqueness) but is satisfied with the first solution discovered. So at that moment I gave him a slight impetus; otherwise he could have stopped there (or maybe not). I told him, "You are on the right track." He got the point. "On the right track" means you have to go further.

Some time later he came running and said that he got 83 but the division gave the quotient 3 (which is correct) and the remainder 5. I told him to check the division.

He checked, "Yes, the remainder is 11, it's OK."

> *I only ran to Dad to check to see if* 83 *was incorrect, or if I had to divide again. I wasn't very keen to divide once more. When Dad told me to check, I understood it would be correct, and checked it in a slipshod way.* — *Dima.*

Then I explained that to get a complete solution we have to carry out the verification to the end, that is, to check $k = 12$ and $k = 13$. We did it together.

"Do we go further?"

"No, the numbers won't be two-digit any longer."

That's about it. I have to add that the problem was solved mentally and that the whole thing took about 40 minutes (clock time — I cannot isolate the "net time").

Whereupon Alla and I had a long discussion about whether we should consider him to be a genius or if this conclusion was still premature.

September 1984.

No math during the summer. At the beginning of the school year (second grade) I gave Dima a few puzzles.

(1) I have already mentioned this one in a simplified version.

> A chicken-and-a-half lay an egg-and-a-half in a day-and-a-half. How many eggs will 9 chickens lay in 9 days?

Of course, Dima said right away, "Nine".

Then he pondered a minute and gave another answer: 18.

The logic of his reasoning was as follows: 9 chickens is 6 times more than 1.5 chickens, and 9 days is 6 times more than 1.5 days. That means they will lay 12 times more eggs. 1.5 multiplied by 12 makes 18. I told him to think again. Then it dawned on him that he had to multiply 1.5 eggs not by $6 + 6$ but by $6 \cdot 6$, and he gave the correct answer of 54.

(2) I gave him the well-known "reflexive" puzzle:[1]

> Two mathematicians who haven't met for some time are chatting. One of them tells the other he has three sons.
>
> "How old are they?" asks the second one.
>
> "Find it yourself: the product of their ages is 36."
>
> The second mathematician says, "The information is insufficient."
>
> "OK, I'll add then that the sum of their ages equals the number of benches in this square."
>
> The second one counts the benches, thinks a little, then says,
>
> "The information is still insufficient."
>
> "Then I'll tell you that my oldest son is red-haired", answers the first mathematician.
>
> "Now we're talking! Your sons are...," and he gives their ages correctly. What are the ages of the three boys?

Unfortunately, Dima didn't have the slightest idea as to its solution.[2]

(3) We also dealt with fractions. Dima solved three or four puzzles correctly but each time in an *ad hoc* way. This time he got stuck with calculating the

---

[1] *P. Z.'s Note:* In American folklore, this is called the "Census-taker problem."

[2] *Solution.* First, find all possible factorizations of 36 into three factors: $1 \cdot 1 \cdot 36$, $1 \cdot 2 \cdot 18$, $1 \cdot 3 \cdot 12$, $1 \cdot 4 \cdot 9$, $1 \cdot 6 \cdot 6$, $2 \cdot 2 \cdot 9$, $2 \cdot 3 \cdot 6$, and $3 \cdot 3 \cdot 4$. Then find the sums of these factors: $1 + 1 + 36 = 38$, $1 + 2 + 18 = 21$, etc. All these sums prove to be distinct, except for two that sum to 13: $1 + 6 + 6$ and $2 + 2 + 9$. Since the second mathematician said, after having counted the benches, that the information wasn't sufficient we conclude that the sum is in fact equal to 13 (otherwise knowing the sum would have been sufficient). The critical information in the sentence "my elder son is red-haired" is that there *is* an elder son. Thus, the correct answer is $2, 2$ and 9 (there is no elder son in the second version $1, 6, 6$).

difference $\frac{1}{7} - \frac{1}{9}$, and failed completely. But I observed the first hint at the right approach: he tried to represent $\frac{1}{7}$ as $\frac{2}{14}$ or $\frac{3}{21}$, and $\frac{1}{9}$ as $\frac{3}{27}$.

> *As I said earlier, I had the basic idea, but $7 \cdot 9 = 63$ was too big a number to find by trial-and-error. — Dima.*

His math grades are ranging from 2 to 4. At a parents' meeting, the new teacher announced, "Penmanship is now our most important goal."

That was said while discussing mathematics. True, it was a broad vision of penmanship: how many squares to leave empty, where to put a full stop, what words to write with a capital letter, whether to write "Problem 32" or "Problem #32" and so on, endlessly. If I am not mistaken, the official term is "unified orthographic presentation."

Sadly, Dima has lately started to make lots of computational mistakes. There are many reasons: the monotony of classroom math, inflamed adenoids constantly giving him low-grade fevers, a general state of fatigue.

October 25, 1984. We try "regular" lessons.

At Dima's request (I thought about it myself) we decided to have a lesson once a week. Today is our first lesson.

(1) We analyzed the mistake he made while calculating the sum $1+2+\cdots+n$. He came up with two solutions; one was $1 + \cdots + 10 = (1+10) + (2+9) + (3+8) + (4+7) + (5+6) = 5 \cdot 11 = 55$, and the second was $1 + \cdots + 10 = (0+10) + (1+9) + (2+8) + (3+7) + (4+6) + (5+5) = 6 \cdot 10 = 60$.

He said the second solution was wrong "because you should never begin with zero." He was unable to utter anything more reasonable than that (for about a year), always saying it had to do with zero. Perhaps this is a holdover from a poorly understood principle of conservation. I made him write out all the operations systematically. At first it didn't help, but then he saw the mistake.

(2) We did a few problems "with x's." He understands them very poorly. If only I could get this through to the people who spout the nonsense that first-graders can easily handle variables for unknown quantities!

In school, variables are introduced as yet another notation for puzzles or their solutions. Certainly, algebraic notation is very handy for solving puzzles. But first graders don't have the slightest idea that it is. For them, among an enormous swamp of rules for notation it is just another one, apparently devoid of any meaning.

When a puzzle contains two unknown values, Dima doesn't think that they are to be denoted by x and y. Indeed, he protests vigorously: "We don't know this one either, so it's also an x."

For homework, I asked him to read the chapter from Perelman's book *Fun Algebra* on how to construct equations. By the way, I discovered that he has *unlearned* multiplication and addition with carry!

November 6, 1984. Common denominators.

This took place unexpectedly, in the kitchen after dinner. Dima at last grasped the idea of common denominators, and learned how to add and subtract fractions. However, he views the existence of a common denominator as a lucky accident (he finds them by exhaustive search). For homework, I ask him think about why there will always be a common denominator.

November 18, 1984. Another entrance examination problem.

(1) Still doesn't see why there is always a common denominator. Says all kinds of silly things on this subject.

(2) We factored the numbers 48, 216, and 1001 into primes. Dima didn't understand why we should do this. When we got $1001 = 7 \cdot 11 \cdot 13$, I said, "Fascinating, isn't it?"

He asked, bewildered,

"What's fascinating?"

(3) We did several puzzles from Trudnev's book. He did them easily, but with a few mistakes.

(4) I gave him this puzzle: A pupil multiplied two numbers but made a mistake, and got 5 less than it should have been. To check his solution, he divided his "product" by one of the original numbers, and got the quotient 29 with a remainder of 7. What numbers did he multiply?

This is a slightly more complicated version of an entrance-exam problem for the Moscow Construction Engineering School. Dima had no idea how to approach this problem; he tried several things without really thinking. His dullness got on my nerves.

An Olympiad puzzle. The other day I gave Dima a problem from the Novosibirsk Regional Olympiad for students in the 7th–9th years of school: The sum of the ages of the two of us is 35 years. I am twice as old as you were when I was as old as you are now. How old are we?

He solved it the next day. But, as always, by exhaustive search. This is the reason why he failed with the previous problem. Exhaustive search doesn't help there; you have to reason, albeit not deeply.

November 19, 1984.

At lunch Dima solved in five minutes the problem of three fishermen: What is the smallest number of fish there can be if each fisherman, in turn, throws away one fish and then takes one-third of the remaining fishes? The answer was 25. Then I told him about "Dirac's solution" of −2.

November 25, 1984. Divisibility by 3 and infinite series.

(1) Is the following number divisible by 3?

$$101001000100001000001\ldots1\underbrace{00\ldots00}_{300\text{ zeros}}.$$

(It is, because the sum of its digits is 300, i.e., divisible by 3.) At first, Dima was stumped. We were talking, I was counting how many digits the number contained (45,450); then we computed together whether an entire notebook would be sufficient to write it down. We learned how many times 10^{300} is larger than 10^{27}. Then Dima said he would solve the puzzle later, but now he wanted to solve something else, not just sit watching me.

We solved a couple of puzzles from the Ignatiev's book, *The Land of the Clever*. Alla came in and I told her the original puzzle. Just then, Dima had an insight concerning the sum of digits, and he solved this puzzle and then another one, the divisibility of the same number by 9.

(2) Next, is this giant number a perfect square? (It is not, because it is divisible by 3, but not by 9.)

Dima advances the hypothesis that "almost all round numbers[1] are squares." We check it by means of a calculator, it fails. Two questions remain as homework: first, concerning this giant number (is it a square?); and, second, when will 10^n be a square?

(3) From Ignatiev's book, I select the famous puzzle about the fly (with slightly simplified numerical data): The distance between the towns A and B is 300 km. Two cyclists, X and Y, start to ride simultaneously towards each other from the two towns at a speed of 50 km per hour. At the same time, a fly leaves town A at a speed of 100 km per hour, and flies between the cyclists; having reached Y, it flies back to X, then back to Y, again to X, etc., until the cyclists meet. How much distance will the fly cover?

Strange as it seems, Dima solved this puzzle by summing the infinite series. This is how it happened. He undertook a long and intense calculation of how much the fly would cover until it first reached Y, and got 200 km; then he calculated how much it would cover until it reached X, and got $66\frac{2}{3}$ km. Then he found that the distance to second meeting with Y was $22\frac{2}{9}$ km. At this point, he saw that the series would be infinite and exclaimed, "Hey, Dad, it will be infinite!"

"Right you are!"

"So it has no solution?"

"Why shouldn't there be? First, you could think about a more ingenious way of solving it. Second, sometimes it's even possible to sum up an infinite series."

"What do you mean?"

---

[1]*P. Z.'s Note:* A number ending with one or more zeros, i.e., a multiple of ten.

(4) I stepped back from the initial puzzle and wrote the following sum.

$$1 + \frac{1}{2} + \frac{1}{4} + \frac{1}{8} + \frac{1}{16} + \frac{1}{32} + \cdots,$$

explaining that the number of addends is infinite. Then I asked, "What do you think it adds up to?"

Then a strangest thing happened. Without a moment's reflection Dima shrugged his shoulders and said, "Two…"

After a pause, I asked, "Why so?"

"Look, first its two, missing one half. Then its missing a quarter, then an eighth, and it will keep going this way."

In other words, he gave an absolutely correct proof (Figure 131).

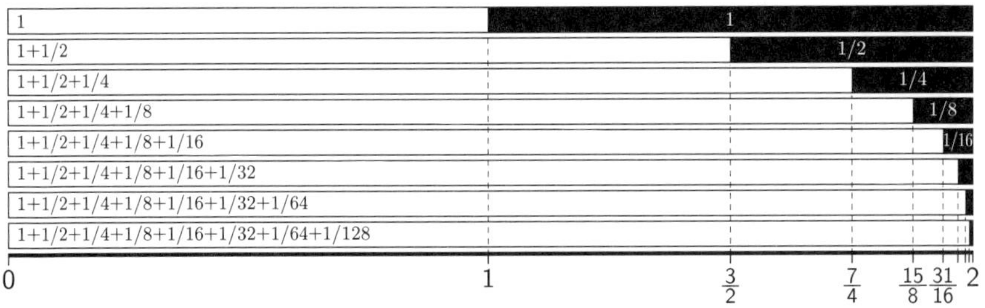

Figure 131.   Summing the infinite series $1 + \frac{1}{2} + \frac{1}{4} + \cdots$. It's quite "visible" that the result is 2, since after each step the distance to 2 is decreased by half; we fall short of 2 by the quantities shown in black.

I agreed with him, repeated his reasoning in greater detail, drawing a picture with adjacent segments of lengths $1, \frac{1}{2}, \frac{1}{4}, \ldots$. More than anything, I tried to make an impression that nothing special had happened though I was excited to the point that my knees were trembling. What if he really is a genius?

My next question was: "And our fly, how much less did it fly each time?"

Dima pondered and said, "Three times less." (That is, the distance was divided by three.)

(I was, of course, giving him leading questions. Dima had not yet guessed on his own that the distance at each step decreased by in same proportion. But after my question, he naturally guessed this was the case, without any proof.) I wrote down the following series:

$$1 + \frac{1}{3} + \frac{1}{9} + \frac{1}{27} + \frac{1}{81} + \cdots,$$

asking, "How much does this add to?"

"Three," answered Dima, as casually as before (clearly reasoning by analogy).

I felt relived. No, not a genius, just a normal bright kid.

I laughed and said I didn't see how it was possible that each addend was smaller and the sum was bigger than in the previous case. Dima first didn't see the point; I explained and he answered, "So what?" However, it made him think and compute, as before, how much was missing from 2 at each step, while I was noting what he was saying: $\frac{2}{3}, \frac{5}{9}, \frac{14}{27}, \ldots$. Soon it became clear that one half was lacking, so the answer was one-and-a-half. I didn't insist on having a proof, though we did draw segments.

> *I think we should have verified that the distance to one-and-a-half was divided by three each time. For a long time I didn't have complete confidence in "one-and-a-half," fearing that it was just a guess. — Dima.*

(5) Back to the fly puzzle.

I asked, "So, what should we now multiply by one and a half?"

Dima was at first completely bewildered. He obviously had forgotten what it was all about. Then he said, "Two hundred kilometers. It will make three hundred kilometers."

"So the answer is. . . ?"

"Three hundred kilometers."

I tell him the "canonical" solution: the cyclists rode for three hours until they met. That means the fly was also flying for three hours, and its speed was 100 km per hour. So she traveled

$$100 \, \text{km/hr} \cdot 3 \, \text{hr} = 300 \, \text{km}.$$

But Dima didn't seem enthralled.

> *I had been racking my brain, inventing things, and then it turned out it was all for nothing; there was a much simpler solution. — Dima.*

I doubted if he had really grasped my solution, and gave him a modified version of the same puzzle with the cyclists' speed equal to 20 and 40 km/hr and the fly traveling at 80 km/hr. It turned out that he had understood it well, since he attempted the correct calculations. But it was already half past nine and he was unable to divide 180 by 20 (he kept getting 8) or to multiply 80 by 5 (he got 450). So we called it a day, though he kept asking me for half an hour why they didn't teach math at school the way I did. How touching, but what a shame! God, if only we could have no school, but just our one session per week!

November 26, 1984.

I discovered that Dima hadn't understood after all, exactly what the sum of an infinite series was, and considered both of his answers as approximate.

December 19, 1984.

Today, after a great number of trials, errors and much confusion Dima has learned at last how to multiply fractions.

December 26, 1984. The Tower of Hanoi.

Somewhere in the middle of the week Dima also learned how to divide fractions.

Our daughter Jane got a version of the Tower of Hanoi for a birthday present. This game is called "Arrangement" and instead of disks it has chips with figures, up to 8 (not up to 5 as in the Hungarian version). The rule is not to put a bigger figure on a smaller one. To my mind, 8 chips are too much, since 255 moves are required to solve the puzzle.

Dima and Pete immediately guessed that it was a modification of the Tower of Hanoi, which stimulated Dima's new interest towards the puzzle. He spent a few days fiddling around with it and finished by announcing he had found the optimal algorithm. However, the formulation proved to be extremely difficult. He didn't know where to begin, which words to choose and only repeated rather hopelessly, "First this one here, then this one here, this one here ..."

The moves he made were completely correct, but it was next to impossible to convert them into words. The algorithm did prove to be optimal. Here it is:

(1) The moves must be made in turn by the smallest chip possible and by another chip;
(2) The move of that other chip is unambiguous since it can't be put on the top of the smallest one;
(3) The moves of the smallest one always go in a cycle.

I talked with Dima about the need for a proof, even though it's very premature; he is nowhere near ready for this. I myself should point out that I never came up with an algorithm myself (I looked it up) nor a proof of its optimality (Vadim Bugaenko provided one after I posed the problem to him).

This semester, Dima and I had a total of six formal sessions, not counting our casual mathematical conversations.

First graders

Here are a few scattered notes about two different first-grade classes. I ran a circle in Dima's class for a semester, and worked for a month in another school, testing an experimental curriculum. If I wrote a journal about these experiences, 95% of its contents would be devoted to the problem of discipline. It is impossible to get anything done in a classroom without establishing a working atmosphere; that is, until the kids stop running, fighting, romping, singing (you name it). How to achieve it, while allowing for creative inquiry, is an enormous enigma; only real virtuosos can accomplish this. I am far from being one of them, so I'll write only about things that I think I have something to say.

What is the origin of talent?

Everyone is fascinated by this question. Did I develop Dima's aptitude for math with our circle, or was he already born gifted and the circle was so successful because of it? I'm inclined toward the latter. The role of the circle was to make him know that mathematics exists as a dynamic, joyful and passionate activity. Another question is how many gifted kids are there, and how often do they miss their vocation and never achieve the life they could have lived. In the first class I worked in, I came across a boy who was distinctly more gifted than Dima, who had no one to develop his capacities before. His name was Gleb and his schoolwork was quite mediocre. I don't know what became of him.[1]

Here are some of my observations from my work with Gleb.

(1) The $\binom{5}{2}$ puzzle (see Chapter 3). Some kids didn't understand the question, others only found 3 or 4 solutions, still others claimed to have found 24–26 solutions, not paying attention to repetitions. Gleb was the only one who found 10 solutions and firmly announced there were no more. (Albeit his explanation was that $5 + 5 = 10$.)

(2) He immediately figured out the trick of summing up invisible numbers (p. 170). His solution, like Dima's, used the table's periodicity, rather than adding up to 20.

(3) He also guessed right away another trick based on the fact that the sum of the numbers on the opposite faces of a die is always equal to seven (p. 173). I will long remember his concentrated gaze while he was studying the dice, looking at what was under, and then his face lit up. . .

It was noteworthy, that when I proclaimed him "champion" for calculating something faster than the others, he confessed he had made a mistake.

What is a puzzle?

After one of the sessions Gleb gave me a puzzle to solve (Figure 132):

"Here is a lake (he draws it). On this side of the lake lives the Old Woman, and on the opposite side lives the Old Man. Reeds grow here, and a cucumber lies there. The Devil lives in the lake and he won't let anyone go by. You can't go around the lake 'cause there's a forest. How can the Old Man go to the Old Woman?"

"Does the Old Man have a boat?"

"No."

"And if he goes round the forest?"

"Hey, he can't!"

I'm thinking. . .

---

[1] My book, after being published, circulated not only in Russia itself but also throughout the Russian-speaking community abroad. Gleb recognized himself in the book and contacted me. He now works at Microsoft Research.

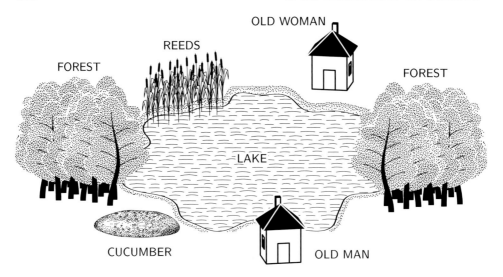

"You give up?"

"Indeed."

"OK! This Devil was very obedient. The Old Man told him, "Devil, Devil, go eat the cucumber!" He did. Then the Old Man said, "Devil, Devil, go mow the reed!" He did. Then the Old Man said, "Devil, your grandchildren are crying and calling you." So the Devil dived under the earth. That made a hole and the water of the lake went down there. So the Old Man went across the bottom of the lake — pitter-patter — and came to the Old Woman."

Should we conclude that kids find the "enrichment" puzzles that we give them to be as meaningful and logical as Gleb's? Is it possible that, to them, no relationship is assumed to exist between the puzzle formulation and its solution: "A puzzle is when they tell you something and then ask a question you don't know how to answer"?

A model pupil.

At one session we did the $\binom{5}{2}$ problem, and at the next one, we tackled $\binom{5}{3}$. I explain why these two puzzles are equivalent. To choose and color two squares out of five is the same as choosing and not coloring three squares out of five. Thus we could have deduced that this puzzle is similar to that of the previous session and say right away that it would have 10 solutions. A boy raises his hand.

"Yes, Alex?"

"I have guessed that this puzzle is similar to the one from the previous session..."

He wasn't at the previous session.

A subtraction problem.

I am teaching at an experimental class with only 18 pupils. I put some beans into a milk bottle and ask the kids to guess how many. Everybody shouts "One hundred!" I say it's not fun; there is no winner.

"Let's each tell me his or her guess, and they must be different! We'll write them on the blackboard and then check."

We note names and guesses on the blackboard. Then we all count the beans together. It will do them no harm to practice counting. The number we get is 49.

"So, who is the winner?"

"Nobody is!"

They mean nobody has given this exact number.

"OK, but who is the closest to this number?"

"Tanya is."

That's correct, Tanya said 52.

"How big was her mistake?"

"Three beans," answers the class.

So far so good. The puzzle is over; we go on to other tasks. About a quarter of an hour later, I give them a subtraction problem: $52 - 49$. The result is staggering: no one got it. No one!

Feel free to interpret this as you wish.

You can touch it!

I'm at the same experimental school, but this time we are in a computer classroom. I have already mentioned the language of *Logo*, specifically adapted for children. By means of very simple commands and programs, they can control the movements of a turtle-robot on the screen. But they can also write text and do many other things. Some of the pupils obviously enjoy working with *Logo*; others are bored and even start wandering about the classroom (discipline!). Suddenly one of these wanderers discovers an old mechanical adding machine forgotten in a closet.

"What's this?"

I say this is an adding machine.

"It can add?"

The fact that computers can add is no surprise for them but here is a mechanical device!

"Can we see it?"

The entire class is no longer at computers: they have surrounded us and watch eagerly. I put 6 on the display and say I am going to add 1. I turn the handle — click-click-click — and the display shows the figure 7.

"Wow!," responds the class.

Now everybody is eager to turn the handle to make the machine make such a cute click and add a unit. Forgotten are dull computers; here you can turn the handle yourself! And I remember a pertinent quotation I recently copied into my notebook, from the essay "Without stereotypes," by the teacher T. Sluzhevskaya (*Yunost* (Youth), #1, 1986):

> ... Another excursion, this time to the zoo with the fourth graders. We stroll along the alleys: predators, monkeys, crocodiles behind glass, an elephant behind bars. The kids swarm about the cages, read the inscriptions; in a word, the learning process is moving along at full speed. Suddenly a boy is missing. I haven't had the time to get frightened when he shoots out from around the corner, red-faced, out of breath, eyes shining.
>
> "Quick, everybody come! You won't believe it!"
>
> What can it be, after all these hippopotamuses and pythons?
>
> "There is a horse, and you can touch it!" shouts the boy.
>
> In a moment there is nobody in front of the elephant, the whole crowd rushes round the corner. Indeed, there is an old chestnut mare with a sagging belly, a draft horse that delivers feed in a cart. And you can pet her, and give her a bunch of grass that she takes politely with her soft lips...

What an amazing story! I could make it an epigraph to this book.

Children outdoors (taken in 1980). From left to right:
Galya (a daughter of our friends, who now works for
Google), and then four participants of the circle: Dima,
Pete, Andy, and Gene.

Our daughter Jane puts Dienes blocks into the box.

Dima helps Jane. Jane is two years old, Dima is six.

One of our sessions. From left to right: Dima, Pete, Gene.

One of our sessions. From left to right: Dima, Pete, Gene.

One of our sessions. From left to right: Dima, Pete, Gene.

One of our sessions. From left to right: Dima, Pete, Gene.

Chapter 9

The Girls' Math Circle, Year One

Introduction

Our new circle has three participants: my daughter Jane, and two of her friends, Sandy and Dinah. The circle started in January 1984. At this time, Jane was 4, Sandy 4 years and 8 months, and Dinah was 5 years and 3 months old.

The most frequently asked questions

I am often asked if there was any profound meaning in the fact that my first circle was all boys and the second was all girls. No, there was none. That's just how it happened. I had to put Dima with his friends, and then did the same with Jane. It was also convenient that Dima and Pete, both had little sisters, Jane and Sandy, who were almost the same age. So this is how it was: "elder boys" and "younger girls." The kids were friends, and by and by their parents also became friends.

Another frequent question was whether the girls' circle was different from that of the boys? Indeed, it was. But a circle with other boys would have also been different. Kids have varied personalities and interests, and this can readily explain the difference. I can't say whether there is a gender difference; to examine this issue, we'd need much broader experience and a serious investigation.

The boys' circle took place over four years and included about 80 sessions, while only 20 sessions were held with the girls. (More precisely, I only recorded notes on 20 math circle sessions; later Jane took computer lessons with me at the Children's Computer Club and in the Pereslavl' summer camp.) Why? Did we treat the mathematical education of the girls less seriously than that of the boys?

I don't know whether you believe me or not; anyway, I can only say what I feel I have to say. An honest answer to this question is, "No." There are several reasons.

First, I was undoubtedly very much stimulated by Dima's passionate interest to math, as well as his above-average talent; as to Jane, her interest in math was non-existent. But I would say this reason accounted for no more than 20% among other ones. The most important reason was that *perestroika* had begun. As events around me started spinning around frantically, so too did my life. I vividly remember going home at 4 AM with my friend, the biologist Boris Berenfeld, after another prolonged discussion of future school reforms, while thinking, with dread, that I have to get up at half past six to go to work. There's a limit to human strength...

One more fussy question: Why did I even try a math circle with Jane, if she wasn't interested in math?

Shame on you, dear reader, for asking this question!

I am not kidding. For any child, communication with parents is absolutely vital. Even a negative communication like scolding or punishment is better than no communication, that's why kids often provoke it if they are unable to attract parents' attention otherwise. More often than not, this communication takes an impersonal, businesslike form with a slight negative nuance: "Go wash your hands. It's time to go to bed, you can't sit in front of the TV all night long. Have you prepared your schoolbag for tomorrow morning? Look, he has a fever again!" The time when adults, peasants or artisans, made kids participate in their work is long gone. The only thing a contemporary child knows about his parents' job is that it's a place where they go in the morning and come back from in the evening. Another thing they know is that it's tiresome, "Leave Dad alone, he is tired after work." Moments of comprehensive communication with kids, like common participation in a meaningful activity, are extremely rare and extremely valuable. This is what happened when I started the circle with Jane. She was delighted, not because it was math, but because Dad was devoting his time and attention to teach her a serious matter that he had earlier taught to her elder brother.

By the way, Dima's interest in math shouldn't be exaggerated; he was much more enthusiastic about activities organized by Gene's father Boris. Led by him, the boys crossed a ravine using a rope, "tracked deer," navigated with a map, dug caves to hide in, and so on. I think Boris was carried away by the general atmosphere of contributing to the kids' education: I was teaching math, Alla taught English, Andy's mother taught music, etc.

But why not choosing another subject that would correspond more to Jane's aptitudes? The reason is, I didn't have any other subject! I was doing what I loved to do and what I knew how to teach. Jane was more than anything, crazy about drawing (see below), but she already belonged to a group guided by the remarkable artist and teacher Nadezhda Stolpovskaya. So I was free to wash my hands and feel my parent's duty to be fulfilled: the child's needs are taken care of, and I am legitimately entitled "to be tired after work."

Still, we decided to set up a circle also for Jane. And trust me, the enjoyment was mutual.

Cast of characters

Dinah has a quiet and stable personality with a slightly "draggy" side, but this was an asset in our sessions. With Jane and Sandy, I am entitled to have problems. Both girls have explosive temperaments, to put it mildly. Their relationship is largely based on passions and emotions. One minute they are the best friends in the world, then suddenly a terrible dispute risks ending their friendship forever! Whereupon they burst into tears, embrace each other or find shelter in Mom's arms, swear eternal love and behave like angels, for about half an hour.

In a word, though I drew on a lot of experience — with boys — here I came across new difficulties, or sometimes the same kind, but much more pronounced.

There was another candidate for our circle, a girl named Katya, but on second thought I decided not to take her: first she was even older than Dinah, that is, almost two years older than Jane; second, she was quite mathematically gifted, so Jane might have felt left out in such a circle.

Jane and her drawings (a long digression)

Let me tell you a little more about Jane.

It's really amazing how children from the same family can be different! The initial conditions seem to be similar, the same is true of education, as well as of parents' influence. I know of course that the first child grows up alone in the company of adults while the second one has another elder family member, apart from the parents. This fact could probably account for certain traits of character. But I am unable to see how it can account for specific aptitudes and interests, which is our chief preoccupation in this book. Largely anticipating and looking back from today's perspective I can assert that both Dima and Jane have grown up to be good persons. But this is probably the only thing they have in common.

We have a snapshot of Jane at the age of 15 months: she is drawing, holding a magic marker exactly as they teach at school to hold a pen. It would be hard to believe without this documentation.

I don't remember at what age she began to draw, I didn't pay much attention to it. All the kids scribble something. But once I glanced at one of her scribbles (she was 3), and got a shock of my life. On a sheet of yellowish spotty paper of approximately 6 inches the whole vertical space was occupied by a long leg ending with a foot below and going away to infinity above. That was a leg of an adult. Also from above came a hand, at which held a kid occupying the rest of the sheet. Or else, there was a kid and an adult's leg at his side. The drawing itself wasn't really a masterpiece, but its composition was striking!

From this time on we (Alla and me) paid more attention to these activities. I couldn't participate, as I am no artist. However, Alla is quite handy with a pencil. But no participation was necessary, at least not literally.

Imagine a child of 5 who draws for *six hours, non-stop*, besides short bathroom breaks. Naturally, the paper supply at home was exhausted almost right away. There were no real shortages for ordinary copy-books but they were not always on sale. You had to be there at the right moment to buy them. Then I started to bring home used computer printer paper. Those who are my age probably remember these broad perforated rolls of paper. The paper was so thin that pen marks bled through to the other side. But we had no other solution, the more so that soon these rolls were not enough either. Sometimes she used old newspapers: their margins rapidly became animated by episodes of the life of fictitious characters. Once we took away her paper, for her bedtime was overdue, but there was a newspaper on the table with a picture from an exposition of wooden ready-built houses. In no time at all the house was decorated with tiny figures playing in the yard, others were looking out of the windows, still others hammering on the roof.

It is not the quality of drawings that I am discussing here, though their expressiveness increased every day. Skaters with flowing scarves, piano-players at pianos, cows in the pasture; nothing posed problems for the artist. And more and more often, you could guess the characters if you knew them. We still have a drawing on the wall of our kitchen: Dima talking about something and waving his hands energetically and Jane looking at him in a skeptical but benevolent manner. Believe me, she managed to convey not only the physical resemblance but even the personalities of her subjects.

The most important feature, however, was the constant drive, the relentless need to draw and draw, time and again, without rest. We were watching this miracle called to life without the slightest stimulation from out part. We were walking on tiptoes, afraid to interrupt it. We didn't know what would happen later: would she preserve this drive to draw, or lose it as unexpectedly as she got it? And what are we to do in the second case? Nag the child that she must draw at least half an hour every day? ("OK, then, 20 minutes, lazybones." And to hear from her ten minutes later, "Dad, how much longer?" or something of the sort. I know this won't do, but I don't know what I should do.) It's amazing how helpless we are in front of a natural phenomenon, because this is exactly what it was: a natural phenomenon.

I am sure the reader is anticipating one of the two possible outcomes: "nothing of the sort happened" or "and this is exactly what happened." But in life things often take an unpredictable turn and what happened was a third possible outcome. Indeed, Jane started to draw much less, as soon as she learned to write. Her passion for drawing proved to be derived from another passion, namely, story-telling. Drawing was, for her, a tool for recording her stories, and as soon as she discovered another, more suitable tool for doing so, she switched over to it.

Had we been more perceptive, we would have long ago guessed what was going on. Jane told stories all the time, not only when she was drawing. During summer walks in the country, her stories used to last for hours on end,

Alla being the principal target. She confessed that sometimes she was close to fainting, because Jane instantly noticed when she wasn't paying attention, and would demand it immediately. We were often entrusted with certain lines and had to pronounce them, cued by Jane. I felt somehow that such a mechanical participation lacked interest and ventured to contribute my own lines into the story. Every such contribution was, however, immediately followed by a punishment which I found more severe than the crime.

One more amazing thing to say concerning Jane's drawings. Once, when she was already an adult, she started to sort out her old drawings (we brought a small portion of them, about half a suitcase, to France). It turned out that she remembered the stories she had composed at the age of 4 perfectly well and could tell them now looking at the drawings.

Having learned how to write, Jane began assimilating various genres and styles of writing. She learned there was a genre of memoirs, and started to write memoirs. We read a Schiller drama out loud, and she wrote a Schiller-style drama. Of course, she composed stories too. A bit later she wrote a telephone conversation with three actors (herself, her friend and a meddling elder brother). Both Dima and Jane had English lessons with Alla, and with her scarce English vocabulary she wrote a story in English. The most hilarious episode was when by chance she discovered a textbook of Japanese on the shelves. After our explanation that in addition to ideographs, the Japanese also have two syllabic alphabets, she composed a story (actually it was in Russian rather than in Japanese, as the majority of its vocabulary consisted of onomatopoetic words like "mama" or "moo") and recorded it by means of such an alphabet. Our neighbor's daughter Anya Shubina who was studying Japanese, being shown the text, had a side-splitting fit of laughter. But Jane's interest in Japanese was short-lived, since its expressive means were quickly exhausted.

When Jane was about 11 years old, she and her friend Masha filled a thick writing book with a story symbolically entitled *A Childhood Summer*. The title was symbolic because a crucial moment was approaching, partially anticipated by the authors, the creative crisis when childhood would soon be over and they would no longer be able to write in a childish and care-free manner. For Jane, this difficult moment coincided with the passage to another language.

The last "childhood" episode I will cite occurred in France. Jane was 12 and studying in a French junior high in a language she knew nothing about six months earlier. Her homework assignment was to compose a tale in the style of Marcel Aymé. Jane handed in such a delightful text that, they say, her tale was read out loud in the teachers' common room. She got 17 out of 20 in spite of numerous errors of orthography.

To appreciate this fact, one should know that French system of grading is a scale ranging from 0 to 20. While it is possible to get 20 in math (it suffices to solve all the exercises correctly), in the humanities, the tradition is not to give a grade higher than 16. When Alla was teaching at the Slavic department of the university, she twice gave a 20 for on the oral conversation exam to two students of Russian origin.

The head of the department gently rebuked her saying, "You know, we never give a score above 16."

"But look, Catherine, these girls are Russian, they speak Russian as well as I do. That was an oral conversation exam!"

"All the same, we never give scores above 16."

In fact they do, if they want to emphasize that something extraordinary has happened.

I think I must stop here if I am not going to transform this book into Jane's biography. I am asking myself why I decided to write about that at all. I think I know the answer: to do her justice. Jane's made modest progress in math. "There were two kids in the family, one very bright and the other mediocre" seems to be the unavoidable conclusion for the reader of this book. But that's false and insulting. The truth is that there were two kids in the family, one gifted in math and the other in drawing and story-telling. In fact I should have written a similar passage about every one of my pupils. Unfortunately, I don't know them well enough to do it.

Once, a few years ago, I saw a video of Sandy, now a young girl, speaking English. I was stunned. Our children also speak English fluently, and after so many years of living abroad it's not something that could amaze me. But when they speak English you can see right away that they are not native speakers. Sandy was speaking as a native American. How could she achieve such a degree of fluency without living there since childhood? This begs another question concerning gifted persons that can't be answered in a rational way.

That's why I repeatedly appeal to you, dear reader, *please bear in mind that I am speaking here of one small facet of extremely rich and versatile personalities.*

Back to math

Before starting the circle, i.e., before she was 4, I did math with Jane only once, for a short period of time, when she was 2. I mentioned it briefly on p. 118. Here is the entry of January 23, 1982:

> The session has an unexpected sequel. I have not yet put the blocks away when our little daughter Jane comes in from a walk and immediately asks to play with them. I give her an age-appropriate assignment (she is 25 months old): I toss out all the shapes from the box and suggest that she put them back.

I am not sure I ever explained what the box for the Dienes blocks looks like. Recall that there are 8 pieces of each shape, half with holes and half without, and there were two compartments for each shape in the box. The pieces fit in their respective compartments.

Jane gets into it enthusiastically. At first, she shoves the pieces in any old way, trying to force big squares into the small triangular compartment. Sometimes she'll put a piece into the right place, but turned the wrong way, so she chooses a different space. Each time she correctly matches a piece with its resting place, I exclaim "Woo!" to encourage her.

When she puts a small circle into a big round compartment — it must be right since the piece went in! — I'm silent. Gradually she learns which placements are right and which are wrong and starts to say "Woo!" herself.

She explains that she is putting the pieces to bed. Our activity lasts for an hour and we have time to put the pieces to bed three times. Jane has learned to distinguish pieces of the same shape and size, but not how to recognize the proper compartment for a piece. She took, for example, a big circle and shoved it into all the compartments in a row. As soon as the right one was found, she selected all the big circles from the pile of pieces and put them into this compartment. For a while it went smoothly: she could always put five pieces into the same space (even if it was meant for four). But the sixth circle wouldn't go in, forcing her to change course in a surprising way.

Jane's method showed that she had already formed an idea of shape "conservation" but not of number conservation. (The first is more surprising than the second, for number conservation normally occurs between the ages of five and seven, while shape conservation, according to Piaget, happens after two.) Jane knew that since other circles fit, the next one would as well. So she had to remove out all the circular pieces, put the newest one on the bottom and then stack the remaining ones on top (they had already proved their ability to go in, so they would go in again). Since she couldn't take the pieces out by herself, she had to ask me, "Please, Dad, pull 'em out."

She would repeat the same procedure several times and after a number of failures she would start to look for another compartment that could welcome the "extra" piece. If she succeeded, the big circles were OK (though sometimes she tried to extract all the big circles from the previous compartment and put them into the new one, but I lost patience and stopped her).

Towards the end of our game, Dima came back inside and made his contribution to the learning process. Basically, he pestered her, saying she shouldn't put five pieces into one space and three into another one. Or nagged her to separate the pieces with and without holes. I managed to get him to let her do as she pleased and avoided a fight.

This went on, with a few variations, for some time. Jane enjoyed the game immensely, often asked me to play it and could easily spend an hour or more at it. Then she started to play in my absence and sometimes lost pieces. I usually found them, but once after I searched for an hour, a piece was still missing. I had to hide the box and didn't give it to her any more. I know it was a nasty thing to do but where on earth would I find another one?

[Summer 2005; I am finishing this book. Jane notices the Dienes blocks on my desk. She is 25 now but she says every time she thinks about them, her heart leaps with delight.]

During the next two years, our mathematical studies were limited to two activities. We enjoyed reading out loud from *The Adventures of Cubarik and Tomatik, or Merry Math*. Jane was crazy about this book, not so much for the math as for the story and illustrations. She considered the puzzles in the book to be unavoidable chores to do in exchange for fun. We tried to teach her to count beyond "two." We encouraged her by awarding her as many sugar-coated hazelnuts as the number she would arrive at without errors. Eventually this strategy paid off, somewhat.

The following anecdote shows how counting is perceived as purely formal at this age. One time, having correctly counted up to "seven, eight, ..." Jane suddenly stopped and said,

"But seven and eight is the same thing, isn't it, Dad?"[1]

Since then I use this question as a touchstone. When I meet a kid who is supposed to know how to count I ask him, "Seven and eight is the same thing, right?"

If he doesn't agree, that means he indeed can count. (Once, however, I came across an intermediate case: a kid very seriously told me that seven and eight was by no means the same thing, but seventeen and eighteen were.)

Session 1. Piaget's phenomena, again

Thursday, January 5, 1984, 10:35–11:15.
Jane, Sandy, Dinah.

Introduction.

I show the girls my little bell and explain that at school every lesson is preceded and concluded by ringing a bell, and we'll do the same at our circle. I throw in a heap of well-meaning words as to how everybody should behave and be friendly and listen to what I say and then it will be fun and so on and so forth. (Jumping ahead, I can tell you that the girls behaved perfectly.) Now, while I speak, they listen seriously and attentively, enviously eying the bell.

Activity 1. Which soldiers are there more of, yellow or red?

I start to make a row of red plastic pawn-shaped pieces ("soldiers").

"I know!" shouts Dinah, "We'll be counting!"

---

[1] In Russian, the words for 7 and 8 are phonetically close: семь (sem') and восемь (vosem').

The others join in chorus asserting they, too, know how to count. I ask Dinah to count the soldiers: we get nine. Then Sandy counts them.

I remark, "Look, Sandy, you started from the other end."

"Because it's closer."

"But how come you've got nine too?"

"Because I counted", declares Sandy.

Then comes Jane's turn. She also counts: one, two, three, four, five, six, seven, seventeen, nine. Also nine!

I make a parallel row of yellow soldiers.

"Are there more red or yellow soldiers?"

"Neither is more, equal."

"But if they start to fight, who will win?"

"Nobody will!"

I move apart the yellow row so that it becomes longer than the red one (Figure 133).

Figure 133.   Are there more yellow or more red soldiers?

"And now, which soldiers are there more of?"

"The yellow ones."

"So who will win if they start to fight?"

"The yellow ones!"

"Of course, those who are more numerous win, don't they?"

"Yes!"

"Sandy, take away a few yellow soldiers so that there remain as many as red ones."

Sandy picks up two "extra" soldiers and we put them into the box.

"Now which ones are there more of?"

"Neither!"

I move apart the yellow row again. Again yellow soldiers are more numerous and they will win the fight. We count the soldiers: there are 9 red ones and 7 yellow ones, but still yellow ones are more numerous. I ask Jane to take away yellow soldiers to make the number equal to the red ones: she takes away one soldier.

The procedure is reiterated a couple of times; finally we have a row of 9 red soldiers and the opposite row of 2 yellow ones. Dinah and Sandy keep asserting their number is equal but Jane suddenly won't have it,

"No, there are less yellow soldiers."

"Why?"

She points out the empty space between two yellow chips,

"Because there is nothing here."

Sandy gives her very enthusiastic support, Dinah keeps silent, embarrassed: she is a very polite girl and doesn't know how she should respond not to spoil the game.

[Recall Dima's commentary on p. 17: Dad didn't say otherwise, so it should be correct.]

I exclaim heatedly, "But you've just said there were more yellow ones and now you say there's less!"

Sandy answers in an equally heated way. I am unable to quote her literally, but the idea is that what they said earlier was correct *then*, and what they say now is correct *now*. She hasn't learned that mathematical assertions that were true yesterday are also true today, so she doesn't see any contradiction.

"What shall we do now?"

By way of an answer, Jane picks up the yellow soldiers earlier relegated to the box and puts them back into the row; once again we have nine of each color.

"Who will win the fight now?"

"Nobody will."

I say, "Well, if this is so, there is no point in fighting, they just go back home peacefully", and I collect the soldiers and put them into the box.

Activity 2. Soldiers on stools

From another box, I take 11 plastic game pieces and 10 counters. The game pieces are soldiers (why soldiers? why the military bias? I'm not trying to cater to boys any more...) and the counters are stools. I ask the girls to give the soldiers seats. They do it, but one soldier remains without a stool.

I suggest they try another way of seating them, so that every soldier has a seat. For instance, put all the red soldiers on red stools, green soldiers on white stools, etc. The girls willingly get to work, but unfortunately, once again there is one soldier too many. I make other suggestions, but nothing seems to work.

"How come every time there's one soldier too many?"

"Because he hasn't got a seat."

"But how can we seat them so that he also would have a place?"

"No way!"

"Really no way?"

"Nope!"

"OK, let's try in another way!"

I make a new suggestion — big soldiers seated on white and yellow stools, and the rest on the remaining ones — and meanwhile steal a soldier and pocket it.

This time we did it! The girls are happy, but only Dinah looks suspicious and regards the stools and the soldiers with a slightly puzzled air. I am ready to pass on to another assignment when she says,

"What if we do the way it was before?"

"You remember how it was?"

Dinah tries to explain, a bit shakily, how the counters and chips were positioned before.

"OK, let's do it that way."

While we are busy moving chips I sneak the stolen soldier back on the table, and there is again a soldier without a seat!

Dinah is totally bewildered and tries to seat two soldiers on one stool. But at this moment Sandy denounces me,

"I know, Sasha has just hid a stool, that's all!"

Curiously she didn't notice anything when I made the trick the first time (stole a soldier). I suspect this is because that problem was happily solved. But now, when everything has already been OK and all of a sudden we are again in a blind alley, there is obviously something fishy, so my second cheating looks suspicious. Of course I could fake righteous indignation and declare my innocence — indeed, I put the stolen soldier back! — but that would be rather shabby.

Activity 3. Odd one out.

I show the girls the following sets of pictures:

(1) A hat, a fur coat, an overcoat, a mushroom (Sandy);
(2) A dog, a cat, a monkey, a balance scale (Sandy);
(3) A sheep, a goat, a cow, a spool of thread (Jane);
(4) A watering-can, a barrel, a bucket, a fence (Dinah);
(5) An Indian, a fireman, a knife-grinder, a giraffe (Sandy);
(6) A heron, an owl, a crane, a squirrel (Jane);
(7) A beetle, a butterfly, wasps, a vase (Dinah);
(8) A rabbit, a dog, a hedgehog, a pillow (Sandy).

The first two sets were shown to everybody but Sandy answers first, and so quickly that the others seemed not to have time to even see what was on the cards, let alone thinking about it. Also, Sandy gives correct explanations. To give the others a chance, we go in turn. Jane is the next one. Just in case, I decide to give her a simple set, the third one, exactly analogous to the second one. Jane answers correctly (the spool, or as she says, the bundle is odd) but when I ask why she says,

"Because it's not a lamb, a goat or a cow."

With the help of my leading questions and Sandy prompting (that they are all alive) we manage to extract from her the idea of the sheep, goat and cow being animals, and the spool not being an animal. She gives the correct answer for the next set saying that a heron, an owl and a crane are all birds while a squirrel isn't a bird.

All the remaining answers are correct. Only once Dinah, having given the correct solution to set 4 (the fence is odd) tries to form Piaget's "figural collection," i.e. an illogical classification: she says that we can water a fence from a watering-can and from a bucket.

The final set is for everyone, and again Sandy is the first to answer. After each set I ask standard questions, like: "Can we also wear a mushroom? Is a vase an insect?" With the boys this strategy used to produce roars of laughter, while the girls for some reason respond more calmly; only when I ask if it is possible to sleep on a hedgehog, do they react more emotionally.

Activity 4. Mirror symmetry.

I make a straight line of pegs in the middle of the pegboard and call it "a mirror." Then I lay out multicolor shapes to the left or to the right from it; the assignment is to lay out a similar symmetrical shape on the opposite side of the "mirror." Having done that, we check with a real mirror whether these two shapes coincide. To set an example, I make the first shape myself. Jane watches and says, sad-faced,

"I will not be able to do that."

Indeed, when her turn comes, she fails completely, even though I made a very simple shape for her. She is only able to manage after Dinah and I help. In contrast, Dinah gets it immediately, and even asked me not to show her; she wants to do it alone. Her sure and correct actions and the way she counts the number of pegs inspires confidence.

Sandy almost gets us into a conflict. She looks distracted, and suddenly asks, pointing to the bell, "May I ring it?"

I promise I'll let her and suggest she watches Jane's performance. To which she announces that she is not going to watch, as she can do everything herself, and walks away from the table. However, when her turn comes, she fails. Dinah rushes to help her, as she has done with Jane, but Sandy starts screaming and pushes her back. [I wonder why I had the impression that the girls behaved irreproachably. Perhaps I had feared it would be much worse?] Nevertheless we manage to placate everyone, and even solve the puzzle.

Conclusion.

I have a hard time ending the pegboard activities, as the girls want to go on. Then comes the bustle of getting everyone's coats on, interrupted by telephone calls. In the middle of all this, Sandy suddenly comes up to me and says, "I know, this isn't mathematics at all!"

"What is it, then?"

"Just playing with dad, that's all."

I do my best to persuade her that all this is very serious mathematics.

Outside, Dima and Pete rush to intercept the girls and eagerly ask them what they were doing (both wanted to be present at out lessons; I might have allowed one of them but both would be too much for me). Jane shouts gleefully, "We put soldiers on stools!"

"Aha, I see," pronounced Dima sagely.

. . .

Almost all of these puzzles have been described earlier. Should I avoid this repetition below?

After some hesitation, I decide that repetition is OK. The puzzles are the same, but kids' reactions are not. Besides, the kids are different.

Session 2. Princes and princesses

> Thursday, February 9, 1984, 10:35–11:10.
> Jane, Sandy, Dinah.

As it often happens, our circle, just started, takes a month-long break. First, it's flu, then I have a conference in Voronezh. The next session is five weeks later.

Compared with the boys, the girls seemed more enthusiastic about their first session. Jane and Sandy keep asking when the next session will take place and shout "Hooray" when it is finally announced. As to Dinah, her reaction surpasses all possible expectations. When asked what she liked most of all during her New Year holidays (tree decoration, meeting Grandfather Frost, theaters, walks in the woods, etc.), she firmly asserted that her favorite thing was our session (which was not even one of the choices).

Activity 1. A fairy tale.

I place two big green chips on the table, a king and a queen. Once upon a time, they had a great ball in their palace, and invited many princes (red chips) and princesses (yellow chips). There were many guests and everybody was having fun.

"I wonder," said the queen at one point, "who are there more of, princes or princesses?"

She wanted to count them but it was impossible, because they were all walking to and fro and some of them even left the ballroom. (Dinah tries to count the chips but I make everyone laugh by moving them around, taking some of them away, etc.) Then the king had an idea. He asked the orchestra to play a dance. The princes started to invite the princesses (we put red and yellow chips in couples). There was one extra prince, but he wasn't sad at all. He danced alone and was very happy. Without waiting for my question the girls say there were more princes than princesses.

After the dance they sat down to table. (We arrange the chips in a long oval and put in front of each a "plate," red for princes, yellow for princesses.)

However, the food wasn't ready yet. The cook wanted to make a cake for each princess and an ice-cream for each prince. But he didn't know how many portions there should be, because he didn't know the exact number of princes and princesses. Since there was no food, the guests decided to go and walk in the garden. (We remove all the chips leaving only the "cook," a big green chip but thicker than that of the king and the queen, and "plates.")

What shall the poor cook do? He wanted to count princes and princesses but they have left. How is it possible to count then now?

Dinah starts immediately to count the red plates and gets 11. Then Jane does the same. At first, the two processes, pointing with a finger and announcing a number, go together, but after a while they diverge, so that the resulting number of plates is "fourteen-fifteen." (This is not an adult approximation like "about 14–15" but rather a composite name like "Anna-Maria." Jane doesn't yet know that the size of a group of objects can only be denoted by one number. Also, 14 and 15 are "the same thing," much like 7 and 8.) Then comes Sandy's turn and she also gets 11.

I tell Jane, "Look, both of your pals have got 11. Try to count so as to get 11 as well."

Very obediently, she recounts, but again gets 14–15. I have to put up with it.

Then we count yellow plates and I say the cook was very clever, for he guessed that there were as many plates as princesses, so he was able to count the plates instead of princesses. The cook made 10 cakes and 11 ice creams. The treats were devoured and the guests went to bed (into the box). And they lived happily ever after.

Activity 2. Odd one out.

As at the last session, I give the girls sets of four pictures. Each gets two sets. They all give correct answers but the explanations aren't always correct. For instance, Jane says that in her set (a pigeon, a hedgehog, a dog, and a teapot), the teapot is odd "because it doesn't fly, or prick, or bark." I demand that they think of one word applicable to the three objects (pigeons, hedgehogs and dogs are alive, unlike teapots).

Then I say, "We four are sitting at this table. If we were on pictures, who would be the odd one?"

Dinah says it would be me, as they are children and I am not. Suddenly Jane protests and says that it is Dinah and herself who are odd as Sandy and I could be called by one word "Sasha."[1] I have to agree with her, remarking that if we were to find two odd persons, her answer would be correct; otherwise it's Dinah who is right.

---

[1]*P. Z.'s Note:* Recall (p. xiii) that Sandy's "real" name is Aleksandra, which can also have the same nickname — "Sasha" — as its male counterpart.

Activity 3. Symmetry.

We repeat the activity from last time. This time all three, Jane included, manage perfectly well. Jane keeps talking under her breath while others work,

"OK, don't forget the little blue one... Oops, not here; here! Good!", etc.

It's not the first time that I come across this enigmatic phenomenon but every time it stuns me. A true miracle of nature, indeed! Just a month ago, Jane was completely unable to do this activity. In the interim, there was no private coaching whatsoever. The only thing that changed is that she has become one month older. And voilà, now she can do it all by herself! Who knows what little wheels were turning in her head, what new links were forming.

Dinah, having finished her work, says, "Only please let's do it again!"

I suggest instead that the girls give me assignments. They agree happily, and I solve three symmetry puzzles. Sometimes I "make mistakes," but they correct me immediately.

Pictures.

At the end, I show them pictures with symmetrical patterns from Hermann Weyl's *Symmetry* and from a collection of papers *Patterns of Symmetry*. They like the pictures, but perforated cards I use as bookmarks are a bigger hit. Sandy asks permission to take them home. Dinah wants to, also, but Galya (her mother) reminds her that her dad is a programmer and at home they have these cards galore. A quarrel breaks out, then sharing takes place, and the pictures are forgotten.

This is the end of the session. Jane rings the bell (next time it will be Dina's turn). It takes us a good ten minutes to tear Sandy and Dinah from the pegboard and send them outdoors. (Of course it is the parents' job, not mine.) As soon as they are gone, Jane and Dima monopolize the pegboard and rapidly fill in the entire surface.

Session 3. How many differences?

> Monday, February 20, 1984, 16:00–16:45.
> Jane, Sandy, Dinah.

The salient feature of this session is that I am completely unprepared for it. I've moved all three of my circles (with the boys, with the girls, and at Dima's school) to Monday (this is my "library day" at work). Therefore I don't have time to prepare anything on Monday itself. For the last three days, I was busy checking the proofs of a joint paper with Misha Shubin (as is often the case, it should have been finished "yesterday"). Consequently, the session was poorly prepared and isn't really a success.

Activity 1. Odd one out.

I don't even have time to get the cards out of the box, but this turns out to
my advantage. I suggest that the girls pick the sets like in a lottery, and all
the three solve their puzzles at the same time. Jane still gives the same kind
of explanation. About her set (cabbage, cucumbers, spinach, water faucet),
she says that the faucet is odd "'cause it's not cabbage, cucumber or leaves."
I suggest that the cabbage might be odd since it's not cucumbers, leaves or a
faucet. Or, for that matter, cucumbers might be odd for the similar reason.
In answer to my sneering Jane says gloomily, "No, it's the tap which is odd."

I think I've come across a very peculiar stage of development: Jane always gives correct answers but can't explain them. Younger kids' answers
are guesses as they don't really understand the meaning of the puzzle. Older
children (like Sandy and Dinah) are already poised to give correct explanations. Jane is in between.

Activity 2. All are odd, in turn.

I take out my favorite set of four geometrical objects, each of which can
become the odd one: My set consists of three squares and one triangle; or
three shapes without a hole, and one with a hole; or three red shapes and
one green shape; or three small objects and one big one (Figure 134).

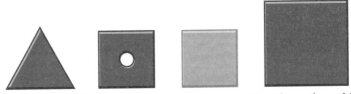

Figure 134.   Each of the shapes can be considered as the odd one,
depending on one's point of view.

The girls' points of view diverge immediately. For Jane, the odd one
has a hole, while Sandy and Dinah are inclined to choose the triangle. I
propose a different odd one, but the girls are adamant and each shouts her
opinion. I have to employ a ruse and propose "fair play," that is, that every
object becomes odd in its turn. This proposal is accepted. Curiously, they
have trouble explaining why the green object is odd; the same is true below
in the next activity; they just don't see the difference in color. I thought
that would be the first feature they would notice! Anyway, all the four
explanations are eventually discovered.

Activity 3. How many "differences"?

I take four Dienes blocks and ask again to find the odd one. I must say
that I chose my set poorly, for there are two shapes that are plausibly odd
ones (i.e., the puzzle has two correct solutions). That starts an argument.

Also, I think they are tired of this type of puzzle. I start with lengthy reasoning about features (color, shape, size, etc). It's boring, and the girls look around restlessly. Then I start to talk nonsense. I put a big red square on the table and ask them to place, next to it, the figure it most resembles. At first there's no problem: four big squares without holes are placed side by side. Then it becomes obvious that either the girls don't understand the assignment or they have forgotten the original question. They start constructing a small hut on wheels, a triangle above, circles below. I try to make them put figures in a line, stammering about the "wrong solution," to no avail. I am more and more vexed with myself for not being prepared, which only contributes to the general mood.

As a last resort I take two figures differing by only one attribute, and ask them to indicate the difference. This is done. The next two figures differ by three attributes. I ask how many differences there are. The girls see only one; for the second attribute, the only thing they can say is that the figures "don't resemble each other." After a little reflection, they manage to find two more differences. As I have mentioned above, the most difficult feature to discover is color. I praise the girls. Things seem to be working out. The next two shapes differ by four attributes. The first difference is discovered by Dinah, the second one by Jane. I ask Sandy, and she stands up and becomes red-faced with effort, but fails to discover any difference.

"Think, think," I say to everybody. Suddenly Jane discovers the third difference, and right after, the forth one. I praise her, and start expounding about just how many differences there are—Four! Imagine that!—enumerating them, getting so carried away that I fail to notice that Sandy is pouting.

Katya (her mother) asks her, "Sanechka, what's wrong?"

All of a sudden she starts to blubber and screams at the top of her lungs, "It was me-e-e who was supposed to find it!"

Everyone tries their best to console her, but it only encourages her. She sobs more piteously. Demagogy comes to the rescue. I say, "Sandy, how many people are sitting around the table?"

"Thre-e-e!"

"How come three? Who is not a human being here?"

"Fo-u-ur!"

"Right! You see: four people; four differences, each has a difference of her own! It all works out fairly."

By this moment she has forgotten that she personally had not discovered a difference of her own, and the storm calms down.

Activity 4. Symmetry with respect to a diagonal.

I make the symmetry puzzle more complicated by choosing a diagonal as a symmetry axis. I was not sure in advance it would work, so we start with problems that the girls give to me. It turns out, however, that they are quite at ease with this new idea, so that I allow myself to make a mistake, which Sandy corrects with a triumphant howl.

Then I give them problems, and they do them fairly well. As usual, when we play with the pegboard, it's next to impossible to take it away from them.

A Japanese top.

For lack of other things, I show them my Japanese top, how it spins and turns over. Katya seems to be much more impressed than the girls are.

Sorting Dienes blocks.

At the end of the session, I ask the girls to put the Dienes figures back in their box so that the shapes with and without holes are separated. They do as they are asked, though their hands tremble to grab as many figures as they can. Eventually they start picking a few shapes at a go to have a look (otherwise while I am shoving this one, the others will get the rest and nothing will be left for me!) and the tension eases.

At the end, Sandy creates a bit more drama, demanding that I give them homework (to write something in a note-book, letters or figures, as her elder brother Pete does). Unfortunately I am unable to think of something that would suit her.

Session 4. Building from diagrams

> Monday, March 12, 1984, 16:00–16:45.
> Jane, Sandy, Dinah.

Activity 1. $\binom{5}{2}$ with the pegboard.

Now we make necklaces[1] with the pegboard. Each necklace has to be composed of 5 beads, two white ones and three red ones. Of course, all the necklaces must be different.

The girls do amazingly well, actually as well as the first-graders at Dima's school. It's also true that they rarely notice repeated solutions unaided, so after each new necklace I ask them to look carefully to see whether it is one that we have already made. As soon as they start comparing, they usually discover the repeats themselves. Sometimes they regard symmetric solutions as the same. It only becomes difficult when we get to the 9th

---

[1]*P. Z.'s Note:* Actually, what we refer to as a "necklace" is really a "linear chain," since in this context, the start and end beads are not joined up. If we were considering "true" necklaces, the number of distinct configurations would be just 2: WWRRR and WRRWR; all other configurations can be found by cycling the beads. We will use the word "necklace" here and below since it is less cumbersome and more fanciful than the more precise "linear chain."

solution (Jane's turn). If there had been just the two of us, I am sure she would have solved it by herself, but she starts to sort out all the solutions, and repeats her work; Sandy and Dinah get bored, so I have to delicately hint to her as to where to put a peg. She then discovers a new necklace right away.

For the final, 10th necklace, I discover it myself, making a point of sorting it out slowly and logically in front of the girls. They help me to find already-made necklaces for each new one that I try, cheering loudly each time. I should have tried to find an 11th necklace, but for some reason it didn't occur to me at the time.

Activity 2. Odd one out.

The game proceeds as usual. I try to solicit "one word" classifications for the three "non-odd" pictures. Jane, happily responds to her set (cup, teapot, vase, rabbit), "Three odd ones!"

Apparently I have fostered the idea that the non-odd are always alive.

Activity 3. Building from diagrams.

Recall the tangram puzzle that we worked with (starting on p. 160). I've got a new version of this puzzle now. It also contains seven figures but of different shapes and they tile a rectangle, rather than a square. As it doesn't have a special name I'll call it the "Hungarian tangram" (it's amazing how many wonderful things we've got from Hungary!). In Figure 135 you can see the shapes and their position in the box.

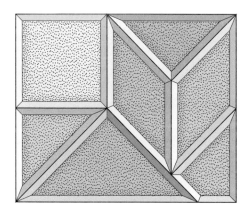

Figure 135. The "Hungarian tangram puzzle." The plastic shapes fit together like this in their rectangular box.

In fact, it was Jane who inspired this activity. She was playing with shapes from this puzzle, but when I asked her to put them back in the box, she couldn't do it. I then showed her the diagram that depicted the placement of the shapes (identical to Figure 135). It turned out that following the diagram wasn't that easy. With some effort she eventually managed to do it.

She was so thrilled by her success that she tossed the figures out and started to put them back again. Curiously, the second time she failed altogether, because she placed the diagram horizontally and the box vertically. I had to help her.

This gave me an idea: to draw several simple diagrams and give them to the girls to assemble in the order of increasing difficulty. I prepared ten problems, of which they did six (Figure 136).

Figure 136. Assemble these figures using the Hungarian tangram pieces.

The sixth problem was too difficult for Dinah; I had to help her. Jane was doing as well as the others; it was a joy to watch her grasping the diagram, selecting the needed shapes and deftly and rapidly assembling the figure.

At the end of the session, my blood ran cold as I remembered that I had promised Sandy homework and hadn't prepare any. Luckily for me, Sandy herself forgot all about it, so the session ended quite peacefully.

Session 5. Permutations

> Monday, March 19, 1984, 16:00–16:50.
> Jane, Sandy, Dinah.

The session didn't go well. First, the problems that I chose were a bit too hard, so the girls couldn't do some of them, which naturally caused frustration. Furthermore, there were disputes, fights, etc.

Activity 1. Permutations.

Again we make necklaces, this time using just three beads, all different colors (red, yellow and blue). The girls competently find all six necklaces.[1] I try to find a seventh necklace and sort out all the possible configurations one by one. Every time a configuration coincides with what we already have, it provokes such a storm of cheers that I almost go deaf. When the assignment is over, the girls don't want to part with the pegboard, so I have to let them make four-color necklaces. This is too difficult for them; they can't determine whether a new configuration coincides with an old one. They mostly pay attention to the position of the blue peg; apparently it is the most visible to them. So, having made seven necklaces (out of 24 possibilities), we call it a day.

Dinah quietly amuses herself, making necklaces symmetrical to Sandy's. However, when this is pointed out, Sandy protests in a most determined way.

At one point, Sandy and Jane start arguing about whose turn it is. I say that the one who behaves better will be the next. Both immediately fall silent so that it's again impossible to determine whose turn it should be. To avoid hard feelings, I suggest tossing a coin. Jane wins. Of course, Sandy bursts into tears. I ask who has hurt her, and propose that she spank the coin (which she does). This provokes Dina's hearty mirth, she says, "Sandy, but the coin is stupid!"

I am only too happy that Jane didn't intervene to assert that the coin was clever.

Activity 2. Odd one out.

It may be that I am too grouchy today, but for some reason all the girls give the same explanations that before only Jane (as the youngest one) used to give: an axe is odd because it's not a bee, a beetle or a butterfly. I sarcastically suggest other odd candidates (using their flawed explanations), but to no avail.

---

[1]*P. Z.'s Note:* Once again, had these beads been connected as a "true" necklace, there would be just two distinct possibilities, or even just one, if you consider turning the necklace upside down. Notice how counting linear chains is much simpler, even though there are more possibilities.

Noteworthy, however, that the answers were correct throughout all the sessions.

Activity 3. Building from diagrams.

I should have been more cautious after Dina's difficulties last time but somehow I thought today it would be OK. Four diagrams remain from last time. After some squabbling, each girl chooses one (Figure 137).

Figure 137.   The girls' diagrams, left to right: Sandy's, Dina's, Jane's.

Dinah is the only one who succeeds. Sandy fails completely. I try to help her but she won't listen, starts to hum and pretends she doesn't give a damn. Katya is worried and wants to help her, but when she sees the assignment she even gives out a whistle, so difficult it seems. Dinah also rushes to help but Katya holds her back. Sandy declares that she doesn't feel like solving this puzzle and we leave her alone.

At first, Jane's situation is a bit better. She correctly places four of the five pieces, but can't find fit the remaining one. Suddenly she feels wounded and says I give her tasks that are too difficult. I try to justify myself by saying that difficult tasks are the most interesting ones but she firmly responds, "No, they are not!"

Only Dinah takes my side, saying that she loves difficult puzzles.

We decide that after the session those who wish will try to solve these puzzles together. But after the session Jane tells me she doesn't feel like it.

Activity 4. Symmetry on graph paper.

This series of puzzles is similar to the one we did on the pegboard, only this time I have drawn the symmetry axis with a black marker on graph paper. Then with markers of different colors (chosen by the girls), I draw on one side of the axis various figures, and the girls draw symmetrical ones on the other side. On the whole the girls do well, though only Dinah makes really accurate drawings; Sandy and Jane just follow the general contours. Once Jane makes a peculiar mistake: she draws a figure which is centrally symmetric to the initial one.

Session 6. The boy's morning

> Thursday, March 29, 1984, 10:30–11:30.
> Jane, Sandy, Dinah.

I recorded this and the following session almost a month later (on April 24), so I am not sure I remember all the details. I think this entry will be shorter than the previous one.

Activity 1. Building from diagrams.

I decide not to give up and do the remaining two puzzles, no matter what. On the whole I succeeded. The girls solve each puzzle together. They quarrel and fight over the pieces, but eventually both puzzles are solved without my help.

Activity 2. Continue the pegboard pattern.

I make a pattern of several pegs, while the girls, by means of a parallel translation, have to make "a ribbon," by repeating the initial figure many times. They do very nicely.

Activity 3. Odd one out.

Now we've exhausted my stock of pictures. Next time I'll have to ask Alla to draw us pictures, or we may use real objects. We can also use the same patterns to try to discover other, more "mathematical" ones (like three triangles and a rectangle, etc.).

Activity 4. The boy's morning.

I display a series of pictures showing a boy doing all kinds of morning activities: he eats breakfast, puts on his clothes, does calisthenics, makes his bed, is asleep, wakes up, washes his face, walks outdoors with a sled, puts on outdoor clothes. These pictures are to be ordered so that activities follow one another like they do in real life: first he is asleep, then he wakes up, washes his face, etc. On the whole the girls are doing well though there are some quarrelsome moments. For instance, what do we do before: have breakfast or make one's bed? I try to solicit a "logical" answer. On the picture the boy is making his bed in pajamas but having breakfast in his day clothes. But the answers I get are of a different sort ("My mom always does it this way" or "Good children must always make their bed," etc.). For

them, my answers have no explanatory power. The question "How do you
know that?" is of no help, either.

Polyhedrons.

At the end of the session, I show them pictures from M. Wenninger's *Polyhedron Models*. Of all pictures, only the most stellated polyhedra are welcomed
with some interest; the others don't produce any effect whatsoever. Alla and
I have already noticed that Jane, despite her passionate love for pictures,
is only interested when there is a story in it, that is, when something is
happening. They may be black-and-white, of poor quality; it really doesn't
matter. But bright glossy pictures of butterflies, parrots or seashells, which
I personally find absolutely irresistible, don't interest her at all.

Session 7. Play trumps science

> Monday, April 9, 1984, 16:00–16:40.
> Jane, Sandy, Dinah.

Activity 1. Symmetry on graph paper.

We repeat the activity from Session 5. Jane confirms her inclination to draw
centrally symmetric figures. I have never observed that at the boys' circle.
On the contrary, I always thought it to be more difficult, and indeed, so it
was.

Activity 2. Errors of symmetry.

On a sheet of paper I draw an axis of symmetry and symmetrical figures on
both sides of it. Some of them contain errors (Figure 138). The girls are to
point them out.

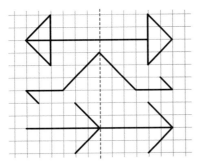

Figure 138. This design is
symmetrical with respect to the
vertical axis but contains a few
mistakes.

Then I try a similar problem, but with multi-colored figures, so that
errors in colors should also be taken into consideration (symmetrical parts
of figures must be of the same color).

As always, Dinah is doing better than the other two. Sandy mostly finds
irrelevant faults stemming from imperfect draftsmanship.

Activity 3. Unordered pairs.

When we make arbitrary sequences of pegs on the pegboard, we have to consider two sequences different if the colors are the same but their order of appearance is not. Consequently, I think it would be difficult to use the pegboard to explain to the girls that we *could* consider, say, the pair (red, blue) and (blue, red) to be the same.

Instead of the pegboard, I use a set of two-colored plastic cubes to identify pairs of colors (not counting order). Each cube is composed of two halves, so that it can be assembled all red, or red-blue, red-yellow, etc. The task is to assemble all possible cubes of this kind. Using four colors (red, blue, yellow, black), it is therefore possible to make six different two-color cubes and four monochromatic ones (Figure 139).

Figure 139.   The cubes are composed of two plastic halves. We assume that the order of colors is irrelevant; i.e., a red-blue cube is the same as a blue-red one. Thus ten different color combinations are possible.

The girls are doing well but don't want to be separated from the shiny, colorful cubes even when the task is over. When all the two-color combinations are composed, they pass on to monochromatic ones and then start again to assemble the same two-color cubes. I try to oppose this behavior and even solicit public opinion, "Let's see; we have probably made this cube already."

The girls waiting for their turn would willingly point it out, "Here it is!"

But the one who is assembling would not agree, "No, this one is red above and mine is red below!"

I have to give up and change the assignment: we now turn each cube so that it attains all possible distinct orientations, given its coloring. (This leads to an idea for a new problem: take various other shapes, not completely symmetrical, and turn them to attain all distinct orientations. One possibility is a cube divided into two parts by a plane cutting it diagonally; we could make them from another kit, not as beautiful as this one, see p. 271). When the girls solve the second puzzle they still go on making more and more cubes, and I am unable to stop them.

Tessellated designs.

My intention is to show the girls the tessellated designs, i.e., tilings of the plane, from Steinhaus's *Mathematical Kaleidoscope.* I thrust the pictures under their noses, call them over, start to draw a tessellation of arrows, like in Figure 140, but no one pays me the slightest attention. They continue to construct palaces and fences from the cubes of the previous activity. They're not even interested in Escher's lizard tessellation. This happened once before in another circle of mine with other kids (I haven't preserved any notes). I must make a mental note that activities with such beautiful cubes should be the very last ones in a session.

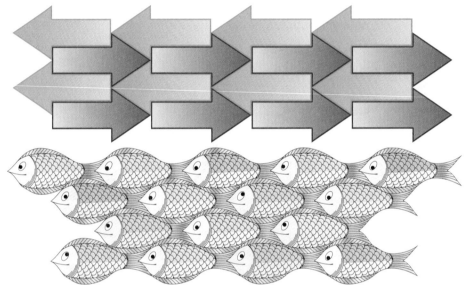

Figure 140.   Top: The tiling of the plane by identical arrows that I showed to the girls. Bottom: tiling with fish (drawing by M. Panov).

If I weren't so lazy, I could make a more interesting tessellation puzzle, perhaps cutting out many identical cardboard figures (squares, triangles, arrows, even Escher's lizards). Then it could be a really captivating activity!

Session 8. Between two mirrors

> Tuesday, May 1, 1984, 18:30–19:15.
> Jane, Sandy, Dinah.

The long interval between this and the last session was due to a business trip.

Activity 1. Pairs of pegs on the pegboard.

The girls are to make all possible pairs of pegs, with the order of colors taken into account (pairs of two pegs of the same color are also allowed). There are 5 colors, so the puzzle has 25 solutions. The girls do amazingly well, finding 24 solutions entirely on their own. My only contribution is the last one. They discover repetitions right away and indicate symmetric solutions, "This one is that one reversed."

When we're done, I ask Dinah to count the number of solutions, which she does.

Activity 2. Find differences between the pictures.

I show them two pictures containing the same figures (in almost identical positions). They are to find all the differences between the pictures (Figure 141). I have prepared two puzzles of this sort.

Figure 141. Find differences between the pictures.

Activity 3. Sort the digits.

On a sheet of paper, ten digits are written in random order (see Figure 155). The girls must point and name them in the right order. For some reason the fact that the last digit is always zero is a source of great merriment. Dinah wants to start with zero but than thinks better of it saying, "It's better to be funny," and starts with one, like everyone else.

Activity 4. Continue the ornament on graph paper.

This activity is identical to one done two sessions ago (p. 261), but now using graph paper instead of the pegboard. I draw the beginning of a pattern ("a fence"), and the girls are to continue it (Figure 142).

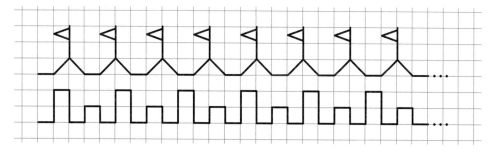

Figure 142. I draw the beginning of a pattern on graph paper, to be continued.

Dinah is the only one who accurately stays on the graph paper lines. Both Sandy and Jane can only repeat correctly the general contours of the pattern. But from the point of view of understanding the pattern, their performance is OK. It's interesting that while doing this and other assignments on the pegboard the girls reproduce correctly not only the general structure of the pattern but also the sizes of its features. But they are unable to do this on graph paper. Can it be that the notion of a number (of pegs, in our case) is better assimilated than a more difficult notion of a length?

> *Whenever I was bored at school, I drew the bottom pattern from Figure 142 on notebook margins, which always gave me a sort of irrational pleasure. I don't know whether it has any connection with our circle. — Jane.*

Games with two mirrors.

I take two small looking-glasses (it's a pity we don't have middle-sized mirrors) and, putting them on the table, show what happens when a chip or a paper clip is reflected in both and what happens if we change the angle between the looking-glasses. Then we all go to the corridor. I bring another mirror from the kitchen, and the girls place themselves between two parallel mirrors watching, with great interest, the infinite chain of their doubles.

The entire activity is welcomed with great enthusiasm and delight.

Session 9. In the courtyard

Monday, May 7, 1984, 18:30–19:15.
Jane, Sandy, Dinah.

It's a wonderful, sunny spring day. It would be a pity to make the girls come back from the outdoors. I decide first to postpone the session and begin at 18:30 instead of 16:00. But when it's almost 18:30 and still fine outdoors, Alla has an idea to have a session in the courtyard! The program is concocted on the spot and not all goes smoothly, but a new challenge should be welcome!

Activity 1. How many steps from a shed to a shed?

In our courtyard, not far from the kids' playground, there are two large concrete transformer sheds on a small expanse of asphalt. At first the girls try to sit around a flat surface, as if it's a table. Mostly, they choose to congregate around a stoop at one of the transformer sheds. I can barely get their attention.

I ask them to guess how many steps there are between the two sheds. The girls start calling out numbers having nothing to do with reality, one person saying "twenty" and then "a hundred" a moment later.

Then we start to measure the distance by taking steps. Dinah goes first, but instead of steps, she measures the distance by counting her feet, heel-to-toe, so it takes quite a lot of time. Then it's Jane's turn. Her behavior is very typical. First the numbers correspond to steps but when the numbers become bigger, the correspondence is lost; she easily takes three or fours steps while pronouncing "twenty-four." Then she reaches numbers she is not very sure about. And while she is painstakingly making efforts to remember the next number, her little feet are going on and on "measuring the steps."

I feel like I still have problems with that ... — Jane.

Dima is jumping around and as usual, overbearingly tries to explain to Jane that she is doing everything wrong. Jane waves him away, "Dima, Dima, don't bother me!" and forgets altogether which was the last number.

"How much was it, Dad?" she asks, frowning.

"Thirty-six."

"And what comes next?"

Dinah tries to prompt her but Jane explodes, "I am not asking you!!"

And all the time, during this dialogue with four participants, she diligently marches on.

The same thing, though less pronounced, happens when it's Sandy's turn. No wonder each of them gets a completely different number. We try to compare the "real" number of steps with the predicted ones (which they have by now forgotten). Making these comparisons is not very meaningful for them; the only conclusion they arrive at is that their predictions were wrong. Sandy gets extremely resentful and starts counting steps again, trying to get the predicted number. I manage to calm her down by saying her mistake was the smallest one (which is true).

I decide to cheer them up and also measure the distance with my steps, only I make giant steps. They split their sides laughing but no mathematical conclusions follow, like the number of steps also depends on the size of a step. And when my last step lands on the wall, much joy ensues.

Activity 2. Build a tower of the same height.

I give the girls the same task that I once gave to the boys: on the table (here, a step) we build a tower of blocks; they have to build a tower of the same height on the "floor." The result is naturally the same: both groups try to build the tower that would reach the same horizontal level (Figure 143).

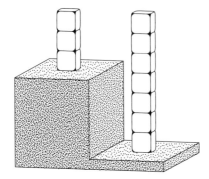

Figure 143. The girls consider these two towers to be the same height.

Unfortunately we are not in a position to discuss this fact; the wind keeps blowing the towers away (and the asphalt surface isn't smooth). We have to postpone it.

By the way, it has just occurred to me that this problem should be presented differently. The first tower should be built on the floor and it should be lower than the table. This way it will be impossible to build a tower on the table that would reach the same level. There is hope that in this case they would build the second tower of the same height that the first one, e.g., they will take the same number of blocks. And then I can ask them to build a third tower, again on the floor, and of the same height that the second one. It will be interesting to compare the first one and the third one.

[An original idea, huh? The fact that I already had it before, and even tested on the boys (p. 97), seems to have gone with the wind.]

Activity 3. A map of the playground.

This activity turns out to be so amusing that even now, twenty years later, the scene is still vivid in my memory.

We come to the playground and I ask the girls to memorize everything that they see on it: a swing, a bench, a sandbox, monkey bars, paths, etc., and how they are situated. I tell the girls they will next have to draw the playground as if seen from above ("imagine you are birds").

We return to the asphalt between the sheds, and each girl gets a piece of chalk, and starts to draw a map of the playground. I allow them, if need be, to run back to the real playground to refresh it in memory.

Sandy does the best job. She makes quite a decent map with correct locations of almost all major objects. The sandbox isn't there. I ask where it is and Sandy draws it where it should be.

Dinah seems to have grasped the idea better than others and sets to work with extreme meticulousness. First she spends a lot of time accurately designing a right-angled bench (Figure 144).

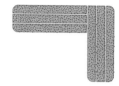

Figure 144. This is how the bench looks if seen from above.

Then she explains to me in an equally lengthy and detailed way that if we look at the bench from above, we won't see its legs, so there is no need to draw them. Then she remarks that the bench is green and starts to color it with green chalk. When, having finished with the bench, she sets to draw the swing (a view from above is rather tricky), it's time to wrap things up. Sandy has finished long ago and is getting antsy, and Jane has long since strayed from map-making. Dinah is hugely upset and asks me to give her some time to finish her map, but it's hopeless; at her speed even two hours wouldn't have been enough.

Jane started the job correctly. In a second there is a large circle on the asphalt meant to be a sandbox. But then she draws a bucket and a scoop, then a boy and a girl scooping the sand, then a doll which the girl puts to bed... I try to divert her from the story and ask where the swing is. Two dashing strokes, and there it is! The boy and the girl go to the swing but then it starts to rain, they rush home forgetting the doll... In no time there is a complete story, while the courtyard, the plan and math in general are completely forgotten.

What can I say? This is one of the times when I can't tell a win from a loss. On one hand, from the point of view of teaching math, two of the three participants failed the task. On the other hand, it's such an incomparable joy to watch three completely different personalities, each at her best, with each one's character so vividly displayed, that the math means little. I am even tempted to exclaim, "To hell with math! Kids are much more interesting!"

Tricks with magnets.

Finally, I show them a few tricks with magnets. Here's one: a small magnet is in a toy truck and when I bring a big magnet close, the truck rolls away. In the second trick, paper clips, pins and other small metal objects run to and fro on a vertical piece of cardboard.

The girls guess that it is the magnet which is responsible for these effects; indeed, I don't try to conceal it.

The session is rather messy. Because of fine weather the courtyard is full of children with parents and grannies. We are surrounded by a small crowd of kids, they interfere, ask for the chalk, the girls shout, "This is our circle, not yours!"

I have to remind them to be polite. Besides, we have our own rather numerous audience: three mothers, Dima and Pete.

The session ends in a fairly unexpected way: while Dima fools around, his bicycle has been stolen! We start an investigation that goes on for two hours. It's a real detective story, with active participation by neighborhood urchins who assist us. Dima is extremely impressed not so much by the fact that the bike was stolen, but that we retrieved it. He has never seen any detective films as we don't have a TV set at home, so he keeps asking if this is how policemen track thieves.

About a fortnight later, Jane confesses that she likes more to have sessions at home than in the courtyard. More proof that kids appreciate routine (cf. Dima's remark on p. 56).

Session 10. Bi-colored cubes

Monday, May 14, 1984, 16:00–17:00.
Jane, Sandy, Dinah.

Activity 1. Oral questions.

(1) To go to my office, I take a bus, then a trolley car, then the metro, and then a tram. How do I get back?

   Dinah replies correctly, Jane and Sandy sometimes correctly and sometimes not, so it's hard to see whether these are just random errors or they don't understand.

(2) What do you call a collection of cows (herd), birds (flock), flowers (bunch), and so on? Some of the words the girls don't know.

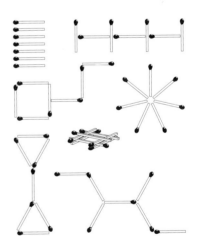

Figure 145. Figures made of seven matches.

Activity 2. Seven matches.

I place seven matches on the table, and start making figures with them (Figure 145).

Each time, the girls are to count how many matches there are. And each time the number turns out to be seven. Dinah asserts that there will always be seven, but when her turn comes, she counts them quite willingly. Finally, remembering my first session with the boys, I make a three-dimensional "well." It's Jane's turn and the matches are hard to count: the well keeps collapsing, just like the last time we built it (p. 18). Perhaps that's why there are only 6 matches. I sum up: all the figures contain 7 matches except that the well contains 6. Nobody protests, not even Dinah.

Activity 3. Finding patterns.

I don't remember the precise activity.

Activity 4. Orienting cubes.

Now we will try the cube-counting activity that I thought about earlier (see p. 263). I give the girls a bunch of identical black-and-while cubes, each divided diagonally by a plane (Figure 146).

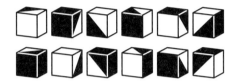

Figure 146. Find all distinct positions for the two-colored cube. There are 12 distinct orientations.

The cubes are to be oriented in all the possible distinct ways (it goes without saying that cubes' axes are parallel to the same coordinate axes (see Figure 146). It would be nice to have special receptacles for the cubes but I don't have any, so we merely put the cubes side by side. In general the girls' performance is good though there are some difficulties towards the end. It's hard for me as well: when a new position doesn't come easily, nobody wants to let me try.

I am quite upset by Jane's reaction to this problem. She's far more creative at coming up with psychological defenses to avoid it rather than actually work on it. At first she declares that thinking will take her a long time "'cause I'm still small and can't think quickly." She continues to dwell on this idea with gusto, and I am unable to make her switch from self-defense to mathematics. She frowns dramatically, pretends to be submerged in a profound meditation, bats her eyes at me to get a smile or asks, as if she has forgotten,

"Dad, what do you call it?"

Meanwhile, her eyes are on me or off to the side, but never on the cubes.

I really don't know how to fight such an attitude. I feel exasperated by it but that, naturally, doesn't help. The slightest criticism gets her hackles up and, once in her element, she forgets about the problem altogether.

Session 11. Fives

> Saturday, May 26, 1984, 11:00–11:50.
> Jane, Sandy, Dinah.

Our last session of the school year has a different structure.

Geometry for Kids.

I read the first chapter of this book, by Zhitomirsky and Shevrin.

Fives.

The geometry book discussed lines (straight, curved, etc.). I declare, "Now we are also going to draw a line."

Each girl gets a sheet of paper with 10 points labeled by the digits $0, 1, 2, \ldots, 9$. They are to be linked together in the order of the digits. Sandy and Dinah do it with ease; Jane has problems, mainly because she is afraid to make a blunder. Zero is the last to be discovered, which produces general laughter.

When they're done, it turns out that on every sheet a "5" has been drawn. I announce solemnly that all three participants have received a grade of 5 in mathematics for the year.

Six five-cakes.

Alla baked biscuits in the form of fives: three big ones and three small ones. We present them to the girls. Entirely on their own, they decide to eat the small ones on the spot and to take the big ones home as a treat for the whole family. And thus the year is over.

Chapter 10

The Girls' Math Circle, Year Two

Session 12. Something's amiss with probability theory

Thursday, October 25, 1984 , 10:00–11:10.
Jane, Sandy, Dinah.

Activity 1. Taking shapes out of the bag.

I put nine large Dienes blocks into a bag: three circles, three squares, and three triangles, and ask the girls to remove, without looking, a specified shape. They take turns (so that each girl gets shapes of all three kinds). They must determine the shape by touch alone.

The assignment is easy and the girls do quite well.

Activity 2. Logical inclusion of classes.

I show the girls four big Dienes blocks (Figure 147) and start asking questions: What are there more of, big ones or squares? Squares or red shapes? Sometimes the questions are simpler: How many squares are there? How many big figures? How many red ones?

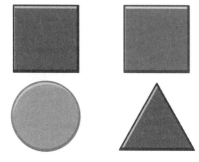

Figure 147. A red square, a blue square, a red triangle, and a green circle.

Their answers to the simple questions are all correct. What surprises me is that, except for Jane, they also correctly answer the more complicated questions that involve intersecting sets. Jane alone answers in accordance with psychology:

"What are there more of, squares or big figures?"

"None is more, they are equal."

"And how many squares there are?"

"Two."

"Big figures?"

"Four."

"So, there are two squares and four big figures, but their number is equal?"

"Yes, it is."

Sandy intrudes with, "Jane's answers are funny. I don't understand."

I ask classical questions of the type, "What are there more of, animals or rabbits?" This time, too, everybody answers correctly, even Jane, while Dinah and Sandy also give correct explanations.

Nevertheless I don't believe they really have full understanding of class inclusion. I'll catch them one day!

Activity 3. A probability game.

Each of the four players (I participate too) get three chips and place them in the cells of the first row of the play board (Figure 148).

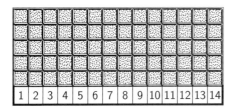

Figure 148. We count the sum of the numbers on two dice and the corresponding game chip makes a step forward. We played this game with the boys. Sums of 1, 13, and 14 are impossible; the most probable sum is 7.

Here's how the game works: We roll two dice, count the total and if, say, we get nine, the chip on cell #9 moves a step forward towards the finish. For the girls the goal of the game is "to win," that is, to arrive at the finish as soon as possible (before starting the game we agree that in this game the dice determine what happens, and since dice are silly, nobody should feel offended if she loses).

I have several educational goals in mind. First, that while playing they learn how to add small numbers. Second, that they remember how the numerals are written (it has turned out that Sandy and Jane do not know them well). Third, to develop a sort of "probabilistic intuition" (I want the girls to observe that certain numbers come out more often than others, and therefore to put their chips on more "profitable" positions).

Unfortunately, the last goal (probability) is a flop. To begin with, Jane has no idea that two symbols "14" at the right edge signify the number "fourteen." Even less obvious for her would be the fact that two dice cannot produce such a sum. Of course, she could have remarked that this number never appeared. But it was just our luck that seven, the theoretically most probable sum, doesn't appear for a very long time (and even then, rather sluggishly, with no wish to catch up).

Basically, Jane has no luck in this game. Three of Dina's chips have already reached the finish line (since I don't want her to be bored, I allow her to put them back at the start and they are again advancing very quickly), while Jane is still almost at the beginning (even with a chip on seven!). I'm eager to have at least one of Jane's chips reach the finish. That's why the game lasts so long, ending at 11:10, making Dinah late for her music lesson.

Regarding addition skills, it's very amusing to watch how the same pair (for example, 5 and 4) comes out again and again, and each time, the girls diligently count the dots: one, two, three, ..., nine. Sometimes I remark, neutrally, "Remember, you've already had 5 and 4. I believe that that time, it also made 9."

But nobody pays any attention to my comments. Which doesn't mean they wouldn't be able to guess the sum if I asked them in so many words. But "to guess" and "to count" isn't the same thing. To count means to dab each object with a finger and say: one, two, three... You may already know how much it will make, so what? You are told to count.

Session 13. Intersecting classes again

Thursday, November 15 1984, 10:10–11:00.
Jane, Sandy, Dinah.

Activity 1. Taking blocks out of a bag.

Just like last time, but now I put the entire set of Dienes blocks into the bag, and the girls can take out any figure they want but they have to say what it is, without looking. They do it with ease, but for some reason they don't announce the size (only doing so when I ask). Apparently size is perceived more as a "visual" property, to be seen (like color), and not be determined by touch.

For fun, I put a few novel star-shaped pieces into the bag. Indeed, they split their sides laughing when Dinah takes out a star for the first time. Sandy even starts fishing exclusively for stars.

Activity 2. Putting blocks back into the box: intersecting classes.

I came up with this activity on the fly, but I am very proud of it. As a rule, the girls squabble about each block when they are putting them back into the box. This time it occurs to me not to chastise them for quarreling, as usual, but to channel their behavior into a special activity. At this point, the activity practically invents itself:

I announce that we are going to put the figures back, one at a time, taking turns. Jane is in charge of small shapes, Sandy does circles, and Dinah handles shapes with holes. (Half of the shapes are small; likewise, half have holes, but only one-third are circles; so afterwards, I allow Sandy to handle the triangles.) So far so good. Jane is busy putting back small shapes, but not all of them; only those that don't have holes and that are not circles, so as not to "invade the other's territory." Sandy only picks big circles without holes, while Dinah takes the big circles with holes. After four turns, we come across the first problem: Sandy says she is out of figures.

I ask, "Are the circles done?"

"Yes, there are none."

"Let's look for them once more."

Sandy pokes with her finger in a heap of circles "looking for a circle."

"So, there are none?"

"No."

"Isn't this a circle?" (I indicated a small circle with a hole.)

Sandy (after a pause), "It's for Jane."

"But this is a circle?"

"Yes, it is."

"Sandy, you are allowed to put back any circle, be it big or small."

Jane is indignant, "What about me? It's me who puts back the small ones!"

Me, "So what? It's still a circle."

Dina's turn to interfere, "It has a hole!"

However, it has dawned upon Sandy that I have *allowed* her to put this circle back in the box, so she can ignore the points of view of the other participants. The work goes on accompanied by disputes and discussions. Jane is the first to realize (and even to declare) that she is entitled to all small blocks, independent of color, shape, and presence/absence of a hole. But she is not ready to acknowledge the same right for the others; whenever someone fancies a small block, she protests vehemently. Gradually she becomes resigned to this, not because she has understood that her protest is groundless but because she sees it is useless. Soon Sandy and Dinah become aware of their rights as well, but quarrels, though less frequent, continue until the activity comes to the end.

At last the work is over. There are four blocks left: big squares without holes. I ask the girls to explain why they are not in the box. Of course their answers aren't very articulate, but they manage to come up with a few ideas. After encouragement ("Yes! Good work!"), I pretend to repeat their statements, making them more accurate. I allow each of the girls to put back one square. Dina's younger sister Asya is visiting our session, and she puts back the final square.

Activity 3. A map of the room.

The girls watch me draw a rough map of the room on a big sheet of paper. After the outline is done, I place the sofa, piano, writing desk, etc., and ask them which is which. Then I ask them to indicate where I should draw the table and to denote with letters who is sitting where. I also ask them to

put in the bookshelves and the record player. They don't draw a plan, i.e.,
a view from above; Jane makes a simple sketch and Sandy, like an ancient
Egyptian, draws a view simultaneously from above and from the front.

Then I draw Pinocchio's head, viewed from above (Figure 149: in this
case it's easy to indicate the front and the behind), and ask what is in front,
behind, to the left and to the right of him. (When asked what's behind him,
Dinah says, "A little pompom.") Almost all the answers are excellent.

Figure 149. Long-nosed Pinocchio.
You can cut him out and put him in
different places; then you can ask
what is in front, behind, to the left or
to the right of him.

Geometry for Kids.

I have decided to read the entire book, a chapter at a time. Although we
read the first chapter in the spring, I start from the very beginning. Like
before (on May 26), after reading the first chapter, we draw dots, curves,
straight lines, etc. This time Jane also does quite well.

. . .

At lunch Jane made the following pronouncement:

"It seems that a year will pass, and Dima will catch up with Pete. But
a year passes, and Pete also grows, and always stays older than Dima. But,
Dima, don't be sad! In return, Pete has only short time to live but you have
much more!"

Two conservation laws at once!

Session 14. The Tower of Hanoi

> Thursday, November 22, 1984, 10:10–10:50.
> Jane, Sandy, Dinah.

Activity 1. The Tower of Hanoi.

I show the girls a plastic Tower of Hanoi (a gift from Hungary) and give a
lengthy and detailed explanation of the rules. Then I give them home-made
cardboard towers, and invite them to try. Jane refuses on the spot, "because
I'll do it wrong!"

Nevertheless, she lets herself be persuaded and finishes first. At the
beginning, she gets stuck several times but I help her and she's able to move
on. I realize that while I've been paying attention just to Jane, Sandy has

moved forward with the puzzle, but I am not sure if she followed the rules. I observe her, and indeed, she does break the rules now and then, mainly replacing two disks at the same time. After I intervene, she gets stuck for some time and I have to help her. Then she too moves along nicely.

Dinah is behind the others. I am sure that this is precisely because she hasn't broken the rules. At least that's my assumption; I've left her pretty much on her own. Her mother Galya tries to prod her, not with hints so much as urging her to work (instead of concentrating on the job, Dinah watches the others). Of course, Jane and Sandy don't fail to remark that Dinah was last, and Jane adds she was first. Before we started, I took care to tell them it was no competition, and now I repeat this, emphatically. Then I help Dinah with a few hints.

Dinah keeps working for some time, while Jane and Sandy get bored and start to fiddle around. When Jane finished, I suggested she try it again, but she refused. Even the plastic version didn't tempt her; she said she wasn't interested.

Activity 2. Putting blocks back into the box.

We put the Dienes blocks into the box again but I've changed the rules and assigned different attributes for each girl to handle. This time they understand things better and fight less.

Geometry for Kids.

We continue our reading, but we get into trouble, because they demand an assignment, like last time, but the book doesn't have one. I'm flooded with nagging; as soon as I placate one girl, another starts in again. The moment I think all is quiet and start reading, someone asks for a magic marker. Finally, I lose it, shut the book, and I say they're not behaving. We end on this unhappy note.

Session 15. Towers of equal height

> Thursday, December 6, 1984, 10:00–11:00.
> Jane, Sandy, Dinah.

Activity 1. Tower of Hanoi, again.

This time they need much less help. Sandy finishes first, then Jane, and then Dinah. Sandy asks me for one of the cardboard towers and I promise to give her one (though I strongly doubt she will use it at home).

Activity 2. Towers of equal height.

We did this earlier : a tower of blocks is built on higher ground, and the kids are to build another one, of equal height, on lower ground (Figure 150).

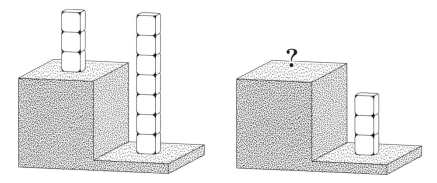

Figure 150 (left) and Figure 151 (right).   Déjà vu (see Figure 143 on p. 268). To forestall the notion that "same height" means "top at the same level", I make the tower on the lower ground low enough that it doesn't reach the upper ground. It is impossible to make the two tops be at the same level.

The idea was that the kids would surely build the second tower so that its top would be on the same level as the first one, which would give me an opportunity to help them see the contradiction.

This is how it went, more or less, but the last time we were outside, and the wind kept knocking down the towers. This time I decide to build the first tower on lower ground (on a stool) while the girls are to build a tower of the same height on the table (Figure 151). This way, you can't have both tops at the same level.

However, this activity doesn't yield anything worthwhile. At first everything goes rather nicely. The girls sensibly build the second tower on the same stool and then carefully transfer it to the table. I ask, "Are the towers of the same height?"

"They are."

"And which one is higher?"

"This one."

"How come? I asked you to build a tower of the same height, and it turns out to be higher."

"Because it's on the table!"

Dinah builds a tower with the type of blocks and in the same sequence as the one on the stool. But she makes mistakes and sometimes mixes up the blocks. This inspires me to come up with a somewhat cumbersome idea of checking transitivity: to try to build two towers each as tall as the first one, yet of different heights. To do this, we should use different blocks (plastic instead of wood) for one of them.

[Indeed, my forgetfulness is appalling: I could have at least re-read my own journal from time to time!]

Apparently, I have another vague idea floating around, since I ask the girls build the two towers on the piano lid. Perhaps this was so that the girls would try to make the tops on the same level because the piano is just a bit higher than the table. As a result I have not clearly formulated the assignment, which was my first mistake; second, the piano lid is not completely horizontal; last, but not least, the blocks I have chosen aren't suitable for building towers. Even I can't make one; the blocks keep scattering. The cubes fall apart into triangles, the girls giggle, rush to retrieve them, crawl under the sofa to look for pieces, and then we have to start all over. It gets so messy that we stop without finishing.

The Spirograph

I show them a spirograph (see Figure 95 on p. 157), and Galya and I proceed to draw all kinds of curves and spirals. Unfortunately, the major drawback of the spirograph is that girls can't use it alone. Even when the girls try to do it with my help, something goes wrong: either the big wheel goes astray or the little one jumps off. When the session is over, Dima tries, but his drawings are far from being satisfactory.

Geometry for Kids.

We continue our reading.

Session 16. Turning 90°

> Thursday, December 20, 1984, 10:10–10:50.
> Jane, Sandy.

This time, I'm pretty much prepared for the session, but at the last moment Galya calls to say that Dinah is sick. I have to switch gears and think of something else on the spot. Actually, if I hadn't, Dinah wouldn't have suffered much, since she's the most mathematically advanced of the girls. But I wasn't nimble-minded enough to have realized this. In particular, I hadn't planned on continuing with the Tower of Hanoi, but instead we do it again, for lack of better ideas.

Activity 1. The Tower of Hanoi.

Sandy finishes first again; she even had time to play twice. That encourages her in her wish to take the game home as a gift (she wanted to do it last time but forgot). This time Katya does take it away.

Activity 2. 90° turns on the pegboard.

I make different figures on the pegboard and ask the girls to make the identical ones but rotated by 90° (in other words, "turned on its side"). I do an example. At first Jane is completely stymied; gradually she adapts, and solves the puzzles almost independently. Finally I give her a rather difficult task, to rotate a figure that contains angles of 45° and 135°. Unfortunately, this one stumps her.

Sandy does all the problems rather smoothly, without mistakes or lapses. But I didn't give her difficult ones. Curiously, Jane and I always turn 90° clockwise, while Sandy turns her figures counterclockwise. Is it because she's a lefty?

Geometry for Kids.

We continue our reading.

Session 17. Snowflakes

> Thursday, December 27, 1984, 10:00–11:10.
> Jane, Dinah.

This time, Sandy is absent, but I decide not to change my holiday-themed activities, since New Year's is just a few days ahead.

Snowflakes.

The entire session is devoted to snowflakes. First we look at a big plastic snowflake and find its axes of symmetry (using a looking-glass). Then I show them pictures in Hermann Weyl's *Symmetry* (I also show them Kepler's book, *A New Years Gift, or On the Six-Cornered Snowflake*. Unfortunately, there are no pictures inside, so I just show them the cover and the title.) Then on a square pegboard field I make a dot with a blue peg ("the center") and explain central symmetry. The process is slow and painful but finally we manage to fabricate something resembling a snowflake (not six-pointed of course). Then we proceed to make a real six-pointed snowflake on a round pegboard. It comes out so beautiful that we decide to leave it for Alla to admire when she comes home.

Then we cut out paper snowflakes.

I remember as a child how I was struck dumb by this dazzling miracle: you take a simple sheet of paper, fold it several times, cut out an arbitrary squiggle — the squigglier the better! — and, anticipating the result, gingerly unfold it and — voilà! — an incredibly lacy, symmetrical, ornamental marvel!

Dinah reacts in much the same way, but the snowflakes don't do much for Jane. Instead, she's fascinated by the remnants of our paper-cutting: "Look, Dad, legs with knees! Wow, and these are a head and two arms!

And this is a fist! A man dancing, here is his leg, and he touches his head with his hand!"

Meticulously, I show all the stages of making a snowflake: folding the paper in halves, in quarters, etc. and how the ornament doubles, quadruples and so on. Dima joins us in these activities.

Geometry for Kids.

At Dina's request we read again what was read at the previous session, when she was absent.

Session 18. Faces, vertices, and edges of a cube

Thursday, April 11, 1985, 11:00–12:00.
Jane, Sandy, Dinah.

As is obvious form the date of the session, we've missed almost three-and-a-half months. Illness was mostly to blame. Dinah and Sandy had whooping cough, Jane and I were down with flu, then it was my throat, etc. In the rare moments when we could have had sessions, I felt like an out-of-shape athlete. During all this time I had just one private session with Jane, and that was quite unpremeditated. Dima was working on puzzles in B. A. Kordemsky's *Mathematical Insight*.[1] One of them was this one:

> Two boys are boating on the river. Two fishermen ask them
> to take them to the other bank. But the boat can only take
> either two boys or an adult. How can the fishermen cross the
> river if the boat must afterwards remain with the boys?

(In another version of this puzzle instead of two fishermen, the boys have to transport a squadron of soldiers.)

Strange as it may seem, Dima, who already knew how to solve the puzzle of the wolf, the goat, and the cabbage (which will be discussed below, on p. 286), gave an incorrect solution, having one of the fishermen swim across the river. He was, however, full of misgivings, and at lunch asked me whether this solution would be acceptable. We started a lengthy discussion as to what it meant to *stay within the framework of a problem*. Jane overheard us and asked us to give her the same puzzle. We gave her two matches, two halves of matches and a little thingum as a boat and she set to solve it. I find the fisherman puzzle more difficult that the wolf, goat, and cabbage puzzle, since its non-trivial "trick" (two boys sailing to the other bank and one returning) must be used twice. Jane used this trick only once and then was stuck. Dima gave her a hint (I didn't have time to stop him), and she solved the puzzle. Typically, she failed to remember the hint: when she wanted to show her solution to Alla that night, she got stuck in the middle.

---

[1] *P. Z.'s Note:* This lovely book is available in English, edited by Martin Gardner, as *The Moscow Puzzles*.

This time I stopped Dima before it was too late. Jane thought a bit and finally got it.

I was quite impressed by her performance. I am already accustomed to her being behind Dima's progress at the same age. But in this case she is clearly ahead of him. At the age of 5 Dima failed to solve the puzzle of the wolf, the goat, and the cabbage (it was in summer, in the country; we drew the river on the ground and were transporting objects to and fro, but to no avail).

All this happened about a month ago. Today I wanted to give the wolf-goat-cabbage puzzle to the girls but didn't have time.

Activity 1. Faces, vertices, and edges of a cube.

I give each girl a cube and ask them to count first its faces, then vertices and then edges. They all do well, except that Jane, while counting edges, gets eight: she has counted the edges on top and on the sides, and at the moment she moves to the bottom, Sandy shouts at the top of her voice, "Twelve!"

I turn to look at her, see that Dinah isn't counting but watching Jane and tell her to count; she says she has already finished, Jane is distracted and forgets to finish her counting.

When they count vertices, Jane says, "Eight. Four and four makes eight, we could have guessed right away."

She's certainly progressing.

Activity 2. Counting $\binom{5}{2}$ two-colored necklaces.

I give each girl a sheet of paper with 12 identical uncolored five-bead necklaces (Figure 152).

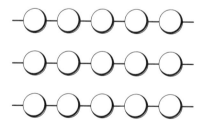

Figure 152. The "paper version" of the problem discussed in detail in Chapter 3.

They are to color two beads blue, and leave the remaining three white, in different ways and preferably without repetitions. I am surprised to see that Jane is doing best of all. She's apparently made a big leap forward.

Sandy is under the weather or distracted by something. She works in a rushed, haphazard way, and repeats the same configurations as many as six times. When we discover this (we check them together to find repetitions), she says she didn't know she couldn't do that. I give her another sheet with necklaces but she only finds one new solution (borrowed from Jane) and the rest are again repetitions made hastily and thoughtlessly. In two sheets she has six good solutions.

Compared with Sandy, Dinah works thoughtfully but very timidly. As soon as she finds, with difficulty, three solutions, she wants to capitulate but I won't have it, saying that Jane is still working and she must do the same. Dinah looks at Jane's sheet, sees her new solution, says "Aha!" and draws the fourth necklace.

(And Jane, the little pest, shouts, "Hey, Dinah! No cheating!" and covers her sheet with her elbow.) After the fourth one, Dinah tries to give up once again, but then finds new solutions (on her own). As a result she also has six solutions (like Sandy) but only one repetition. Jane is not really much ahead as far as the results are concerned: she has seven solutions. What is different is her manner of working. She has worked as attentively and seriously as Dinah, and as boldly as Sandy. In other words, had it not being for my prompting and pushing, Dinah would have got three necklaces without repetitions, Sandy would have got five with seven repetitions, and Jane seven solutions and one repetition. Besides, Jane isn't stopping. But I have to stop her as the other two do nothing and start fooling around. After counting, Jane says, "So I got more than anyone!"

Dinah chides her with, "And you, Jane, you shouldn't brag!"

This, unexpectedly, silenced Jane.

At the end we check the solutions to find all the repetitions. Everybody is doing well, which proves once more that intellectually they are quite capable of solving this puzzle. If they lack anything, it's concentration, boldness and creativity, i.e., the imagination to hunt for new solutions.

Activity 3. $\binom{5}{2}$ on the pegboard, reprise.

We worked on this last year, at our fourth session (p. 256). I ask the girls if they remember a puzzle similar to the one we have just solved. Sandy says she remembers that they were drawing crosses "like this" (drawing with her finger). I don't know what she's thinking of, but suspect she thinks the puzzle was similar because they were also drawing. Neither Dinah nor Jane remember anything similar. Then I get out the pegboard and ask them to make "necklaces" with 5 pegs, using 2 blue ones and 3 white ones. Now everybody remembers that, indeed, we had a similar assignment.

We make necklaces in turn. Again Sandy seems distracted: she can't find the second (!) configuration after Dinah finds the first one. Sandy starts by putting three white pegs into the same places that Dinah did, and then she is buried in thought (Figure 153). But there is nothing to think about, since there is no choice for blue pegs.

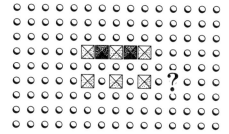

Figure 153. This "new" necklace goes nowhere, for it precludes any different configuration.

I suggest that she replace the white pegs. She takes them away, thinks a little, and then puts them back in the same places. I try explaining more carefully, but Sandy seems mesmerized: again she picks up the three white pegs and puts them back in the same place. Risking offending her, I let Jane take a turn. She does it in a flash. Having seen her solution, Sandy seems to come to her senses and says, "Now I also know how to do it."

Indeed, very soon she finds the third necklace, and then the fifth one, getting stuck only at the eighth one, when we use Jane's help again. After making a new necklace on the pegboard we look for it on our sheets of paper (i.e., the girls do the searching while I observe). If we find one, we mark it with a plus; if not, we add it to other necklaces already on paper.

The search for the last, tenth necklace is Dina's job. She works without success for a long time. I give a hint, asking whether someone has on her paper a necklace unmarked by a plus. Jane has one, and she makes this last necklace on the pegboard. I point out that now we have exactly 10 necklaces on the pegboard and also on paper.

Then I start to hunt for an 11th solution. I carefully and *systematically* sort out all the possibilities and each time we see for ourselves that we already have such a necklace. Together we come to the conclusion that there are no more necklaces. The session is over.

In fact, Jane also used a somewhat systematic approach, though only once: she put a blue peg in the first position, and then sorted through all possible positions for the second one, and thus found a new configuration. She certainly made me quite happy today.

. . .

Math has influenced Jane's favorite pastime — telling stories to herself out loud — in an amusing way. Immediately after today's circle she began narrating, but her characters were digits, with Five as the leader. She spoke in a very excited, emphatic voice: "They caught the Five and dragged her into prison!! Then the Four rushed after them to save her, and Threes and Twos helped, but it was too late!!! (A tragic pause.) She was gone – forever!! 'How will we live without our leader?,' asked. . ." I don't remember who asked that.

Session 19. The wolf, the goat, and the cabbage

Thursday, April 18, 1985, 11:00–12:00.
Jane, Sandy, Dinah.

Activity 1. The Wolf, the Goat, and the Cabbage.

Here is the statement of the puzzle from Kordemsky's book:

> This is also an ancient puzzle that dates to the 8th century,
> preserved as a fable: A man must ferry a wolf, a goat, and
> a cabbage across a river with his boat. The boat is so small
> that it can only carry the man, and with him either the wolf,
> or the goat, or the cabbage. But if the wolf stays alone with
> the goat, it will eat it; the same is true of the goat and the
> cabbage. However, when the man is present, no one eats
> anything. Finally the man manages to bring all of them
> across the river. How did he do that?

My childhood memory still holds the picture accompanying the puzzle:
a bearded peasant in bast shoes[1] stands beside a boat, scratching his head.
At his side are his three "charges," the wolf eyeing the goat malevolently.

Today I give this puzzle to the girls. And Jane can't solve it! I don't
get it. Is this puzzle harder than the fishermen puzzle? In what way? And
how come, in the first-grade circle at Dima's school, nobody could solve it,
not even Gleb the genius?

The wolf, the goat, the cabbage, as well as the man and the boat are
quite "real," not abstract chips, but small toys. The crack between two
parts of the folding table is our river.

Dinah attentively examines the small figurines and says, "I think I can,"
and performs the correct solution.

Then, just like before, neither Jane nor Sandy can reproduce what they
have just seen. Sandy is the first to try. At the decisive moment (when the
goat is to be taken back) she stops and hesitates. Dinah helps her. When
it's Jane's turn, she is stuck at the same stage. This time I ask Dinah not
to help her and the puzzle remains unsolved. I ask Dinah to demonstrate
her solution again and for Jane to watch her carefully. Jane says she's "got
it," but falters at the same crucial moment, and manages only after Dinah
helps her. It may be that if a puzzle demands logical organization, it's
impossible to remember the solution in a purely mechanical way, without
understanding this logical structure.

I am reminded of one of Piaget's memory experiments. A young child,
who is not yet aware — as verified by special tests — of the concept of an

---

[1]*P. Z.'s Note:* Shoes woven from bark fibers; a type of primitive footware that was
once common in Eastern Europe.

ordered set is shown a picture of line segments ordered by length (Figure 154, left) and asked to remember what is in the picture.

"Sticks," says the child.

"Draw them," asks the experimenter.

The child then draws a chaotic set of parallel segments (see the same figure, right).

Six months later, the child is asked if he remembers the old assignment. Yes, he does remember. "Then draw what you saw then." He reproduces in an absolutely correct manner the (left) picture with segments set in the order of their length. He is even able to explain that they are ordered, which he couldn't do before. After this experience I have a feeling that the mechanism of memory is altogether enigmatic.

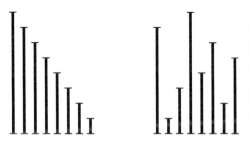

Figure 154. Left: an ordered set of segments. Right: the way a child who hasn't yet mastered the idea of order "memorizes" and reproduces it. Six months later the same child will reproduce it as it appears on the left.

We could follow the pattern of this experience and ask Jane in about six months if she remembers the solution of the wolf and the goat puzzle. Though in our case it would be impossible to tell whether she really remembers it or has solved the puzzle anew.

I've always had problems with this puzzle. I would forget the solution and, horrified, would look at the pictures of the protagonists with a certainty that in a minute I'd fail and bring shame on myself (having solved it correctly before never gave me confidence).

Besides, I completely forgot the puzzle about the two boys and two fishermen; but when I am thinking of it now, a posteriori, it seems I understand what was going on: it all hinges on the goals of the characters in the stories — yes!

The fishermen want to cross the river, which they do assisted by the boys. The boys don't have any special goal besides guarding their boat; they don't go to any special place, they just sail. No action of the participants is in contradiction to their goals.

But the solution to the wolf puzzle contains a psychologically absurd move: the man takes the goat who was intentionally brought across the river back to the original side. I suspect that this is where I always got stuck. — Jane.

Activity 2. A triangular prism.

Last time, we counted the faces, vertices and edges of a cube. Today we do the same with a triangular prism. Sandy and Dinah do well, but Jane's a bit sketchy.

Activity 3. Polygons.

We draw all kinds of polygons and count how many vertices and sides they have. I don't remember the details but it seems we didn't always have the same results. It was fairly chaotic.

Activity 4. $\binom{5}{2}$, yet again.

Dinah is the only one of my pupils who has professional mathematicians in her family, people who thus have their own particular opinions about my style and methods. It seems to me that they're often exasperated by my silly tendency not to give any explanations whatsoever (that is, not to explain the solution of a puzzle).

Like many other mathematicians, they believe that the central educational goal is clear and comprehensible ("accessible") explanation. Thus, creative energy should be used to find logical moves, visual images, allegories, comparisons, etc. For instance, how to better explain to a novice the difference between Riemann and Lebesgue integrals? Here's how: take a handful of coins and demonstrate two summing methods. The Riemann method adds them one by one, while Lebesgue adds coins of various values separately.[1]

I suspect that they see my avoidance of explanations not so much as a strategy, but as an inability to provide good explanations. Several times they shared with me their ideas about how to explain this or that to kids, and how they explained something to Dinah and she understood it perfectly well. However, when Alla once told Galya that my idea was not to impose any explanations on the kids, Galya seemed to think that this was eminently reasonable. So it may be that I am imagining things.

Whether I am or not, at today's circle, Dinah brought a notebook which she proudly showed to me. Almost half of it was filled with "necklaces" and computations. It contained the entire series of combinations out of five elements:

$$\binom{5}{0}, \binom{5}{1}, \binom{5}{2}, \binom{5}{3}, \binom{5}{4}, \binom{5}{5},$$

with an explicit demonstration of the connection between $\binom{n}{k}$ and $\binom{n}{n-k}$. Furthermore, other examples were also analyzed, like $\binom{7}{2}$. Dinah told me that her grandmother had explained everything to her: that the bead to be colored should be fixed in turn, and the remaining ones to the right

---

[1] *P. Z.'s Note:* Unfortunately, this is a mathematical joke of the "If you have to ask, you won't understand" variety.

of it should be changed, and how it was possible to calculate the result beforehand. In a word, she received a precise, coherent and well-thought-out lesson that would be perfectly appropriate for 10-year-olds (at least, that's what *I* think, having never taught this age group).[1]

I must say that Dinah was recounting Grandma's lesson correctly and fairly coherently. I am sure I could confuse her by asking something to which she was not prepared (e.g., why the beads must be colored in this order; I think she would have said "Grandma says to do it this way"). Of course, I did nothing of the sort.

Anyway, today's activity included the task of writing out all distinct combinations of two Bs and three Ws:

BBWWW

BWBWW

BWWBW

. . .

I never doubted what would happen: when it was Dina's turn, she did neither better nor worse than the two other girls, straining, unsystematically, to find only six strings. (I am afraid her Grandma would have been upset on seeing this, and would have thought that Dinah learned nothing. But she would have been wrong again. Or else she wouldn't have given her time to think and started to corner her with leading questions until Dinah would have done everything "mathematically." And that would have been another "educational success," avoiding exasperation over the the child's boneheadedness.)

We repeat the same procedure as at the previous session: check all solutions, look for repetitions, add the missing solutions, etc., and finish with a final list of 10 solutions. I say,

"Have you guessed what B, B, and W, W, W mean? That means Blue, Blue, White, White, White!"

And I show them necklaces from last time, indicating that two Bs mean two blue beads and three Ws are the remaining white beads. For some time we are busy looking for correspondences between the two assignments. The girls work willingly and effortlessly, but they don't display the enthusiasm of discovery manifested by the boys under similar circumstances. In general, when compared to the boys, the girls respond with a significantly greater delight to the fact of just having a session (when announced it will take place the following day, they shout "Hooray!," clap their hands, jump with joy) but at the actual sessions, when we make our small discoveries, their glee is less pronounced; in fact, they barely display any special emotions at all.

---

[1]*P. Z.'s Note:* Indeed, this estimate is rather optimistic, by American standards!

A Child's Guide to Stars and Planets.[1]

I lent *Geometry for Kids* to Sasha Pachikov, and so as not to break our tradition, I read from a book, about astronomy.

Session 20. A chain with one difference

> Monday, October 21 1985, 14:30–15:20.
> Jane, Sandy, Dinah.

Once again, I start with excuses. We missed almost six months, because I was unable to muster up the energy and find the time to squeeze the circle into my already full schedule. During this period (in August) the magazine *Znanie–Sila* (Knowledge is Power) published my article about the circle, which provoked an explosion of interest. I was ashamed of neglecting the circle, but at the same time, I was confronted with new responsibilities. I had to write responses to questions, to talk to people, to meet with colleagues, and so on. To say nothing of the terrible change in my work schedule and my niece Anya's marriage. This is how we arrived at the end of October.

As before, when the impending circle was announced, the girls howl with delight.

Activity 1. Warm up: looking for digits.

Each girl gets a sheet of paper divided into various geometric shapes containing digits (each sheet is different); see Figure 155. They are to indicate and name the digits in the right order. They do it hands down. Jane and Sandy begin with 1 and go up to 9, so they have to end with zero. Dinah sees this drawback and begins with zero. In the past, this provoked great merriment, but today everything goes on calmly.

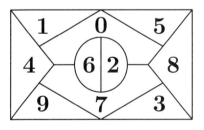

Figure 155. Find and show all the digits in the right order.

Sandy says, "Did you draw this yourself?"
"Yes, I did."
"And how come it's so neat?"
"I've made it with a ruler."
"And the circles?"
"With a compass."
"Ahh..."

---

[1]*P. Z.'s Note:* By E. P. Levitan.

Activity 2. A chain of objects with one difference.

Again we use our precious Dienes blocks and discuss once more how the pieces are different from one another. It used to be difficult to explain, but no longer: now everybody understands that there are four different attributes, enumerating them: "color, shape, size, and 'hole.'" Their task is to construct a line of pieces so that every new one differs from the previous one by exactly one property (only by color, or by shape, or by size, or by presence/absence of a hole). All remaining properties mustn't change. This takes up almost the entire session. Several times I ask the girls if they are tired of it but they deny it unanimously.

Dinah and Jane are doing very well indeed. But poor Sandy began school this year. Which means the whole deadening bouquet: fatigue, inattention, and diminished initiative. I may not have described the "old" Sandy that well, but her normal state was... radiant. Imagine a kid who has just been given a puppy. This was Sandy's usual state of mind, but without any puppy. Now she seems literally "turned off." Her gaze drifts away, into space. She picks up an arbitrary piece; quite by chance it's a correct one. She stares at it for a long time, clearly unable to isolate its properties and to compare them with the previous ones. Finally she puts it back into the pile. Then, without really looking, she picks up another, and the whole process repeats. At some point this tires her so much that she just inserts the piece she is holding into the chain, even though it doesn't fit, and her eyes drift away again. Sometimes she holds a piece, but instead of looking at it or at the chain, she gazes somewhere into space.

To take her out of her torpor, I ask her, "Are these figures of the same size?"

"Of the same color?"

"Is there a hole? And here?"

Her answers are all correct but she is unable to take action from them. The hardest thing is to see how many differences there are and how many there should be. Sometimes, when the figure is already in the chain, she notices that it differs from the previous one (as it should be, by one property; but this seems to have escaped her memory); she would then think better of it and take the figure back. I have to explain that actually she has been right. Sometimes I have an impression that she is confused about the names of the attributes. There are triangles, circles and squares, so far so good, this is easy, but there is also something called "shape," and it's not clear what it means and how it is related to all the rest. A triangle is different from a square, there is no doubt about that, but it's also different in what is called "shape;" is this a second difference? She is also confused by the meaning of the words "shape" and "size." These are, roughly speaking, the "symptoms" of her "academic failure." I am sure she will soon be OK, but right now, today, she can't do anything.

Watching Jane, I notice a peculiar phenomenon. When others are working on the problem, it's as if she has an *instantaneous vision* of the correct
solution, that is, she solves the puzzle pretty much the way I do. She is
eager to hint, she whispers in my ear that Sandy doesn't see the solution
just under her nose, utters a small excited cry when a suitable figure would
fall out of the pile and so on. It is obvious that she determines good and
bad solutions at first sight. But the moment her turn comes, she loses this
ability and acts "explicitly" (to use a psychological term); she enumerates
all the attributes, verifies whether they coincide, counts non-coincidences,
etc. And she can easily omit a property or make a mistake in counting
(count the same property twice or forget the first difference after the second
is discovered), and that will lead to an error.

Furthermore, she takes from the pile not the right figure, but an arbitrary
one. She is as different from herself at the moments of "non-responsibility"
as someone who can tell prose from poetry is from a person who can only
do this by counting syllables. The latter will easily make mistakes, due to
counting, while the former won't even need to count, instantly apprehending
by *listening*.

This spontaneous comparison is a good demonstration of a "theory of
stepwise formation of mental activities." Imagine how its practitioners would
teach us to tell poetry from prose. We must begin with "explicit object
activities." For instance, a stressed syllable is marked with a red pencil,
an unstressed syllable with a blue one. Now you make row of red and
blue cardboard pictures corresponding to each line of writing, and discover
patterns. The next stage is passing from object activities to "symbolic"
ones: draw a pattern like $- \wedge - \wedge - \wedge -$, where $\wedge$ and dash signify stressed
and unstressed syllables, respectively. Gradually the teacher must get the
pupils to internalize these patterns, i.e., that they draw them mentally,
"implicitly" (I am not sure what this means); and of course the counting of
syllables, should also be internalized, becoming more and more rapid, until
it is completely automatic. This way we learn to tell prose from poetry
hands down.

While actually the best way to learn is to read a lot of poetry, preferably
good poetry, and preferably with enjoyment.

My poetry analogy is no hyperbole. I saw an article that described a way
to teach 12-year-olds who don't see the three-dimensional object depicted in
a two-dimensional drawing, by isolating parts of the drawing and explaining
their geometric interrelationships. For example, in the picture of a vertex
of a cube (Figure 156), one of the lines is explained to be vertical, the other
to be horizontal and parallel to the plane of the picture, and the third to be
horizontal and perpendicular to the plane of the picture.

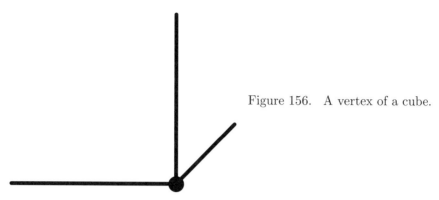

Figure 156.   A vertex of a cube.

The funniest thing is that the pupils did learn! If you apply the above methods of teaching how to recognize poetry, sure enough, the kids will have read a lot of verse! The capable pupils who understood without being taught will also benefit from extra instruction in the foundation of formal prosody. Which doesn't change the fact this theory is an absurdity. Kids never learn this way.

But let's return to our session. Even when it's her turn, Jane makes very few mistakes, and sometimes her "instant vision" wakes up and she gets a solution right away. There's another way to look at her progress: most of the solutions proposed by the girls are "trivial" in that they change only color when compared to the previous configuration. For instance, after a big red no-holed square, they place a big blue no-holed square, then a yellow one, then a green one. When the colors are exhausted, they have to change a less trivial property while preserving the rest, and it's at this moment that things get harder. Jane has an easier time of it than the others and sometimes proposes the non-trivial solutions before it becomes absolutely necessary. Dinah is next best at this, but Sandy is completely at a loss. I have just got an idea that kids recognize color as a property easier because it is verbally expressed by adjectives (blue, red, yellow, green) while the shape is expressed by nouns (a triangle, a square, a circle). On the other hand, size is also expressed by adjectives (big, small) but despite this it is a less obvious property than color.

[Earlier I stated that color difference was the last thing kids noticed. I really have a knack for producing half-baked theories!]

Finally, Dinah faces a situation when there are about a dozen pieces left, but none will fit at the end of the chain. She is stuck for some time.

There is a behavior that I have been observing dozens of times which I can't put up with (I've mentioned it before). It seems to be the simplest thing in the world: when you are sorting figures, and see that the one you are holding doesn't fit, just put it aside, not back in the common pile. *None of the kids ever does that!* It's beyond me to see why. Is the idea really that difficult? They fumble in the pile examining the same solutions time and again, while the situation becomes more and more tedious and hopeless. This is what is happening now. I have to interfere and put aside the figures already considered as unfit. As a result we come to the conclusion that no more solutions exist and the assignment is over. Galya starts to go on at the other end of the chain, but I feel that the assignment (as well as its narrative here) has taken too much time and I ask the girls if they want to go on. They said "no" to the two previous questions, but now they unanimously agree that it's enough.

I think I have two explanations for why kids don't put aside the rejected pieces, but leave them in the pile. First: they are not very sure that they have performed the task without mistakes and that the piece is truly wrong. Second: they don't yet have our adult certainty of the invariance of natural laws (and logic). It may well be that it doesn't fit now, but it will fit five minutes later. Such things used to happen and the reasons for that weren't 100% clear.

Activity 3. Putting blocks back into the box.

As before, I set up intersecting conditions for the task: one girl handles only big pieces, another, only pieces with holes, the third, just yellow pieces. This time the condition is clear for all of them. Jane even points out a piece that both she and Sandy can put into the box. So there are no more arguments. When Jane runs out of yellow pieces, I ask here why she is the first to have no more figures. She thinks the reason is that Sandy also put back a few yellow figures. I explain that it is because half of the figures are big, and half have holes, but only one quarter are yellow, as there are four colors. So we let Jane also take care of red pieces. In the long run what remains are several pieces fit for nobody, complements of all three classes. We just put them back.

The work is going on in a lively and joyous manner, "Hey, Jane, you only have two left!," and so on.

Geometry for Kids

I still have two or three puzzles to propose but our session has already taken 45 minutes. Instead, we spend the last 5 minutes listening to me reading.

· · ·

And so ends our second circle, with no fanfare or festivities. All of our efforts to continue proved fruitless. Life steamed ahead, and I couldn't stop, take a breath, or look back, until now, in 2005.

This is Not an Epilogue

Surely the reader is curious about what become of the heroes of my story. I hesitated for a long time about whether I should satisfy this curiosity. Life goes on, and what is true today may readily change tomorrow. Eventually I decided to write what I know about them.

I have already apologized of dedicating more time and space to my own children. Now the situation is even more unbalanced: I could write a whole chapter about them, while what I know about the others is sparse and mostly hearsay. I hope the reader will understand that, and forgive me.

Of all the boys, Dima is the only one who chose math as his profession. He graduated from École Normal Supérieure in Paris, defended his thesis and is now working as a researcher ("chercheur CNRS") in one of the Universities of Paris. At the very beginning of this book I mentioned the Moscow Center for Continuous Mathematical Education (MCCME, among other things the publisher of the Russian edition of this book) and the Independent University of Moscow. For several years, Dima was responsible (on the French side) for an exchange program between École Normale and the Independent University. He also spends a lot of his time and effort teaching school children; among other things, he organized the Tournament of the Towns in Paris (this is an international mathematical Olympiad spearheaded by MCCME). He has other interests as well; singing, guitar, and helping to run a Russian singing group in Paris.

Pete graduated from the Moscow Institute of Oriental Languages (majoring in Japanese); he spent a year in Japan and works as an interpreter. He is one of the leaders of his church's youth group and supervises its newsletter. These interests inspired him to continue his education, and now he is a student in the psychology department of Moscow State University.

Andy graduated from the State Academy of Finance, majoring in international economics. He works in the Moscow branch of a prominent international bank and specializes in the trading of financial derivatives.

Gene works with a tourist agency and divides his time between Moscow and St. Petersburg.

My daughter Jane graduated from one of the Universities of Paris (cinema department) and defended her Ph.D. thesis, on the Russian film director

Kira Muratova. Recently she got a tenure position of Associate Professor (maître de conférences) in a Paris university. Besides that, she teaches cinema studies to college students and high-school teachers; organizes festivals; makes subtitles; works as an interpreter and translator; was a member of the youth jury at the Cannes festival; shot several short films; toured in Russia, Kazakhstan, and Kyrgyzstan presenting contemporary French cinema; is a terrific swing dancer... I think I should stop here.

Sandy graduated from the history-philology department of the Russian Humanitarian University; like her brother Pete, she spends a lot of time teaching kids in her church, only not Orthodox, but Protestant. She is currently working to open a new private school.

Dinah lives in the United States; she got a math degree from Brandeis University, and now teaches math. She also edits mathematical textbooks. Her hobby is ceramics; she has participated in several exhibitions.

Some of the "kids" are married; some already have their own children.

Now it's time for the punch line.

I know that in theory, the climax should be located roughly at the two-thirds point, and then the tension should diminish. But in fact, the tension and rhythm in my book are more or less homogeneous throughout. In a certain way that resembles a saga (well, of course I am flattering myself; the comparison is misplaced!). As a youth I was astounded and fascinated by Icelandic sagas, and even nowadays they remain my favorite reading. In these sagas, life boils, events rush headlong, and then suddenly comes a short sentence:

"This saga ends here."

An idea doesn't pretend to be in motion; it shows not a path, but a means of travel. It's a good thing when the reader finishes a book with the unmistakable feeling that now his ignorance is greater than he thought it was.

S. Averintsev

M. Gasparov, In Memory of Sergei Averintsev. *Novy Mir*, #6, 2004.

Index of Math, Pedagogy, and Psychology

algebra, 27, 229
angles, 224
area, 172, 221, 222
arithmetic, 27, 113, 115, 163, 175, 191, 193, 204, 209, 214, 220, 223, 226, 230, 237

ciphers, 131, 202, 203
combinatorics, 64, 70, 71, 94, 179, 263, 289
$\binom{5}{2}$, 70–79, 119, 236, 256, 283, 288

even number, *see under* number

folklore problems
  bicycle and fly, 231
  birthday, 196
  boys and fishermen, 282
  census-taker, 228
  chicken-and-a-half..., 193, 228
  extra square, 210
  four color map theorem, 184
  Galileo's apocryphal experiment, 80
  game of fifteen, 135, 151
  Gauss's sum, 190, 209, 213
  houses and wells, 183
  inventor of chess, 214
  life versus death, 149
  magic square, 109, 114, 115, 117, 120, 182
    multiplicative, 116
    with letters, 120
  page count, 172
  pigeonhole principle, 60
  Pythagorean theorem, 222
  Rubik's cube, 191
  Rubik's snake, 169
  seventeen camels, 193
  three fishermen (Dirac's solution), 230

Tower of Hanoi, 43, 234, 277, 280
Ulam conjecture, 224
wolf, goat, and cabbage, 286

games
  arithmetic, 214
  computer, 147
  logic, 168, 171
  Nim-like, 184
  odd one out, 21, 45, 249, 252, 254, 259, 261
  probability, 86–88, 90, 93, 165, 167, 174, 176, 177, 204, 274
  word, 90, 92, 95, 135, 167
graph, 119, 121, 153, 183

infinite series, 231, 233
irrational numbers, *see under* number

logic, 64
  and humor, 185
  and physics, 79
  genealogical tree, 133, 134
  inclusion, 18, 273
  intersection, 118
  proof, 77, 96
  sets, 22, 84, 90, 92
  symbols, 126
  tautology, 130
  transitivity, 41, 45, 154

magic tricks
  counting, 127
  dice, 173
  invisible numbers, 170, 182
  paper cutting, 179
  simple algebra, 134, 175
manipulatives
  blocks, 97, 123, 127, 156, 267, 279
  buttons, 15

chessboard, 211
coins, 15, 84
cutting paper (to measure
    probability), 180
dice, 86, 88, 90, 93, 173, 204, 235, 274
Dienes blocks, 106, 118, 122, 244,
    255, 273, 278
graph paper, 72, 85, 86, 110, 172,
    260, 265
importance of, 237
magnets, 269
matches, 18, 150, 270, 282
mirror, 23, 65, 173, 266
paper clips, 150
pegboard, 23, 51, 65, 70, 72, 85, 111,
    112, 250, 256, 263, 264, 281, 284
pentominos, 158, 160
pins, 150
pouring water, 57
snowflakes, 281
spirograph, 157, 280
sticks, 62, 129, 133
tangram, 160
    Hungarian, 257
maps, 159, 184, 268, 276

numbers
    binary and other bases, 220
    digits, 290
    even, 177, 208, 223, 224
    factoring, 228, 230
    fractions, 225, 230, 233
    irrational, 223
    Mayan numerals, 213, 215
    odd, 208, 209, 223, 224
    prime, 123, 135, 144, 208
    Roman numerals, 211
    round, 231
    square, 135, 208, 209, 222, 231
    triangular, 222

odd number, 177, *see under* number
order, 65, 71, 78, 99, 153, 155, 262, 263,
    287

Pell's equation, 222
periodicity, 170, 235
polygons, 40, 42, 51, 95
polyhedra, 168, 262
powers of two, 214
prime number, *see under* number
programming, 107–109, 123–125, 197,
    200, 205
    Kid, 97–105

Logo, 100, 237
proportion, 176
psychology and pedagogy
    autism, 143
    cognitive conflict, 31, 56
    conservation
        of area, 162
        of length, 180
        of matter, 20, 31, 56
        of number, 16, 25, 180
        of shape, 245
    danger of abstraction, 139, 141, 292
    discovery, 17, 18, 68, 160, 173, 226
    global vs. local reasoning, 201
    language acquisition, 33, 144
    learning to reason, 31
    mental retardation, 141
    nature vs. nurture, 235
    negative effects of school, 164, 217,
        229, 291
    Piaget, 24–26, 204, 226, 245, 250
        memory experiment, 286
        phenomena, 17, 25, 31, 56, 129,
            179, 248
    precocity vs. tenacity, 191
    synesthesia, 61, 91
    types of giftedness, 244
    whole-language method, 145
pyramids, 185, 213, 222

rotation, 65, 281

similarity, 85, 86, 150, 152
spatial orientation, 271
square number, *see under* number
symmetry, 23, 65, 110, 111, 250, 255,
    260, 281

tessellation, 175, 264
tiling, 160
tilted squares, 222
topology, 46, 181, 183

vectors, 73

weight, 132, 221
word problems, 230

Zeno's paradox, 189

Titles in This Series

5 **Alexander Zvonkin,** Math from three to seven: The story of a mathematical circle for preschoolers, 2011

4 **Roman Fedorov, Alexei Belov, Alexander Kovaldzhi, and Ivan Yashchenko,** Moscow Mathematical Olympiads, 1993–1999, 2011

3 **Judith D. Sally and Paul J. Sally, Jr.,** Geometry: a guide for teachers, 2011

2 **Sam Vandervelde,** Circle in a box, 2009

1 **Zvezdelina Stankova and Tom Rike, Editors,** A decade of the Berkeley Math Circle: The American experience, Volume I, 2008